M. GORKY

MY APPRENTICESHIP

★

М. ГОРЬКИЙ

В ЛЮДЯХ

1916

1952

ИЗДАТЕЛЬСТВО ЛИТЕРАТУРЫ
НА ИНОСТРАННЫХ ЯЗЫКАХ
Москва

M. GORKY

MY APPRENTICESHIP

1916

1952

FOREIGN LANGUAGES
PUBLISHING HOUSE
Moscow

TRANSLATED FROM THE RUSSIAN
BY MARGARET WETTLIN

DESIGNED
BY E. KOGAN

I

So HERE I am—an apprentice. I am the "boy"
in a "stylish footwear" shop on the main street
of the town.

My master is a round little creature with a
bleary face, greenish teeth, and bilge-water eyes.
It seems to me that he is blind, and I make
faces at him in the hope of confirming this.

"Don't screw up your mug," he says to me
quietly, but firmly.

I hate to think that those murky eyes see
me, and I don't believe they do—perhaps
the master just guesses that I am making faces.

7

"I told you once not to screw up your mug," he insists even more quietly, scarcely moving his thick lips.

"And stop scratching your hands." His dry whisper seems to come crawling after me. "Remember—you are serving in a first-class shop on the main street of the town. The boy should stand at the door stiff as a stachy."

I have no idea what a "stachy" is, and I cannot resist scratching my arms and hands, which are covered to the elbow with red blotches and ulcers—the itch-mite burrowing mercilessly under my skin.

"What was your job at home?" asks the master, glancing at my hands.

When I tell him, he shakes his bullet head, all pasted over with grey hair, and says hurtfully:

"Scavengering—that's worse than begging, worse than stealing."

"I stole too," I announce, not without pride.

At that he leans on his palms like a cat on its paws, fixes me with vacuous, starting eyes, and hisses over the counter:

"Wh-a-a-t! You say you stole?"

I explain how and what.

"Well, we'll let that pass. But if you go stealing my boots or my money, I'll have you in jail before you ever come of age."

He says this very calmly, but I am frightened, and dislike him all the more.

Besides the master, there are two assistants in the shop: my cousin Sasha (son of Yakov), and the senior assistant, a slick, slimy, ruddy fellow. Sasha wears a brown frockcoat, a starched shirt front, and a cravat, and he is too proud to notice me.

The day grandfather brought me to the master and asked Sasha to help me learn the business, Sasha frowned importantly and said:

"First he'll have to learn to obey me."

Grandfather put his hand on my head and gave it a push.

"Obey him," he said. "He's above you in years and position."

Sasha rolled his eyes impressively:

"Remember grandfather's words!"

From the very first day he took ruthless advantage of his seniority.

"Stop goggling, Kashirin!" the master warned him.

"I—I wasn't," answered Sasha, dropping his head, but the master was not through with him:

"And don't pull in your chin—the customers may take you for a goat."

The senior assistant laughed ingratiatingly and the master stretched his ugly lips, while Sasha, blushing furiously, ducked under the counter.

I disliked such talk. These people used so many strange words that sometimes it seemed to me they were speaking a foreign tongue.

Whenever a lady entered the shop, the master would take his hand out of his pocket, lightly touch his moustaches, and glue on a saccharine smile which covered his cheeks with wrinkles without changing the expression of his vacuous eyes. The senior assistant would draw himself up, his elbows pressed to his sides, his hands flapping fawningly. Sasha would blink in the effort to hide his bulging orbs, while I would remain at the door furtively scratching my hands and watching the ceremonial of the sale.

The assistant always spread his fingers in an amazing manner when kneeling before a lady to try on shoes. His hands would be all aquiver, and he would touch the leg as if afraid of breaking it, although it was usually a fat leg, resembling a droop-shouldered bottle turned upside down.

Once one of the ladies squirmed and kicked out her toe, saying:

"Oh dear! How you do tickle!"

"That's just out of politeness, ma'am," was the assistant's quick rejoinder.

It was comical to see him hovering about the ladies and I had to turn away to keep from laughing. But I could never resist the temptation to turn back, so ludicrous were the shop assistant's devices. And it seemed to me that never in my life could I make my fingers stick out so politely, or fit shoes to other people's feet so deftly.

Often the master would retire to a little room at the back of the shop and call Sasha, leaving the senior assistant alone with a customer. I remember his once touching the instep of a large blonde and then drawing his finger tips together and kissing them.

"Oh, what a naughty fellow you are!" giggled the woman.

"Ah-h-h-h!" said he, smacking his lips.

I laughed so hard that I grabbed the doorknob to keep from falling; the door opened, my head banged against the glass, and the glass fell out. The assistant stamped his foot at me and my master rapped me over the head with his heavy gold signet ring. Sasha tried to tweak my ears, and that evening as we were going home he warned me severely:

"You'll get the sack if you behave like that. What was so funny anyhow?"

Then he explained that the more enchanting the ladies found the shop assistant, the better for business.

"Even if a lady doesn't need shoes, she'll buy herself an extra pair just to get another look at a nice man. Can't you understand that? There's no teaching you anything!"

His words offended me. No one in the shop had ever tried to teach me anything, least of all Sasha.

Every morning the cook, an ailing, cantankerous woman, would wake me up an hour earlier than my cousin. I would heat the samovar, bring in wood for all the stoves, scour the dinner pots, and brush the clothes and clean the boots of my master, the senior assistant, and Sasha. At the shop I swept, dusted, made tea, delivered packages, and then went home to fetch the dinner. While I was busy with these chores, Sasha had to take my place at the door, and finding this beneath his dignity, he would shout at me:

"You lout! Me having to do your work for you!"

Accustomed as I was to living an independent life in fields and woods, along the banks of the turbid Oka, or on the sandy streets of Kunavino, I found my present existence boring and irksome. I missed Granny and my friends. I had no one to talk to, and I was chafed by the false, seamy side of life as I now saw it.

Frequently the ladies would leave the shop without buying a thing, and then my master and his two assistants would become indignant.

"Kashirin, put away the shoes!" the master would command, pocketing his saccharine smile.

"Had to poke her snout in here, the pig! Got tired of sitting home, so the old fool decided to do the shops! Oho, if she was my wife, wouldn't I show her a thing or two though!"

His wife was a lean, black-eyed woman with a large nose, who shouted and stamped her foot at him as though he were the serving-man.

Often, after seeing out a lady with polite bows and gracious remarks, the master and his assistants would say filthy, shameful things about her, making me want to run out into the street, catch up with her, and tell her what they had said.

Naturally I knew that people were inclined to say nasty things behind your back, but it was particularly exasperating to hear these three speak about everybody as though they themselves were the finest people on earth and had been appointed to pass judgment on all others. They envied most people, praised no one, and knew some unsavoury bit of gossip about everyone.

Into the shop one day came a bright-eyed, rosy-cheeked young woman wearing a velvet cloak with a black fur collar. Her face surmounted the fur like an amazing flower. She became even prettier when she had thrown her cloak over Sasha's arm; diamond drops glittered in her ears and her graceful figure was shown off to advantage by a tight-fitting, blue-grey gown. She reminded me of Vasilissa the Lovely, and I was sure that she must be at least the wife of the Governor. They received her with particular deference, bowing before her like fire worshippers and muttering honeyed words. All three of them rushed madly about the shop, their reflections flashing in the glass of the showcases, and it seemed as if everything were flaming and fusing and would presently assume new forms and contours.

When she left, after having quickly selected an expensive pair of shoes, the master clicked his tongue and hissed:

"The hussy!"

"In a word—an actress," murmured the shop assistant superciliously.

And they went on to tell each other about the lady's lovers and the gay life she led.

After dinner the master lay down to take a nap in the little room at the back of the shop. Removing the back from his gold watch, I dripped some vinegar into the works. It gave me the greatest pleasure to see how, on waking, he entered the shop with the watch in his hand, muttering:

"What do you think of that—all of a sudden my watch takes to sweating. Such a thing never happened before. Sweating, mind you! Perhaps that's a bad sign, eh?"

Despite the bustle in the shop and all the work at home, I went about in a stupor of boredom and kept thinking ever more often: "What could I do to make them get rid of me?"

Snowy people sped past the doors of the shop. They seemed to be latecomers at a funeral who were now hurrying to the cemetery, trying to catch up with the coffin. Dray horses jerked their carts through impeding snowdrifts. Every day the bells of the church behind the shop pealed drearily, for the season was Lent. Their incessant ringing was like pillow-blows over the head—painless, but stunning.

One day while in the yard unpacking a new case of goods, I was approached by the church watchman, a lopsided old man, soft as a rag doll and tattered as though he had been mauled by dogs.

"Would you be stealing me a pair of galoshes, my lad?" he asked.

I said nothing. He sat down on an empty packing case, yawned, made the sign of the cross over his lips, and repeated his request:

"Would you now?"

"It's wrong to steal," I informed him.

"But it's done. Come, lad, out of respect for my years."

He was pleasantly unlike the people who surrounded me. He seemed so sure I would steal, that I consented to slip him a pair of galoshes through the window.

"Good," he said calmly, and without any particular satisfaction. "You wouldn't fool me now, would you? All right, all right, I see you're not one to fool people."

For a minute or two he went on sitting there scraping the toe of his boot over the wet, dirty snow, then he lighted his clay pipe, and all of a sudden gave me a fright:

"And what if I be fooling *you*? What if I take those same galoshes back to the master and say you sold them to me for half a ruble, eh? The cost is over two, and you sold them for a half. Just for a little pocket money, eh?"

I looked at him dumbly, as though he had already done what he threatened, and he kept on talking quietly, nasally, his eyes on his boot, his head wreathed in blue smoke.

"What if it's the master himself as sicked me on: 'go try out that boy of mine—see how much of a thief he is.' What then?"

"I won't give you the galoshes," I said angrily.

"You can't get out of it now, once you've promised!"

He took my hand and pulled me over. Tapping my forehead with a cold finger, he drawled:

"How did you come to agree, just like that: 'Here, take your galoshes,' eh?"

"You asked for them, didn't you?"

"I could ask for lots of things. If I asked you to rob the church—would you rob it? How can you go trusting people like that, you little ninny?"

He pushed me away and got up.

"I'm not needing any stolen galoshes. I'm not so fine a gentleman as to be wearing galoshes anyway. I was just joking. But since you trust me, I'll let you up in the belfry come Eastertide. You can ring the bell and have a look at the town."

"I know the town."

"It's much prettier from the belfry."

He walked slowly away, pushing the toes of his boots into the snow, at last disappearing around a corner of the church. As I watched him go I wondered with pained uneasiness whether the old man had really been having his fun with me, or whether he had been sent by the master to test me. I was afraid to go back into the shop.

"What the devil you doing here so long?" cried Sasha, running out into the yard.

In a sudden wave of fury I shook the pliers at him.

I knew that he and the shop assistant stole from the master. They would hide a pair of boots or shoes in the stove chimney until closing time, when they would leave with the stolen goods up a coat sleeve. This displeased and frightened me, for I had not forgotten the master's warning.

"Do you steal?" I asked Sasha.

"Not me. It's the senior assistant does it," he said severely. "I only help him. He says: 'Do what I tell you!' He'll play some mean trick on me if I don't. As for the master— he was a shop assistant once himself. He knows all the tricks. But you hold your tongue!"

As he spoke he kept looking in the mirror and adjusting his tie, his fingers sticking out in the affected manner of the senior assistant. He was forever impressing on me the fact that he was older and could boss me about. He would shout at me in a bass voice and gesture imperiously when giving me orders. Although I was taller and stronger than he, I was lanky and clumsy, while he was soft, stocky, and slippery. I found him very impressive in his frock coat, but a bit ridiculous. He hated the cook, who was indeed a strange woman—you could never decide whether she was good or bad.

"Best of all I like fights," she would say, opening wide her burning black eyes. "And it's all the same to me who does the fighting—cocks, or dogs, or muzhiks—all the same to me!"

If cocks or pigeons started fighting out in the yard she would drop whatever she was doing and stand at the window until the tussle was over, deaf to everything else. In the evenings she would say to Sasha and me:

"What are you sitting here for, youngsters? Why don't you go out and have a good fight?"

Sasha would fume.

"I'm no youngster, you old fool—I'm the junior assistant!"

"Well now, that's hard to see. For me you'll be a youngster till your wedding day."

"You old fool with a foolish noddle!"

"The devil's smart, but God don't like him."

Sasha was especially annoyed by her manner of speech. When he teased her she would annihilate him with a glance and say:

"Phooh, you little cockroach—God's big mistake."

More than once he tried to talk me into putting pins into her pillow, smearing her face with wax or soot when she was asleep, or playing some other practical joke. But I was afraid of the cook and was sure she would catch me, for she was a very light sleeper. Often she would wake up, light the lamp, and sit staring into some corner. Sometimes she would come over to my bed behind the stove and shake me as she whispered hoarsely:

"I can't sleep somehow, Alyosha. Scary-like. Tell me something."

Only half awake, I would tell her some tale, and she would sit there silently rocking back and forth. It seemed to me that her hot body exuded a smell of wax and incense, and that soon she would die. Perhaps this very minute. In my fear I would raise my voice, but she would always stop me.

"Sh! You'll wake up those bastards and they'll think you're my lover."

She always sat in one and the same pose—all bent over, her hands thrust between her knees, her bony legs pressed tightly together. Even under the thick homespun of her shift the ribs of her flat-chested figure stuck out like the hoops of a shrunken barrel. She would sit silent for a long time and suddenly whisper:

"Would I were dead and rid of all this misery!"

Or would I turn to someone and ask:

"Well, I've lived out my day, and what of it?"

She made no bones about cutting me short in the middle of a tale with a harsh, "Go to sleep!," rising, then, and melting greyly into the shadows of the kitchen.

"The old witch" was what Sasha called her behind her back. Once I suggested that he say it to her face.

"Think I'm afraid?" he retorted, but immediately frowned and added: "No, I won't say it to her face. Maybe she really is a witch."

23

Always contemptuous and irascible, she showed me no more mercy than anyone else. At six o'clock in the morning she would yank me by the foot and shout:

"Enough of your snoring! Bring in the wood! Heat the samovar! Peel the potatoes!"

This would wake up Sasha too.

"What you yelling about?" he would whine.

"I'll tell the master you don't let me sleep."

Her eyes, inflamed from sleeplessness, would flash in his direction as she briskly shifted her bag of bones about the kitchen.

"Phooh, God's big mistake! If you was my stepson, wouldn't I give you a stitching though!"

"Damn you!" swore Sasha; then to me later, on the way to the shop: "I'll make them get rid of her. I'll add salt to the food when she's not looking. If everything's too salty they'll throw her out. Or perhaps kerosene. Why don't you do it?"

"Why don't *you*?"

"Coward!" he snorted.

The cook died before our very eyes. Once when bending down to lift the samovar, she suddenly collapsed as though someone had given her a push on the chest, slumping over on one side, her arms outstretched, the blood trickling from a corner of her mouth.

Both of us knew at once that she was dead, but in our fright we just stood there looking at her, unable to utter a word. At last Sasha rushed out of the kitchen while I, at a loss what to do, pressed against the windowpane, toward the street light. The master came, crouched down beside her anxiously, touched her face, and said:

"She's dead all right. What do you think of that!"

Turning to the little image of Nikola the Miracle Worker in the icon corner, he began to cross himself. His prayers over, he shouted into the entranceway:

"Kashirin, run and tell the police!"

A policeman came, shuffled about, pocketed a coin, and went away. Soon he returned accompanied by a drayman. They took the cook by the head and the feet and carried her outside. The master's wife glanced through the door.

"Scrub the floor!" she called to me.

"It's a good thing she died in the evening," observed the master.

I did not understand why that was a good thing.

"Don't put out the light," said Sasha with unwonted meekness when we had gone to bed.

"Afraid?"

He covered his head with the blanket and lay silent for a long time. The night too was silent, as though listening for something, waiting for something. And it seemed to me that the next moment would bring a clanging of bells, and the townsfolk would start rushing about and shouting in a frenzy of fear.

"Let's lie together up on the stove," suggested Sasha softly, poking his nose out of the blanket.

"It's hot up on the stove."

Again he fell silent.

"Didn't she go all of a sudden though?" he said at last. "And me thinking she was a witch. I can't sleep."

"Neither can I."

He began talking about how the dead rise from their graves and wander about the town until midnight, seeking their homes and their kin.

"The dead remember only the towns," he whispered. "They don't remember streets and houses."

It became even more quiet, and seemed to grow darker. Sasha raised his head.

"Want to see what's in my chest?" he asked.

I had long wondered what he hid away in that chest. He always kept it locked, and opened it with an exaggerated air of caution. If ever I attempted to peep inside, he would say harshly:

"Stop! What you looking at?"

Now that I said I should like to see it, he sat up in bed, and with his usual peremptoriness, ordered me to place the chest at his feet. He wore the key on a chain about his neck along with his baptismal cross. After first glancing into the darkness of the kitchen, he frowned importantly, unlocked the chest, blew on the lid as though it were hot, and at last opened it. Out of it he pulled several suits of underwear.

Half the chest was filled with pillboxes, rolls of varicoloured tea wrappings, empty sardine and blacking tins.

"What's all that?"

"You'll see."

Squeezing the chest between his legs, he bent over it and chanted under his breath:

"Father in heaven. . . ."

I had expected to see toys: I had never owned toys myself, and while I outwardly treated them with contempt, I harboured a secret envy of those who possessed them. I liked the idea that Sasha, staid as he was, should keep toys. To be sure he hid them shamefacedly, but I appreciated his bashfulness.

He opened the first box and took out a pair of spectacle frames. Putting them on his nose, he looked at me severely and said:

"It doesn't matter that the glass is gone. That's the way they're supposed to be."

"Let me look through them."

"They don't suit your eyes. They're for dark eyes and yours are lightish," he explained with a matter-of-fact grunt, so unexpectedly loud that he darted frightened glances about the kitchen.

One of the blacking tins contained a collection of buttons.

"Found them all in the street," he boasted. "All by myself. Thirty-seven of them."

The third box contained some large brass pins, also found in the street; some shoemaker's nails and shoe buckles—worn ones, broken ones, a few whole ones; a brass doorknob; an ivory knob; a woman's comb; a *Dream Book and Fortuneteller*; and many other objects of similar value.

In my searchings for rags and bones I could have collected ten times as much rubbish in a single month. The sight of Sasha's treasures filled me with disappointment, embarrassment, and pity for him. He studied every object attentively, lovingly stroking it with his fingers, his thick lips pursed officiously, his popping eyes fondly solicitous. But the spectacles made his childish face look absurd.

"What do you want with that stuff?"

He cast me a swift glance through the frames and said in the cracked voice of his years:

"Want me to give you something?"

"No, thank you."

He did not reply for a moment, apparently injured by my refusal and lack of interest in his treasure.

"Take a towel and we'll shine everything," he then suggested. "They're all dusty."

When the treasures had been polished and replaced, he rolled over on his side with his face to the wall. It had begun to rain, and the wind was beating at the window.

"Wait till the ground dries in the garden and I'll show you something that'll take your breath away," he remarked without turning around.

I crawled into bed without answering him.

A few seconds later he suddenly jumped up, began clawing at the wall and said in a voice that left no doubt of his terror:

"I'm afraid. . . . Oh God, how afraid I am! Lord, have mercy!"

I myself went cold with fright. It seemed to me that the cook was standing at the window with her back to me, pressing her forehead against the pane as she always used to do when watching cockfights.

Sasha sobbed and kept clawing at the wall, his legs jerking convulsively. I plunged across the kitchen floor as though crossing a bed of hot coals, and crawled up beside him.

We wept until we were exhausted and fell asleep.

Some days later we had a holiday when we worked only until noon, returning home for dinner. When the master and his wife retired for their nap, Sasha said to me mysteriously:

"Come along!"

I guessed that he was going to show me the something that would take my breath away.

We went into the garden. On a narrow stretch of land between two houses stood some ten or fifteen ancient limes whose mighty trunks were furry with lichen and whose bare black limbs thrust lifeless into the sky. Not a single rook's nest was to be seen among them. The trees reared like giant tombstones. Nothing but these limes grew here—not a bush, not a blade of grass; the earth of the paths was packed down as hard and black as iron, and wherever patches of soil showed beneath the decay of last year's leaves, they were overgrown with mould like stagnant water with duckweed.

Sasha turned the corner of the house, walked in the direction of the street fence, and came to a halt beneath one of the limes, where for a minute he stood staring at the window of the neighbouring house. Then he squatted down and dug away the leaves with his hands, exposing a gnarled root with two bricks sunk deep into the ground beside it. He pulled out the bricks. Under them lay a sheet of roofer's tin; under the tin, a square board. At last I beheld a large hole extending under the root.

Sasha struck a match and lit a stub of candle which he thrust into the hole, saying:

"Look. Only don't be afraid."

Apparently he himself was afraid. The candle trembled in his hand, he was pale, his lips were unpleasantly lax, his eyes moist, and he furtively slipped his free hand behind his back. I became infected with his fear. With the utmost caution I glanced under the root which served as an arch for a miniature cave. Sasha had lighted three tapers which filled the aperture with blue light. The cave was about as deep as an ordinary bucket, but wider, and the walls were inlaid with bits of coloured glass and china. On a central elevation stood a little coffin plastered with tin foil and half covered with a scrap of material resembling brocade. From under this coverlet protruded the grey claws and the beak of a sparrow. At the head rose a tiny lectern holding a small brass baptismal cross, while on three sides burned the tapers in holders decorated with gold and silver bonbon wrappers.

The pointed flames streamed toward the opening of the cave, the interior of which was dimly lustrous with glints and patches of many-hued light. The odour of earth and warm wax and decay beat in waves against my face, and the iridescence of a shattered rainbow leaped and quivered in my eyes. All of this roused an oppressive sense of wonder, extinguishing my fear.

"Pretty?" asked Sasha.

"What's it for?"

"It's a shrine," he explained. "Doesn't it look like one?"

"I don't know."

"And the sparrow's the corpse. Maybe its body will be turned into a holy relic by some miracle, seeing as how it died, an innocent sacrifice."

"Did you find it dead?"

"No, it flew into the shed and I caught it in my cap and smothered it."

"Why?"

"Just because."

He looked into my eyes and again asked:

"Isn't it pretty?"

"No!"

He leaned over the cave, quickly covered it with the board, the tin, replaced the bricks, stood up and brushed the dirt off his knees as he said harshly:

"Why don't you like it?"

"Because I pity the sparrow."

He fixed me with a blank stare, as though suddenly gone blind, then struck me in the chest, shouting:

"Blockhead! You're just jealous—that's why you say you don't like it. Maybe you think you fixed things up prettier in your garden there on Kanatnaya Street?"

"Of course I did," I answered unhesitatingly, recalling the nook I had made for myself.

Sasha threw off his frock coat, rolled up his sleeves, spat on his palms and said:

"All right then, let's fight it out."

I had no desire to fight. I was wearied by it all and could not bear to look at my cousin's angry face.

He rushed at me, knocked me down by butting me in the chest, and straddled me.

"Life or death?" he shouted.

I was stronger than he, and thoroughly aroused; a minute later he was lying snorting on his face with his hands over his head. Thoroughly alarmed, I tried to raise him up, but he fought me off, and this only alarmed me the more. I moved away not knowing what to do.

"I've got you now. I won't budge until the master finds me, and then I'll tell on you and he'll give you the sack."

He cursed and threatened. This maddened me and I rushed to the cave, tore out the bricks, threw the coffin and the sparrow over the fence, and dug up everything inside, trampling it underfoot.

"There! There! See that?"

Sasha reacted strangely to my fury. He sat up with his mouth slightly open and his brows drawn together, watching me without a word, and when I had finished he rose unhurriedly, dusted himself, threw his coat over his shoulders, and said with calm menace in his voice:

"Now you'll see what'll happen. Just you wait. I made that specially for you; it was witchcraft! So there!"

I slumped as though felled by his words, and everything inside me went cold. He walked away without so much as glancing back, his calmness crushing me completely.

I resolved that on the next day I would run away from that town, from the master, from Sasha and his witchcraft, from all that senseless, dreary life.

When the new cook woke me up the next morning she cried:

"Lord! What's wrong with your face?"

"The witchcraft's working," I thought with a sense of doom.

But the cook went off into such peals of laughter that I myself could not resist a smile as I glanced into her mirror. My face was thickly smeared with soot.

"Did Sasha do it?" I asked.

"Perhaps it was me," laughed the cook.

I began to polish the boots. When I thrust my hand into one of them, a pin stuck me.

"There's your witchcraft for you!" thought I.

Pins and needles were hidden in all the boots, and so cleverly that I was sure to get them in my flesh. I took a jug of cold water and with the greatest satisfaction poured it over the head of the sorcerer, who was still sleeping, or feigning sleep.

But still I was unhappy. I could not get rid of the vision of the coffin containing the sparrow with its grey, shrivelled claws and its pitiful little waxen beak, whilst all around glinted the varicoloured light which seemed futilely trying to assemble into a rainbow. The coffin expanded, the claws of the bird grew, stretching up and up, palpitatingly alive.

I had planned to run away that evening, but as I was warming up the soup on the oil stove just before dinner, I fell to dreaming and let the soup boil over. In my haste to extinguish the flame I overturned the pot on my hands and had to be sent to the hospital.

I remember the nightmare of that hospital. Figures in grey and white shrouds swarmed and groaned and murmured in the wavering yellow emptiness. A tall man on crutches with eyebrows like moustaches kept shaking his long black beard and roaring:

"I'll report you to His Reverence the Bishop!"

The cots reminded me of coffins; the sick people lying with their noses pointing to the ceiling resembled dead sparrows. The yellow walls rocked, the ceiling billowed like a sail, the floor surged, swinging the cots back and forth. Everything was eery and hopeless, while beyond the windows the bare branches of the trees stuck up like whips shaken by an invisible hand.

A thin, redheaded corpse danced in the doorway, pulling his shroud about him with short little arms and squealing:

"I'll have none of your lunatics!"

"His Reverence the Bi-i-shop!" shouted the man on crutches.

Granny and grandfather and everyone else had always said that people were starved to death in the hospital, and I decided that my days were numbered. A woman in glasses —also in a shroud—came and wrote something in chalk on the slate fastened to the head of my bed. The chalk crumbled and the pieces fell on my hair.

"What is your name?" she asked.

"I haven't any."

"You haven't any?"

"No."

"None of your nonsense now, or you'll get a trouncing."

It was just because I was sure they would give me a trouncing that I had refused to answer. She spat out her words like a cat, and vanished with catlike stealth.

Two lamps were lighted, and their yellow orbs hung from the ceiling like lost eyes, swinging and blinking blindingly as they sought reunion.

"Let's have a game of cards," said someone in the corner.

"How can I play with only one arm?"

"Aha, so they cut off your arm, did they?"

I immediately assumed that they had cut off his arm because he played cards, and I wondered what they would do to me before killing me.

My hands burned and ached as though someone were plucking at the bones. I cried softly with fear and pain, shutting my eyes so that no one should see my tears, but they flowed over and trickled down my temples and into my ears.

Night came. The people all crept on to their cots and hid themselves under grey blankets, and with every moment the silence became more profound, broken only by a voice in the corner muttering:

"Nothing'll come of it. He's a beast and she's a beast. . . ."

I wanted to write to Granny, imploring her to rescue me while there was yet time, but I could not write because of my hands, and because I had no paper. I decided to run away.

The night seemed to have settled down for all time. Softly I slipped my feet over the side of the cot and went to the double door. One half was open, and there on a bench in the corridor I caught sight of a smoke-wreathed, tousled grey head whose sunken dark eyes were fixed on me. I had no time to hide.

"Who's wandering around in there? Come here!"

The voice was soft and not at all intimidating. I went over and looked into a round face bristling with beard. The grey hair on the man's head was long and stuck out in all directions, like a silver halo. From his belt swung a ring of keys. Had his hair and beard been longer, he would have looked like Saint Peter.

"Are you the one with the scalded hands? What are you wandering around in the night for? That's not according to rules and regulations."

He blew a cloud of smoke into my face and placed a warm arm around me, drawing me to him.

"Afraid?"

"Yes."

"Everybody's afraid here at first. But there's nothing to be afraid of. Specially with me. I wouldn't let anybody come to harm. Do you want to smoke? That's all right—you don't have to. You're too young—wait a couple of years. Where's your mother and father? You have no mother or father? That's all right—you don't have to. You'll get along without them. That is, if you don't show the white feather."

It had been a long time since I had met anyone who spoke simple, friendly, comprehensible words, and it was inexpressibly pleasant to hear them.

He led me back to my cot.

"Sit with me a while," I begged.

"That I will," he replied.

"Who are you?"

"I'm a soldier, a true soldier who fought in the Caucasus. Real battles. That's only natural; a soldier lives to fight battles. I fought with the Hungarians and the Circassians and the Poles. War, brother, is a b-i-g mischief."

I closed my eyes for a moment, and when I opened them Granny was sitting where the soldier had been, and he was standing alongside of her, saying:

"So they all died, did they? You don't say!"

Like a romping child, the bright sun came and went, swiftly gilding everything in the ward and then vanishing, only to return in another burst of light.

Granny leaned over me to say:

"What is it, pigeon? Have they hurt you? I told that redheaded hyena. . . ."

"Just a minute and I'll fix everything according to rules and regulations," said the soldier, going away.

"It seems that soldier's from Balakhna," said Granny, wiping the tears from her cheeks.

I still thought I was dreaming, and said nothing.

A doctor came and dressed my hands, and then Granny and I set off through the town in a carriage.

"That grandfather of ours has gone clean out of his head," she said. "He's so tight— turns your stomach. Not long ago saddler Khlist—that'll be a new friend of his—stole a hundred-ruble note from his prayer book. My, wasn't there a row then! Oo-o-o!"

The sun was shining brightly and clouds floated like white birds across the sky. We crossed the plank road laid across the frozen Volga where the ice was humming and swelling, and a thin layer of water went swishing under the planks. Golden crosses flashed atop the bulging red cupolas of the market church. We met a broad-faced woman carrying a bundle of silken pussy willows. Spring was coming! Soon it would be Eastertide!

My heart sang like a lark.

"How I love you, Granny!"

This did not surprise her.

"That's natural—you're my kin," she said simply. "But I can say without bragging that even strangers love me, praised be the Blessed Virgin."

With a smile she added:

"She'll be rejoicing soon—with her son getting resurrected. But my daughter, Varyusha. . . ."

And she fell silent.

II

Grandfather met me in the yard where he was on his knees sharpening a pole with an axe. He lifted the axe as though to hurl it at my head, then took off his cap, saying scornfully:

"Welcome to our midst, most Honourable Excellence! So your service is over? Well, now you can make a living as best you know how. Phooh!"

"We know all that," grandmother interrupted with a wave of her hand. When we had entered the room and she was heating the samovar she said:

"Your grandfather's been plucked clean this time. He gave all the money he had to his godson Nikolai to invest for him without taking any receipt. I can't say just how it happened, but it turns out he's been plucked clean. All the money's gone. And all because we didn't help the poor, didn't pity the unfortunate; so the Lord God thought to Himself: why should I be so good to those Kashirins? That's what He thought, and took everything away."

She glanced about before she continued:

"I've been trying to soften the heart of the Lord a wee bit, so's He wouldn't be too hard on the old man. I've been going about nights scattering some quiet mercy out of my earnings. If you like we can go tonight. I have some money."

Grandfather came in scowling.

"Have been seeing what you could gobble up?" he said.

"It's nothing of yours we're gobbling," said Granny. "And if you like, you can sit down with us. There's enough to go round."

He sat down at the table.

"Pour me out a cup," he muttered meekly.

Everything in the room remained unchanged except that mother's corner was sadly empty, and on the wall over grandfather's bed hung a piece of paper on which was written in large printed letters:

"Jesus save my soul. And may Thy mercy attend me all the days of my life until the hour of my death."

"Who wrote that?"

Grandfather did not answer, and after a brief pause Granny said with a smile:

"That paper's worth a hundred rubles."

"It's none of your business," shouted grandfather. "I'll give away everything I have to strangers!"

"There's nothing left to give, and when there was, you grudged it," observed Granny calmly.

"Silence!" shrieked grandfather.

Everything was as it should be—as it had been.

Kolya woke up in his clothes basket on the trunk in the corner. The blue shine of his eyes was scarcely visible under his heavy lids. He had become even more grey and listless and ephemeral. Without recognizing me, he silently turned away and closed his eyes.

Out in the street I was met with sad news: Vyakhir had died—"carried off by the pox" during Passion Week. Khabi had moved into the city, while Yaz had lost the use of his legs and could not leave the house. In telling me all this the black-eyed Kostroma said angrily:

"The boys die off mighty fast!"

"Vyakhir's the only one that's died."

"It's all the same. Once a fellow's off the street he's good as dead. You just make friends and get to know a fellow, when they send him to work or he dies. Some new people have moved into the Chesnokovs' in your yard—the Yevseyenkos. They have a boy named Nushka—he's all right, slick enough—and two girls, one of them's little and the other's lame, walks with crutches. She's pretty."

After a minute's musing he added:

"Me and Churka are in love with her. We keep quarrelling all the time."

"With her?"

"Of course not. With each other. Hardly ever with her."

Of course I knew that big boys and even grown men fell in love, and I knew the coarse significance of love. But now I was upset and felt sorry for Kostroma, the sight of whose gawky frame and smouldering black eyes somehow abashed me.

I saw the lame girl that very evening. As she was descending the steps into the yard she dropped her crutch and stood there helpless, weak and thin, clinging to the railing with waxen fingers. I tried to pick up the crutch, but the bandages on my hands interfered, and for a long time I fussed about in exasperation while she stood there above me laughing softly.

"What's wrong with your hands?" she asked.

"I scalded them."

"And I'm lame. Do you live in our yard? Were you in hospital long? I was. Terribly long," she added with a sigh.

She was wearing an old but freshly starched white dress patterned with blue horseshoes.

Her hair was combed down smooth and lay in a short, thick braid on her breast. Her eyes were large and grave with blue fires glowing in their calm depths, lighting a wan, pinched face. She had a pleasant smile, but I did not like her. Her whole sickly figure seemed to say:

"Don't touch me, please!"

How could my comrades have fallen in love with her?

"I've been sick for a long time," she promptly informed me, with even a touch of pride in her voice. "Our neighbour bewitched me— she had a fight with mama and bewitched me to spite her. Was it awful in the hospital?"

"Yes."

I felt awkward in her presence and went indoors.

At about midnight Granny gently woke me up.

"Shall we be going? If you do good to others, your hands'll heal quicker."

She took me by the arm and led me through the darkness as though I were blind. The night was black and damp, with the wind blowing steadily like a fast-flowing river, and the cold sand chilling our feet. Grandmother would cautiously approach the dark windows of townsmen's homes, cross herself three times, leave five kopeks and three biscuits on the window sill, cross herself once more, her eyes raised to the starless sky, and whisper:

"Holy Queen of Heaven, help all people, for all of us are sinners in Thy sight, Blessed Mother."

The further we went from our house, the darker and more deserted everything became. Moon and stars seemed to have been forever swallowed up in the fathomless depths of the night sky. A dog ran out and stood growling at us, its eyes gleaming in the darkness. I clung frightenedly to Granny.

"Have no fear," she said. "That's just a dog. It's too late for the devil—the cocks have crowed already."

She called the dog, patted its head and said:

"Now, doggy, don't go frightening my grandson!"

The dog rubbed up against my legs and the three of us walked on. Twelve times did Granny approach a window to leave her "quiet mercy" on the sill. The sky brightened. Grey houses loomed in the darkness and the belfry of Napolnaya Church grew as white as sugar, the brick wall of the cemetery seemed translucent, like a wattle fence.

"Your old Granny's tired," said my grandmother. "Time to be going home. When the wives wake up in the morning they'll find the Holy Virgin's left the children a mite. If there's not enough to go around, even a mite's to be welcomed. Ah me, Alyosha, it's a poor life folks live, and no one to give them a care!

The rich man thinks not of the Lord,
Of Judgment Day, the Holy Word;
And to the poor his heart is cold,
So bent is he on getting gold;
In Hell he'll burn on coals of gold!

"That's the pity of it. And we should live caring for each other, with God caring for all. But I'm glad you're by my side again."

I too was glad in a quiet way, feeling vaguely that I had had contact with something I should never forget. Alongside of me jogged the brown dog with a foxlike face and kind, apologetic eyes.

"Will it live with us?"

"Why not, if it wants to? Here, I'll give it a biscuit—I have two left. Let's sit down on this bench a while; I seem to be tired somehow."

We sat on a bench alongside of a gate, the dog lying at our feet gnawing at the dry biscuit.

"There's a Jewess lives here. Nine children she has, one littler than the other. 'How ever do you live, Moseyevna?' says I to her. 'I live with my God; how else should I live?' says she."

Presently I fell asleep, nestled against grandmother's warm body.

Once more life flowed along, swift and brimming. The broad stream of each new day filled my soul with impressions that enraptured, alarmed, pained, or set me to thinking.

Soon I too was filled with the desire to see the lame girl as often as possible, to talk to her, or simply sit silent beside her on the bench near the gate. It was a pleasure even to be silent in her company. She was as clean as a bird and gave wonderful descriptions of the life of the Cossacks on the Don where she had lived for a long time with her uncle, a mechanic in a creamery. Then her father, a fitter, had moved to Nizhni-Novgorod.

"And I have another uncle who works for the Tsar himself."

On holiday evenings all the people in the street came out of their houses. The young boys and girls went to the cemetery for song promenades; the men went to the taverns; only the women and children remained in the street. The women sat on the benches or simply in the sand beside the gates, raising a great rumpus with their quarrelling and gossiping. The children played ball and skittles and "sharmazlo," while their mothers praised them for their skill or chided them for their clumsiness. It was deafeningly noisy and unforgettably gay. The presence and attention of the grownups excited us children, so that we played with fierce animation and rivalry. But however engrossed Kostroma, Churka, and I became, we would be sure to find time to run over to the lame girl and boast of our prowess.

"Did you see how I knocked down all the pins at once, Ludmilla?"

She would smile sweetly and bob her head.

Formerly our crowd had always tried to be on the same side in a game, but now I noticed that Churka and Kostroma sought opposite sides, and in every way pitted themselves against each other in strength and skill, even to the point of fighting and tears. One day they battled so desperately that the grownups had to interfere, which they did by throwing water over them, as if they were dogs.

Ludmilla, who was sitting on the bench, stamped the ground with her sound foot, and whenever the fighters lunged toward her she would push them away with her crutch, crying in fear:

"Stop it!"

Her face grew livid, her eyes filmy and starting, as though she were having a fit.

Another time, after being shamefully defeated at skittles by Churka, Kostroma crouched behind a chest of oats in a greengrocer's shop and began to cry noiselessly. That was a fearful sight. He clenched his teeth until the muscles of his jaw bulged and his lean face seemed turned to stone, while large tears rolled out of his black, brooding eyes. When I tried to console him he swallowed back his tears and gasped:

"Just wait—I'll throw a brick at his head—you'll see!"

Churka assumed an arrogant air. He walked down the middle of the street like the marriageable boys, his cap on one side, his hands in his pockets.

"I'm going to start smoking soon," he said, demonstrating his latest accomplishment of spitting through his teeth. "I've already tried it twice, but it still makes me sick."

All of this displeased me. I could see that I was losing my comrades, and it seemed to me that Ludmilla was the cause.

One evening when I was out in the yard sorting the bones and rags and other trash

I had collected, Ludmilla came over and stood swinging on her crutch, waving her right hand.

"Hello," she said with three little nods. "Did Kostroma go with you?"

"Yes."

"And Churka?"

"Churka doesn't play with us any more. And it's all your fault. They've fallen in love with you and that's why they fight."

She blushed, but answered mockingly:

"You don't say! Why is it my fault?"

"Why did you make them love you?"

"I didn't ask them to love me," she retorted angrily and went away saying: "That's all nonsense! I'm older than they are. I'm fourteen years old. You don't fall in love with girls older than yourself."

"Don't you though!" I cried, trying to wound her. "Look at the shopkeeper, Khlist's sister—she's really old, but just see how the boys play around with her!"

Ludmilla's crutch ground deep into the sand as she whirled to confront me.

"You don't know anything yourself," she said hurriedly, with tears in her voice, her pretty eyes flashing. "The shopkeeper is a loose woman, but I—do you think I'm like that? I'm still little. I'm not to be touched and pinched and—all that. If you had read the second half of *Kamchadalka* you wouldn't say such things!"

She went away whimpering. I felt sorry for her. Her words seemed to contain some truth yet unknown to me. Why should my comrades pinch her? And they claimed to be in love with her!

The next day, wishing to atone for my offence, I bought seven kopeks worth of "barley sugar," which I knew to be Ludmilla's favourite sweet.

"Want some?"

"Go away! I won't be friends with you!" she said with forced anger. But presently she took the sweets, remarking: "You might at least have wrapped them in paper. Look how dirty your hands are."

"I washed them, but it won't come off."

She took one of my hands in hers, which were hot and dry, and examined it.

"You've ruined your hands."

"Your fingers are all pricked too."

"That's from the needle. I sew a lot."

A few minutes later she suggested, after first glancing about:

"Let's hide away somewhere and read *Kamchadalka*; want to?"

It took us some time to find a suitable place. Finally we decided on the entrance to the bathhouse. It was dark, but we could sit at the window, which looked out on a littered stretch between the shed and the slaughterhouse. People rarely came to that spot.

So there she sat at the window, her bad leg stretched out on the bench, her sound one on the floor, a dog-eared book in front of her face, pouring out a stream of dull, unintelligible words. But I was touched. From my position on the floor I could see the two blue flames of her serious eyes moving across the pages of the book; sometimes they would become misted by tears and the girl's voice would tremble as she pronounced unfamiliar words in incomprehensible combinations. I seized upon these words and tried to fit them into verse, twisting them about in various ways. This preoccupation made it utterly impossible to understand what the book was about.

My dog slept on my knees. I had named it "Wind," because it was long-legged and shaggy and swift and howled like the autumn wind in the chimney.

"Are you listening?" asked the girl.

I nodded. I grew ever more excited by the tangle of words and ever more anxious to rearrange them like the words of a song, each one a bright and shining star.

When it became dark, Ludmilla dropped the pallid hand holding the book.

"Isn't it nice?" she asked. "I told you it would be."

After that we frequently went to sit in the entrance to the bathhouse. To my great satisfaction, Ludmilla soon discarded *Kamchadalka*. I could not have told her a word of the contents of that endless tale—endless because there was a third part following the second (with which we had begun), and Ludmilla told me there was even a fourth.

We were especially happy there on rainy days, if they did not happen to fall on Saturdays, when the bathhouse was heated.

The rain would come pouring down, keeping everyone indoors, so that there was no chance of anyone passing our dark window. Ludmilla was dreadfully afraid that we would get caught.

"Do you know what they would think?" she asked softly.

I did, and was also afraid of being caught. We would sit there talking for hours at a time. Sometimes I would tell her Granny's tales and Ludmilla would recount the lives of the Cossacks along the Medveditsa River.

"It's wonderful there!" she would sigh. "Not like here. This place is only fit for beggars!"

I decided that when I grew up I would most certainly go to see the Medveditsa River.

Soon we no longer had to sit in the entrance to the bathhouse. Ludmilla's mother found work with a furrier, her sister went to school, her brother worked at a tile factory.

When the weather was bad I would go help the girl cook and tidy up the room and kitchen.

"You and I live like husband and wife," she laughed. "Only we don't sleep together. We live even better—husbands never help their wives."

If I happened to have any money I would buy something sweet and we would have tea, later cooling the samovar with cold water so that Ludmilla's irate mother would not guess we had heated it. Sometimes Granny came and sat with us, making lace or embroidering while she told us marvellous tales, and whenever grandfather went to town, Ludmilla would come to visit us, on which occasions we feasted without a care in the world.

Granny would say:

"We do have a grand life, don't we? Who'll forbid me to dine if the money's mine?"

She encouraged our friendship.

"It's a good thing when a boy and a girl become friends. Only they mustn't do anything foolish."

And in the most simple way she explained to us what "doing anything foolish" meant.

There was beauty in her words, and inspiration, and I readily understood that flowers were not to be touched until they were full-blown, otherwise they would give off no perfume and bear no fruit.

I had no desire to "do anything foolish," but that did not prevent Ludmilla and me from speaking about that which is usually passed over in silence. Naturally we spoke only when the necessity arose, for the crude relationship of the sexes was too often and too insistently cast up before us, offending both of us deeply.

Yevseyenko, Ludmilla's father, was a handsome man of about forty, with curly hair and whiskers and heavy eyebrows which he raised with a peculiar air of triumph. He was strangely taciturn—I do not remember ever hearing him speak. He would make sounds like a deaf-mute when caressing his children, and he even beat his wife without uttering a word.

On holiday evenings he would don a blue blouse, wide velvet trousers, and shiny boots and make for the gate with a large accordion swinging from a strap over his shoulder. There he would stand like a soldier presenting arms. Soon the promenade would begin to pass our gate. The girls and women would file past like geese, stealing shy glances at Yevseyenko from under their lashes, or gazing openly, with hungry eyes, while he would stand with underlip outthrust, his dark eyes surveying them selectively. There was something revoltingly canine in that silent communication of eyes, in the slow, fatalistic procession of women past the male. It seemed as though an imperious sign from him would cause any one of them to drop prostrate onto the dirty sand of the street.

"Ogling them, the goat! The shameless pig!" muttered Ludmilla's mother. She looked like a worn-out broom—tall and thin, with a long, ravaged face and hair that had been cropped during a siege of typhus.

Beside her sat Ludmilla, futilely trying to distract her attention by all sorts of questions.

"Leave me alone, you miserable cripple," muttered the mother, blinking uneasily. Her narrow Mongolian eyes were strangely pale and fixed, as though they had caught on something that held them fast.

"Don't be angry mama, it's no use," said Ludmilla. "Just see how the matmaker's widow has decked herself up!"

"I'd dress better'n her if I didn't have you three on my hands. You've eaten me out of house and home—swallowed me up," replied her mother with tearful heartlessness, staring at the enormous widow.

The latter resembled a small house, her bosom thrusting out like a balcony. Her red face, clipped by a tight-bound green kerchief, reminded me of a dormer window aglow with sunset.

Yevseyenko swung his accordion onto his chest and began to play. The instrument gave forth rich harmonies which lured to unknown places; children from all over the street came running to fall at the feet of the musician, where they lay in breathless ecstasy.

"Just wait, someone will give you a good thrashing yet," warned Yevseyenko's wife.

He cast her a sidelong glance without deigning to reply.

The matmaker's widow plunked down on the bench in front of Khlist's store, where she sat listening, her head drooping to one side, her bosom heaving.

The field beyond the cemetery was washed with the rosy light of the setting sun. Down the street as down a river floated brightly-clad lumps of flesh with children swirling about them. The air was heady. From the sun-warmed sand rose a conglomerate odour dominated by the fattish, sweetish smell of the slaughterhouses—the smell of blood—while from the saddlers' yards came the salt pungency of hides. The chatter of the women, the drunken roars of the men, the sharp cries of the children, the low hum of the accordion, all merged in a pulsing rhythm, the mighty sighing of the fecund earth. Everything was coarse and naked, arousing a vast, strong faith in that dark life, so shamelessly bestial, so frenziedly seeking outlet for its proud strength.

Through the general clamour, particularly striking words would sometimes smite the heart and lodge in the memory:

"You can't all of you throw yourselves on him at once—have to wallop him in turn."

"Who'll ever pity us if we don't pity ourselves?"

"Looks like God made women just for the joke of it."

Night was at hand; the air grew fresher, the clamour died down; the wooden houses swelled and expanded as they donned the shadows. Some of the children were dragged home at bedtime; others slept right there in the shadow of the fences, at the feet or in the laps of their mothers. At night the older children became quieter and more tractable. Yevseyenko vanished when nobody was looking, as though he had melted away; the matmaker's widow also disappeared, and the deep-throated singing of the accordion now came from somewhere far away beyond the cemetery. Ludmilla's mother sat there on the bench all bent over, her back arched like a cat's. Granny went to have tea with the midwife and matchmaker who was our neighbour—a large, sinewy woman with a duck's beak for a nose and a gold medal "for rescuing the perishing" on her flat, mannish chest. Everyone on our street feared her, considering her a witch. It was said that once she had carried the three children and the sick wife of a colonel out of a flaming house.

Granny and she were friends. Whenever they saw each other coming down the street, they would smile with particular cordiality while still a long way off.

Kostroma and I joined Ludmilla on the bench by our gate. Churka had challenged Ludmilla's brother to fight, and now they were stirring up the dust in a tight clinch.

"Stop it!" cried Ludmilla in fright.

Kostroma, fixing on her a sidelong glance of his black eyes, was telling about the hunter Kalinin, a mouldy old man with cunning eyes, whose bad reputation was known to everyone in the settlement. Recently he had died, but, said Kostroma, instead of burying his coffin in the sands of the cemetery, they had left it on top of the ground, apart from the other graves. The black coffin was mounted on an iron framework, with white pictures of a cross, a lance, a reed, and two bones on the lid.

It was said that every night the old man rose from his coffin, to wander about the cemetery in search of something until the crowing of the first cock.

"Don't speak of such dreadful things!" begged Ludmilla.

"Let me go!" cried Churka, freeing himself from the grip of her brother. Turning to Kostroma he said mockingly: "What are you lying for? Didn't I see them dig in the coffin myself and leave the top of the grave empty for a tombstone? As for his ghost walking about the cemetery at night—the drunken blacksmith just made it up!"

"Go spend the night in the cemetery if you're so sure of it!" retorted Kostroma without so much as glancing at him.

They began to argue, and Ludmilla turned to her mother with a mournful shake of her head:

"Do ghosts walk at night, mama?" she asked.

"Yes they do," confirmed her mother, as though called back from afar.

Valyok, the fat, red-cheeked, twenty-year-old son of the shopkeeper, strolled over and listened to our argument.

"I'll give twenty kopeks and ten cigarettes to anyone who lies on top of the coffin until morning; but if you funk, I'll pull your ears to my hearts content. Well, how about it?"

A strained silence ensued, broken by Ludmilla's mother:

"What nonsense!" she said. "You can't ask children to do a thing like that!"

"Give me a ruble and I'll do it," muttered Churka.

"Scared to do it for twenty kopeks?" asked Kostroma spitefully. "Offer a ruble, Valyok. He won't go anyway. He's just bragging."

"All right, I'll pay a ruble!"

Churka got up off the ground and slowly walked away, hugging the fence. Kostroma stuck his fingers in his mouth and gave a shrill whistle, while Ludmilla said anxiously:

"Oh dear, why must he brag so?"

"A pack of cowards," teased Valyok. "The best fighters on the street—humph! Puppies, that's what you are!"

It was hurtful to take his insults. We did not like this fat fellow; he was always urging the children to mischief, telling them nasty gossip about the girls and women, and teaching them to make fun of them. The children obeyed him, and paid dearly for it. For some reason he hated my dog. He kept throwing stones at it and one day gave it a piece of bread with a needle inside.

But it was even more hurtful to see Churka slinking away in disgrace.

I said to Valyok:

"Give me a ruble and I'll go."

With a guffaw intended to intimidate me, he handed the ruble to Ludmilla's mother.

"I don't want it, I won't take it," she said, and walked off angrily. Ludmilla also refused to take the money, and this only made Valyok tease us the more. I was about to go without demanding any money, but at that moment Granny came up. On hearing what it was all about, she took the ruble and said to me calmly:

"Put on your coat and take a blanket—it gets cold towards morning."

Her words filled me with hope that nothing dreadful would happen.

Valyok made the stipulation that I was to lie or sit on the coffin until morning, remaining there no matter what happened, even if the coffin started swaying when old man Kalinin began to crawl out. Should I jump off, I would lose the wager.

"Mind now!" said Valyok. "I'll keep my eye on you all night!"

When I left for the cemetery Granny made the sign of the cross over me and admonished

"If you seem to see something, don't stir. Just say a prayer to the Virgin."

I went off quickly, anxious to get the business over. Valyok, Kostroma, and some other boys accompanied me. While climbing over the brick wall I caught my foot in the blanket and fell, immediately jumping up as if bounced back by the sand. I heard laughter on the other side of the wall. Something clicked inside of me and cold chills ran up and down my back.

I stumbled over to the black coffin. On one side it was packed with sand, while on the other the squat little legs of the framework were exposed, as though someone had attempted to lift it and been unable to. I sat down on the edge of the coffin and glanced about: the lumpy cemetery was thickly sown with grey crosses whose flaring shadows were skinny arms embracing the bristling grave-mounds. Here and there among the crosses rose thin, emaciated birches, their branches linking up the isolated graves. Weeds thrust through the lacework of their shadows, and this grey raggedness was most terrifying of all. Like a giant snowdrift rose the cemetery church, while a small, waning moon gleamed among motionless clouds.

Yaz's father, the "Rotten Muzhik," lazily rang the watchman's bell. Every time he tugged at the rope it caught on a piece of loose roofing which let out a plaintive zing followed by the short, dreary clang of the little bell.

I recalled the watchman's saying:

"Lord preserve us from sleepless nights."

It was ghastly. And for some reason stifling. I broke out in a sweat, though the evening was cool. Would I have time to reach the watchman's hut if old man Kalinin should begin to climb out of his coffin?

I knew the cemetery well; dozens of times I had played among the graves with Yaz and my other friends. Over there near the church my mother lay buried.

Not everyone was asleep yet. From the settlement came splashes of laughter, fragments of song. Somewhere in the hills, or the railway sandpits, or the nearby village of Katyzovka, an accordion was screeching and sobbing. The blacksmith Myachov, permanently drunk, came staggering along the other side of the cemetery wall—I recognized him by his song:

> Our mama is too naughty
> To hold herself so haughty:
> She turned down every laddie
> In favour of her daddy.

It was encouraging to hear these last breaths of life, but with every ring of the bell things grew quieter, and the quietness surged like a river over the meadows, submerging and blotting out everything else. My soul was extinguished in limitless, bottomless nothingness, was utterly dissolved in an empty ocean where only the unapproachable stars lived and glowed, everything else being annihilated—dead and unwanted.

I wrapped myself up in my blanket and sat with my feet drawn up under me, facing the church, and every time I stirred the coffin squeaked and the sand grated.

Something struck the earth behind me once, and again, and then a piece of brick fell near the coffin. This was fearful, but I immediately guessed that Valyok and his friends were throwing things over the wall to frighten me. The fact that there were people nearby made me feel better.

I began to think of my mother. Once when I had tried smoking a cigarette she had begun to whip me, and I had said:

"Don't touch me—I feel bad enough as it is. I'm sick."

After the whipping I crept behind the stove, and heard her say to Granny:

"Such a hardhearted boy! He doesn't love anyone!"

It pained me to hear her say that. Whenever my mother punished me I felt sorry and ashamed for her. It rarely happened that her punishments were deserved.

And indeed there was much that was painful in life. Take those fellows on the other side of the wall. They knew very well that it was terrifying for me to be alone here in the cemetery, yet they tried to frighten me all the more. Why?

I wanted to shout to them:

"Go to the devil!"

But that was dangerous. Who knew how the devil would take such a thing? Undoubtedly he was somewhere close at hand.

The sand was full of bits of mica, which glittered dully in the moonlight, and they reminded me of how one day, while lying on a raft on the Oka and gazing into the water, a little water imp had suddenly appeared before my very eyes; it rolled over on its side so that it resembled a man's cheek and glanced at me with round little bird's eyes before it dived back into the depths, fluttering like a falling maple leaf.

My memory became intensely active, piling up various incidents from my life into a barricade against my imagination, which insisted on creating all sorts of horrors.

Here, for example, came a hedgehog, tapping across the sand on firm little paws. It made me think of a house-goblin—just as tiny and tousled.

I remembered how Granny used to crouch in front of the stove and chant:

"Good little goblin, gobble up the roaches. . . ."

Far beyond the city, which was out of sight, the sky began to brighten; the cold of early morning nipped my cheeks; my eyelids grew heavy. I curled up in a ball and pulled the blanket over my head. Let come what might!

Granny woke me up. She was standing beside me tugging at the blanket and saying:

"Get up! Are you chilled? Well, was it so fearful?"

"Yes it was, but don't tell anyone. Don't let the fellows know."

"And why not?" she asked in some surprise. "If you had nothing to fear, you'd be left with nothing to boast of."

We went home, and on the way she said tenderly:

"You have to try everything yourself, pigeon-widgeon; you have to learn everything for yourself. If you don't find out for yourself, no one will teach you."

By evening I had become the "hero" of our street. Everyone asked me:

"Wasn't it awful?"

And when I said: "Yes, it was!" they shook their heads and exclaimed: "You see?"

The shopkeeper announced with loud conviction:

"So it means they lied that Kalinin comes out of his grave. If he came out, would he have been scared of the boy? With one slap of his hand he'd have whisked him out of the cemetery, heaven only knows where."

Ludmilla looked at me in fond wonder, and it seems that even grandfather was pleased, for he kept grinning at me. Only Churka said sullenly:

"It's easy for him—his grandmother's a witch!"

My brother Kolya faded away as inconspicuously as a star at dawn. He and Granny and I slept out in a shed, on a woodpile spread with old rags. On the other side of a flimsy wall the landlord kept his chickens. Every evening we could hear the sated hens clucking and flapping their wings, while every morning we were awakened by the full-throated crowing of a golden cock.

"They'd ought to chop your head off!" grumbled Granny one morning as she woke up.

I was awake already, and lay watching the sun streaming through chinks in the wall and the silver motes dancing in its rays like words in a fairy tale. Mice rustled in the woodpile, and little red beetles with black-spotted wings went scuttling back and forth.

Sometimes to escape the stifling fumes of the chicken droppings, I would crawl out of the shed and onto the roof, from where I watched the neighbours wake up—huge and eyeless and swollen with sleep.

Out of one of the windows popped the matted head of boatman Fermanov, a surly drunkard, who turned the slits of his puffy eyes up to the sun and grunted like a pig. Grandfather ran out into the yard, slicking down his scanty red hair with both hands. He was hurrying to the bathhouse to douse himself with cold water. The landlord's tongue-wagging cook looked like a cuckoo, with her sharp nose and freckles; the landlord himself resembled a fat old pigeon, and everybody reminded me of some bird or beast.

The morning was clear and lovely, but I felt sad and yearned to go off to the fields where I could be alone. I knew that people were sure to spoil the bright day.

Once when I was lying up on the roof, Granny called me and said softly, nodding toward the bed:

"Kolya's dead."

The child had slipped off the red calico pillow onto the felt matting. He was blue and naked, his shirt having climbed up about his neck, revealing his bloated belly and sore-spotted legs. His hands were thrust behind his back, as though he had tried to raise himself, and his head had fallen slightly to one side.

"Thank goodness he's dead," said Granny as she combed her hair. "How could he have gone on living, such a measly little creature?"

Grandfather came in and pranced about the body, carefully touching the child's closed eyes.

"Don't touch him with unwashed hands!" said Granny sharply.

"Came into the world—breathed—ate—and all for nothing—" he muttered.

"Think what you're saying!" interrupted Granny.

He glanced at her vacantly and went out into the yard.

"Do what you like," said he. "I have no money to bury him with."

"Ah, you miserable creature!"

I went away and returned only in the evening.

Kolya was buried on the following morning. I did not go to the church and sat out the entire funeral ceremony beside my mother's grave, which had been dug open to receive my little brother. My dog and Yaz's father sat with me. The latter had taken a mere trifle for digging the grave and kept bragging to me about it.

"It's just because you're a friend of mine, else I'd have charged a ruble."

As I gazed into the yellow hole from which issued an unpleasant odour, I caught a glimpse of black, mouldy boards. My slightest movement sent streams of sand slipping to the bottom of the hole. I moved on purpose, so that the sand would cover those boards.

"None of your tricks, lad," said Yaz's father as he drew on his pipe.

Granny carried over a little white coffin; the "Rotten Muzhik" jumped into the hole, took it out of her hands, placed it beside the mouldy boards, jumped out of the hole, and started pushing in the sand with his feet and a spade. His pipe smoked like a censer. Granny and grandfather helped him in silence. There was no priest, there were no beggars; only the three of us among that crowd of crosses.

As she handed the money to the watchman, Granny said in a tone of rebuke:

"But you did disturb my Varya's nest, didn't you?"

"I couldn't help it. Even so I took a bit of the neighbour's earth. That's all right— no harm done."

Granny bowed to the earth before the grave, sniffled, sobbed, and walked away. Behind her went grandfather, pulling at his worn frock coat and hiding his eyes under the peak of his cap.

"We sowed our seed in unploughed earth," he said suddenly, scurrying up ahead of us like a crow over the furrows.

"What did he say?" I asked Granny.

"Lord knows. He has his own way of thinking," she replied.

It was hot. Granny plodded slowly ahead, her feet sinking in the warm sand. Often she stopped to wipe her perspiring face with her handkerchief.

With a great effort I asked:

"That blackness there in the grave—was that mother's coffin?"

"Yes," she said with asperity. "That old idiot of a gravedigger! Less than a year gone by and Varya a-rotting already! It's all account of the sand—lets the water through. Clay's better."

"Does everybody rot?"

"Everybody. Only the saints escape it."

"You'll never rot!"

She stopped, straightened the cap on my head, and said to me solemnly:

"Don't think about that. You mustn't now, hear?"

But I thought to myself:

"How ugly and disgusting death is! How hateful!"

I was feeling very bad.

When we reached home grandfather had already put up the samovar and set the table.

"We'll have some tea; the weather's so hot," said he. "I'll brew my own—for all of us."

He went over to Granny and patted her on the shoulder.

"Well, what do you say, mother?"

Granny waved her hand.

"What's there to say?"

"That's it. The Lord's pouring out His wrath on us, snatching us away bit by bit. If only families lived tight together, like the fingers of your hand—"

It had been a long time since he had spoken so gently and peaceably. I listened to him, hoping that he would ease my pain and help me forget the yellow hole with those black patches showing.

But Granny interrupted him sharply:

"Stop it, father! You've been saying those words all your life, but have they ever helped anybody? All your life you've been eating into people, like rust into iron."

Grandfather glanced at her with a grunt, and fell silent.

At the gate that evening I told Ludmilla what I had seen in the morning, but it seemed to make no impression.

"It's better to be an orphan. If my mother

and father died I'd leave my sister to my brother's care and become a nun for the rest of my life. What else could I do? I'll never get married because I'm lame and can't work. And I'd only bring more lame children into the world."

She spoke sensibly, like all the women on our street, but it seems I took no further interest in her after that evening. Indeed my life became such that I rarely saw her thereafter.

A few days after the death of my brother, grandfather said to me:

"Go to bed earlier tonight. I'll wake you at sunrise and we'll go to the forest for wood."

"And I'll gather herbs," announced Granny.

The fir and birch forest which grew on the marshes some three versts from our settlement, was full of brush and fallen branches. On one side it extended to the Oka River, on the other, it reached beyond the Moscow highway. Like a tall black tent above its soft bushiness rose the cluster of pines called "Savelov's Mane."

All that wealth belonged to Count Shuvalov, who was lax in guarding it. The Kunavino townsfolk looked upon the forest as their own, helping themselves to brushwood, chopping down dead trees or even live ones. In the autumn dozens of people came with axes in their hands and ropes about their waists to collect a store of firewood for the winter.

At dawn the three of us crossed the dewy, silver-green fields. A lackadaisical Russian sun rose slowly above the Oka, above the ruddy flanks of Dyatlovy Hills, above white Nizhni-Novgorod with its green orchards and golden cupolas. From the quiet, turbid Oka came a quiet, sleepy breeze. Golden buttercups nodded heads heavy with dew, bluebells drooped mutely to the earth, varicoloured straw flowers reared stiffly from the grudging sod, while the pinks, those "beauties of the night," burst into crimson stars.

The forest advanced upon us in dark, serried ranks. The winged firs were like great birds; the birches like maidens. Over the fields came the acrid smell of the marshlands. My dog, which was walking beside me with its pink tongue lolling, stopped, sniffed, and shook its foxlike head in some uncertainty.

Grandfather was wearing Granny's warm jacket and an old peakless cap. He smiled to himself as he advanced stealthily on his spindly legs as though he were creeping up on someone. Granny was dressed in a blue blouse and black skirt and had tied a white kerchief over her head. She rolled along so briskly that it was hard to keep up with her.

The nearer we drew to the forest, the more animated grandfather became. He grunted and sniffed in great breaths of air and began to talk, at first spasmodically and inarticulately, then gaily and beautifully, as though he were growing intoxicated.

"The forests are the gardens of the Lord. Nobody planted them but the wind—the Divine breath from out His mouth. Used to be, back in Zhiguli, in the days of my youth, when I was still a boatman—Ah, Alexei, it'll not be given you to see what I saw!

Along the Oka—forests from Kasimov to Murom! Or beyond the Volga—forests running clean up to the Urals! An endless marvel it was!"

Granny glanced at me from under her brows and winked, while he plodded on, stumbling over the ruts as he scattered dry handfuls of words which took root in my memory.

"We were hauling a barge loaded with sunflower-seed oil from Saratov to the fair on Makar's Day, and we had a foreman over us named Kirillo, from Purekh, and a Tatar bailer from Kasimov—Asaf was his name, if my memory's not failed me. Well, when we got to Zhiguli, we were struck by a downstream wind—knocked the strength out of us, brought us to a halt, left us there gasping, so we climbed the bank to boil some porridge. It was May on the earth, and the Volga a sea, and the whitecaps riding her like flocks of swans—thousands of them floating down to the Caspian. And the hills of Zhiguli, green with spring, reaching up to the heaven, and white clouds grazing there, and the sun pouring gold over the earth. So we rested and drank it all in, our hearts melting. Down on the river it was northcold, but here on the bank it was warm and sweet-smelling. Towards evening that Kirillo of ours—a solemn muzhik, well on in years—gets on his feet, takes off his cap, and says: 'Well, lads, I'm no longer your master or your servant. You must go on alone, for I'm off to the woods!' We just sat there with our mouths open. Who'd ever heard of such a thing? We couldn't go on without someone to answer to the master for us—people don't go walking around without a head. To be sure it was the Volga, but even so we might go astray. And Man is the wildest of beasts— he stops at nothing. So we were frightened. But he stuck to it: 'I don't want to go on living like this, being a shepherd to you. I'm off to the woods!' There were those of us who wanted to beat him and tie him up, but there were others who thought his way. 'Stop!' they cried, and the Tatar bailer adds: 'I'm off along with him!' That was bad indeed. The boss owed the Tatar for two trips already and here he was halfway along the third—a great deal of money those days. We shouted until nightfall, but when night came seven went off, leaving us there alone—some fifteen or sixteen of us. That's what the forest does to you!"

"Did they go off to be robbers?"

"Maybe robbers; maybe hermits. In those days people didn't draw much difference."

Granny crossed herself.

"Ah, Mother of God! When you start thinking about people, it sets your heart to bleeding."

"We're all blessed with enough sense to know where the devil's luring us."

We entered the forest along a wet path running between sickly fir groves and lumpy swampland. I thought how fine it would be to enter the forest for good, like Kirillo from Purekh. There was no fighting and drinking and brawling in the forest; there you could forget about your grandfather's greed and your mother's grave in the sand— about everything that hurt you and weighed so heavily on your heart.

When we reached a dry spot Granny said:
"Time to have a bite. Sit down."

Out of her basket she took some rye bread,
green onions, pickles, salt, and some cottage
cheese wrapped in cloth. Grandfather gazed
at it all, blinking uneasily.

"And just to think—me not bringing a
thing!"

"There's enough for all of us."

We sat with our backs against the bronze
trunk of a tall pine; the air was filled with
the odour of resin, and a soft breeze came
from the fields, arching the grass. With a
swarthy hand Granny plucked various herbs,
telling me of the healing properties of plan-
tain and St. John's wort, and of the magic
power wielded by ferns and the sticky rose-
bay.

Grandfather cut the underbrush and I was
to pile it together in one spot, but I
stole away into the thickets after Granny,
who went sailing among the mighty tree
trunks, dipping to the needle-soft earth from
time to time as though diving into water.
As she walked she kept talking to herself:

"The mushrooms have shown themselves early this year—means there'll be few. It's bad care you're taking of the poor, Lord—even a mushroom is food for those as have none."

I followed her soundlessly, trying hard not to be seen; I did not wish to interrupt her conversation with God, the frogs, and the grasses.

But she saw me.

"Ran away from grandfather, did you?"

Bending down to the black earth robed in the rich brocade of the plants, she told me how God had once become so angry with human beings that He flooded the earth and drowned all living things.

"But in good time His Blessed Mother gathered all the seeds in her basket and hid them away. After the flood she went to the sun and said: 'Be so good as to dry up the earth from end to end, and the good people will sing your praises forever.' So the sun dried up the earth and she sowed the seeds she had hidden away. The Lord had a look: there was the earth all grown over again with grass and cattle and people! Who was

so bold, says He, to pit his will against Mine?
Then she confessed; but the Lord Himself
was sorry to see the land forlorn, so He says
to her: 'It's a good thing, what you've done,
Mother.'"

I liked the tale, but it surprised me, and
I said in all seriousness:

"Was it really like that? The Virgin was
born long after the flood."

Now it was Granny's turn to be surprised.

"Who ever told you such a thing?"

"In school—it's written in the books."

She was relieved to hear it and said to me:

"Don't listen to them; forget what's in
the books. The books just lie."

And she gave a gay, soft little laugh.

"Just to think of making up a thing like
that, the idiots! Like as if God could exist
without a Mother! Who, then, ever gave
birth to Him?"

"I don't know."

"That's it. Reached the 'I don't know'
stage of your learning."

"The priest said the Virgin was born of
Joachim and Anna."

This was the last straw. Granny looked me sternly in the eye and said:

"In other words she was Marya Joachimovna? I'll tan your hide for you if you dare to think such a thing!"

A minute later she explained:

"The Holy Virgin always existed—long before anyone else. God was born of her, and then. . . ."

"And what about Christ?"

Granny closed her eyes in perplexity.

"Christ? Ah yes—Christ—"

I saw that I had won; I had tangled her up in the mysteries of creation, and this upset me.

We kept going farther into the forest, into the blue mist pierced by golden sunrays. The warm, snug forest had its own peculiar sound, a dreamy sound, making you yourself feel dreamy. The crossbills twittered, the titmice chirped, the cuckoos laughed, the orioles whistled, the jealous goldfinches sang an incessant song, while that strange bird, the pine finch, warbled contemplatively. Emerald toads leaped out from under our feet; a grass snake raised its golden head from among the roots which served as ambush. With a chatter of tiny teeth a squirrel flashed its plumelike tail through the pine boughs. There was a myriad of things to be seen, but one wanted to see more—to go on and on.

Huge, wraithlike figures appeared among the trunks of the pines, only to vanish in the green depths, whence came glimpses of a blue and silver sky. The earth was strewn with a luxurious carpet of moss embroidered with blueberries and festoons of cranberries; bilberries glistened in the grass like drops of blood, while the scent of the mushrooms rose temptingly to the nostrils.

"Blessed Virgin, light of the world," prayed Granny with a sigh.

It was as though the forest belonged to her, and she to it. She walked along like a great she-bear, seeing everything, admiring everything, and murmuring words of gratitude. Warmth seemed to flow from her into the woods, and it gave me particular pleasure to see the moss rise again and preen itself after her foot had pressed it down.

As I walked I kept thinking how good it would be to become a robber and steal from the rich to give to the poor. If only everyone were gay and well fed, knowing no envy, never barking at each other like vicious dogs! And how good it would be to go to Granny's God and to her Blessed Virgin and tell them the whole truth about how miserably people lived, and how horridly, how hurtfully they buried each other in the dreadful sand. And how much needless suffering there was on the earth! And if the Virgin were convinced, let her give me the wisdom to change things and make them better. Let the people listen to me and trust me, and I would be sure to find a better way of life! What did it matter that I was still a child? Christ was only a year older when the learned men listened to him in the Temple.

Once I became so absorbed in my thoughts that I fell into a deep hole, scratching my side on a dead branch and scraping the skin off the back of my head. As I sat in the cold, sticky mud at the bottom of the hole, I realized to my shame that I was unable to climb out. I did not wish to frighten Granny by shouting, but there was nothing else to do.

She hauled me out in a jiffy and crossed herself as she said:

"Thank the Lord! Happily it turned out to be an empty hole, but what if the bear had been in it?"

And she laughed through her tears. Then she washed me in a brook, put some leaves on my cuts to take out the pain, bound them up with her blouse, and led me to a railway-guard's lodge, for I was too weak to walk home.

Almost every day I would say to Granny:

"Let's go to the forest."

She was only too glad to consent, and thus we spent our time until late in the autumn, gathering herbs and berries, mushrooms and nuts. Granny sold what we gathered and we lived on the money.

"Spongers!" squeaked grandfather, although we never touched his food.

The forest roused in me a sense of peace and well-being; and this feeling soothed

my pain and helped me forget all unpleasantness, while at the same time I developed a
remarkable keenness of perception: sight and
hearing became sharper, memory more re-
tentive, my reservoir of impressions expanded.

And I grew more amazed than ever at
my grandmother. I had always considered
her a person above all others, the kindest
and wisest creature on earth, and she constantly confirmed this conviction.

One evening when we reached the edge
of the forest on our way home from gathering
mushrooms, Granny sat down to rest, while
I went off in the hope of finding more mushrooms.

Suddenly I heard her voice and looked
about to see her sitting calmly on the path,
cutting off the roots of the mushrooms we had
found, while beside her stood a lean grey
dog with its tongue hanging out.

"Go away, go away now, that's a nice
beast," she was saying. "Go away, and God
with you."

Not long before that, Valyok had poisoned
my dog, and I wanted to lure this new one to

come with me. I ran out onto the path. The dog arched strangely without turning its head, glanced at me with cold, hungry green eyes, and leaped into the forest with its tail between its legs. The animal's gait was not that of a dog, and when I whistled it plunged wildly into the bushes.

"See that?" asked Granny with a smile. "At first I mistook it for a dog. Then I had another look—fangs like a wolf, and neck too. I had quite a fright. Well then, says I, if it's a wolf you be, you'd best go away. Fortunately wolves are peaceful in summer."

She never became lost in the forest, unerringly finding her way home. From the scent of the herbs she knew what kind of mushrooms grew in one place, what kind in another, and often she tested my knowledge:

"Under what tree do the red ones grow?" "How can you tell a good *syroyezhka* from a poisonous one?" "What kind of mushroom hides under ferns?"

A tiny scratch on the bark of a tree would lead her to a squirrel's hole. I would climb up the tree and empty the nest of its winter supply of nuts; sometimes there would be as many as ten pounds stored away.

Once when I was occupied in such a way, a hunter buried twenty-seven bits of small-shot in the flesh of my right side. Granny dug out eleven of them with a needle; the rest remained under my skin for many years, gradually working their way out.

It pleased my grandmother to see me endure pain stoically.

"Good lad!" she would say. "Pain overcome is a battle won."

Whenever the sale of mushrooms and nuts brought her a little surplus money, she would place her "quiet mercy" on the window sills, while she herself went about in rags and patches even on holidays.

"Look worse'n a beggar—a disgrace to me," grumbled grandfather.

"That's all right. I'm not your daughter nor yet a maid looking for a husband."

Their quarrels became more and more frequent.

"I've not sinned worse than others," cried grandfather, voicing his injury, "but I'm punished worse."

Granny would tease him.

"The devil knows a man's worth," she would say, explaining to me when we were alone: "The old man has an awful fear of the devil. See how old he's got from his fear? Ah me, the poor creature!"

That summer in the forest strengthened my body, but made me unsociable; I lost interest in the lives of my playmates and of Ludmilla. I now found her cleverness tiresome.

One day grandfather returned from the city soaked to the skin. It was autumn and raining. He shook himself like a sparrow on the doorstep and said triumphantly:

"Well, lazybones, tomorrow you go to work!"

"Where?" asked Granny irritably.

"To your sister Matryona's—to work for her son."

"You've made a bad choice, father!"

"Silence, you old fool! Maybe they'll make a draughtsman out of him."

Granny lowered her head without a word.

That evening I told Ludmilla I was going to live in the city.

"Soon I'm to be taken there too," she said thoughtfully. "Papa wants them to cut my leg off. They say I'll get well if they do."

She had grown thinner during the summer. Her face had assumed a bluish tinge and her eyes had grown enormous.

"Are you afraid?" I asked.

"Yes," she replied, and began to weep noiselessly.

There was nothing I could say to comfort her. I too was afraid of life in the city. For a long time we sat crouching close to each other in miserable silence.

Had it been summer I would have talked Granny into going begging as she had done as a girl. We could have taken Ludmilla with us —I would have pulled her along in a little cart.

But it was autumn. A damp wind swept the streets and the sky was veiled in endless clouds; the earth faded, grew soiled and sullen.

IV

Again I went to live in the city, in a two-storeyed white house resembling a coffin built to hold many people. The house was new, but seemed to be ailing—it was as bloated as a beggar who, upon suddenly inheriting a fortune, has gorged himself. It stood sidewise to the street, with eight windows to a storey on the street side, four to a storey on the side which should have been the façade. The lower windows faced a narrow passageway in the yard, while the upper ones looked out over the fence onto a dirty ravine and a little house belonging to a laundress.

There was no street in the ordinary sense of the word. In front of the house extended this dirty ravine crossed in two places by narrow dikes. On the left it extended to a prisoners' colony, near which the householders had chosen a spot for dumping their refuse over the embankment, so that the bottom of the ravine had become covered with a thick green ooze. To the right the ravine ended in the putrid Zvezdin Pond. The centre of the ravine was just opposite our house. Half of it was filled with rubbish and overgrown with nettles, burdock, and sorrel. The other half had been turned into a garden by Father Dorimedont Pokrovsky. In the garden stood a summerhouse built of green laths which snapped when you threw stones at them.

The place was impossibly dull and bumptiously dirty. Autumn weather turned the weedy clay soil into a sort of red tar which clung mercilessly to your feet. Never before had I seen so much dirt in so small a space, and after the purity of the fields and forests to which I had become accustomed, this sordid corner of the town depressed me beyond words.

Beyond the ravine extended dilapidated grey fences, among which I discovered the brown house where I had lived while serving as boy in the boot-shop. The proximity of this house made me feel even worse. Why must I again live on that street?

I was acquainted with my new master. Formerly he and his brother had visited my mother; it was his brother who had piped so amusingly:

"Andrei-papá, Andrei-papá."

Neither of them had changed a whit. The elder, who had an aquiline nose and long hair, was pleasant and apparently kindhearted; Victor, the younger, had the same horse face and the same freckles. Their mother was Granny's sister, but she was very noisy and irascible. The elder son was married to a dark-eyed woman as white and plump as a wheaten bun.

Twice during the first few days she said to me:

"I once gave your mother a silk cloak with jet beads on it."

For some reason I did not wish to believe that she had made mother a present, and that mother had accepted it. The next time she reminded me of this cloak I said to her:

"If you gave it away, why boast of it?"

She started back, astounded.

"Wha-a-a-t? Who do you think you're talking to?"

Her face broke out in red blotches, she rolled her eyes and called for her husband.

He entered the kitchen with a pair of compasses in his hand and a pencil behind his ear. When he had heard his wife out he said to me:

"You must never be impertinent."

Then he turned impatiently to his wife:

"Don't bother me with such nonsense!"

"What do you mean—nonsense! When your own kin—"

"Damn my own kin!" he cried, and rushed out.

I also disliked the fact that these people were kin to Granny. According to my observation, relatives treated each other worse than strangers. Knowing each other's weak and ridiculous sides better than anyone else, they spread worse gossip, quarrelled and fought more often among themselves.

I liked my master. He had a winning way of tossing back his hair and pushing it behind his ear, and for some reason he reminded me of "That's Fine." He often laughed heartily, at which times his grey eyes would gleam good-naturedly and amusing wrinkles would appear on either side of his hawklike nose.

"Enough of your fighting, you roaring chickens," he would say to his mother and wife with a smile, exposing small, close-set teeth.

The two women quarrelled every day; I was always surprised to see how quickly they flared up. From early morning the two women went rushing through the rooms in a state of uncombed dishabille as though the house were on fire. They fussed about all day long, resting only at the table during dinner, tea, and supper. They ate and drank themselves into a stupor. At dinner they would discuss the food, lazily parrying words in preparation for a serious quarrel. No matter what the mother-in-law cooked, the daughter-in-law would say:

"Mama never made it like that."

"Then it must have been worse."

"No it wasn't—it was better!"

"Then why don't you go live with your mama?"

"I'm the mistress here!"

"And who do you think I am?"

"Enough of it, you roaring chickens!" the

husband would say. "What's the matter—have you gone mad?"

Everything in the house was inexplicably strange and ludicrous. In order to enter the dining room from the kitchen it was necessary to pass through a narrow little lavatory, the only one in the house. Through this room food and the samovar were carried to the table. It was the cause of much joking and, often of amusing incidents. My duties included seeing that the toilet tank was filled with water. I slept in the kitchen opposite the door to the lavatory and next to the door leading onto the front porch. My head became overheated by the kitchen stove, while my feet froze from the draft creeping under the porch door. On going to bed I collected all the floor mats and heaped them on my feet.

It was dull and empty in the drawing room with its two pier glasses, two card tables, twelve straight-backed chairs, and gilt-framed pictures received as gift attachments to subscriptions to the magazine *Niva*. The small parlour was stuffed with gaudily upholstered furniture and with shelves exhibiting the silver and tea sets which were part of the bride's dowery. Three lamps, vying with each other in size, formed its crowning glory. The windowless bedroom was furnished with an enormous bed, trunks, and wardrobes giving off a scent of leaf tobacco and camomile. These three rooms were always empty, while the family squeezed into the tiny dining room where they were constantly getting in each other's way. Immediately after an eight o'clock breakfast, the husband and his brother would extend the table, cover it with sheets of white paper, bring drawing instruments, pencils, saucers filled with India ink, and set to work, one at the far end of the table, the other opposite him. The table was shaky and took up the entire room, and whenever my younger mistress and the child's nurse emerged from the nursery, they were sure to bump into it.

"Can't you keep out of the way?" Victor shouted on one such occasion.

The mistress turned a hurt face to her husband and said:

"Vasya, tell him not to shout at me."

"Then don't shake the table," advised her husband peaceably.

"But I'm pregnant and it's crowded here."

"All right, we'll take our work into the drawing room."

"Heavens! Who ever heard of working in the drawing room!"

In the doorway of the lavatory appeared the face of my elder mistress, Matryona Ivanovna, red as a beet from the kitchen stove.

"Just look at that, Vasya!" she cried. "Here you are working your fingers off and she complaining that four rooms is not enough to have her puppies in! It's a princess you've wed, without a brain in her head!"

Victor laughed spitefully.

"Enough of this!" cried the husband.

But his wife, after directing a stream of abuse at her mother-in-law, fell across the table and moaned:

"I'll go away! I'll die!"

"You're interfering with my work, devil take you!" shouted the husband, white with strain. "This is a lunatic asylum! After all,

it's for you I stand here breaking my back—
to feed you, you roaring chickens!"

At first these quarrels frightened me. I
was especially frightened once when the wife
grabbed up the bread knife, locked herself in
the toilet, and began to scream wildly. For a
moment everything was deadly quiet, then the
husband ran to the door and braced himself
against it, bending double.

"Climb up! Break the window and pull
the hook off the door!" he cried to me.

In a trice I was up on his back and had
broken the glass above the door, but when
I leaned down to take off the hook, the wife
beat me over the head with the handle of the
knife. I managed to unlock the door, however,
and the husband then took his wife by storm,
dragging her into the dining room and wrench-
ing the knife out of her hand. As I sat in
the kitchen nursing my battered head I realized that my suffering had been in vain.
The knife was so dull that it was impossible
to cut even butter with it, let alone one's
throat. Nor had it been necessary for me to
climb up on my master's back; I could have

stood on a chair to break the window; and it would have been easier for a grownup to unhook the door—his arms would have been longer. Thereafter the scenes in this house did not frighten me.

The brothers were members of the church choir. Sometimes they would sing softly at their work. The elder would begin in his baritone:

> *Into the foaming waters*
> *The maiden's ring I tossed,*

and the younger would add in his tenor:

> *And with the ring, contentment*
> *And earthly bliss were lost.*

From the nursery would come my younger mistress' hushed voice saying:

"Are you crazy? Don't you know the baby's asleep?"

Or:

"You're a married man, Vasya, and it's unbecoming for you to sing about the maidens. And besides, the bell will be ringing for vespers soon."

"Well, then we'll sing church music."

But my mistress insisted that church music should not be sung just anywhere, and especially here (with an eloquent gesture toward the lavatory door).

"That's the limit," growled my master. "We'll have to move into another apartment."

Just as frequently he said they would have to get a new table, but he had been reiterating this for three years.

Whenever I heard these people discuss their neighbours, I was reminded of the gossip in the boot-shop. It became clear to me that my employers too considered themselves the best people in town. They knew all the rules for correct behaviour and mercilessly judged everyone else according to these rules, which were beyond my comprehension. Their habit of judging others roused in me a feeling of bitter resentment against them and against the rules, which it now gave me the greatest satisfaction to violate.

I had to work very hard. Fulfilling the duties of a housemaid, I had to scrub the kitchen floor and shine the samovar and other brassware on Wednesdays, while on

Saturdays I had to scrub all the floors and both stairways. I chopped and brought in wood for the stoves, washed the dishes, cleaned the vegetables, went marketing with my mistress so as to carry her basket, and ran to the grocery and the chemist's shop.

My elder mistress—grandmother's noisy, irascible sister—got up at six o'clock every morning. After a brief wash, she would kneel in her shift before the icons and for a long time complain to the Lord about her life, her sons, and her daughter-in-law.

"Oh Lord," she would complain lugubriously, touching her forehead with the tips of her fingers gathered to a point. "There's nothing I want of Thee, Lord—nothing I ask of Thee but a bit of rest—a bit of peace, if it be Thy will."

Her cries woke me up, and I lay watching her from under the blanket, listening in fright to her impassioned prayers. The autumn morning glanced murkily through the rain-washed kitchen window; in the cold dawn her grey figure kept bending to the floor as she crossed herself furiously. The kerchief would slip off her small head, leaving her thin, colourless hair straggling about her shoulders. As she adjusted the kerchief with a brusque movement of her left hand she would mutter:

"This damn rag!"

Violently striking her forehead, shoulders and belly in the sign of the cross, she would snarl out her petition: "If you love me, Lord, punish that daughter-in-law of mine. Make her pay for the way she insults me! And open the eyes of my son—so he'll see what she's really like, and what Victor's like too. And help Victor, Lord. Show him Thy mercy."

Victor, too, was sleeping here in the kitchen on a high bunk. The complaints of his mother woke him up and he cried sleepily:

"Bawling again at such an hour! You're simply a visitation, ma!"

"Now, now, go back to sleep," whispered his mother apologetically. For a minute or two she would rock back and forth in silence, then again cry vengefully:

"And may the very marrow freeze in their bones, and may their blood dry up!"

Even grandfather had never prayed with such malevolence.

She would wake me up when her prayers were said.

"Get up. Enough of your lolling here— that's not what we hired you for. Put up the samovar and bring in the wood.—Aha! again you neglected to get the chips ready in the evening!"

I tried to work quickly so as not to hear the sibilant mutterings of the old woman, but it was impossible to please her. She swept like a snowstorm about the kitchen, hissing:

"Shhh, you little devil! You'll wake up Victor, and then I'll show you! Run to the shop!"

For weekday breakfasts we bought two pounds of wheaten bread and two-kopeks' worth of buns for the younger mistress. When I brought home the bread the women would examine it suspiciously, weighing it on their palms and asking:

"Wasn't there a little piece to make up the weight? No? Come, now, open your mouth!" Then they would shout triumphantly: "He ate the piece! He ate it! There's the crumbs on his teeth!"

I worked willingly. I enjoyed whisking away the dirt in the house, scrubbing the floors, shining the brassware, doorknobs, and stove plates. More than once when things were peaceful I heard the women remark:

"He works hard."

"He's clean."

"But very impudent."

"You must remember who brought him up."

Both of them tried to make me respect them, but I considered them half crazy, had no use for them, refused to obey them, and always answered them back. The young mistress must have noticed how I reacted to some of her remarks, and for that reason she kept saying to me:

"You mustn't forget that we've taken you from a family of beggars. I once presented your mother with a silk cloak trimmed with jet beads!"

One day I said to her:

"Do you want to skin me in exchange for that cloak of yours?"

"Heavens! Why, he's capable of setting the house afire!" she cried in fright.

I was taken aback—why should I set fire to the house?

Both of them kept complaining to my master about me, and he would say sternly:

"You better watch your step, young man!"

But one day he turned wearily to his wife and mother:

"You're fine ones, you are. You ride that boy like he was a horse. Any other'd have run away long ago, or simply died of overwork!"

This angered the women to the point of tears.

"How dare you say such things in front of him, you long-haired fool!" shouted his wife, stamping her foot in fury. "How's he going to obey me after listening to things like that? Don't forget I'm pregnant!"

His mother wailed plaintively:

"God forgive you, Vasili, but remember my words: you'll spoil that boy yet!"

And they walked away in a huff.

"See what a scene you've caused, you little devil? I'll send you back to your grandfather, that's what I'll do, and you can return to your ragpicking," he said sternly.

"Better to be a ragpicker than live with you," I retorted, unable to bear the insult. "You brought me here as an apprentice, but what are you teaching me? How to carry out the garbage?"

My master grabbed me gently by the hair and looked me in the eyes as he said:

"You're a little ruffian all right! That won't do, brother, not at a-a-all!"

I was sure he would send me home, but two days later he entered the kitchen with a pencil, ruler, T-square, and roll of paper in his hands.

"When you finish polishing the knives, copy this," he said.

The drawing represented the façade of a two-storeyed house with innumerable windows and plaster ornamentation.

"Here's a pair of compasses. Measure all the lines, mark them off on the paper with dots, and join them with the ruler. First lengthwise—that will be horizontal, and then up and down—vertical. Go ahead."

I was delighted to be given clean work and to begin studying, but I gazed in awe at the paper and instruments, understanding nothing.

However, I immediately washed my hands, and set to work. I marked out all the horizontals and connected them. Very good! Except that for some reason there were three extra lines. Then I put in all the vertical lines, and to my great astonishment discovered that the house had strangely changed its appearance. The windows had climbed over onto the intervening wall space, while one of them hung in the air beyond the house. The main entranceway had also clambered up to the second floor, the cornice was higher than the roof, and the dormer window was on top of the chimney.

Almost in tears, I stood for a long time surveying this monstrosity, trying to understand how it could have happened. At length I decided to remedy things with the aid of my imagination. On all the cornices and along the ridge of the roof I drew sparrows and crows and pigeons, while on the ground in front of the windows I drew bandy-legged people with umbrellas which did not quite hide their deformities. Then I covered the entire picture with slanting lines and took it to my master.

He raised his brows, twisted a lock of hair, and remarked sullenly:

"What do you call this?"

"It's raining," I explained. "When it rains houses always look crooked because the rain is crooked. The birds—those are all birds—are hiding on the cornices. They always do that when it rains. And these people are running home. Here's a girl who fell down, and this is a lemon vendor."

"I certainly am grateful to you," said my master, leaning over the table until his hair swept the paper, shaking with laughter:

"I ought to wipe you off the earth, that's what, you roaring little sparrow!"

The young mistress came in, her belly swaying like a barrel, and looked at my drawing.

"Give him a thrashing," she said to her husband.

"Oh no, I didn't do any better myself when I just began," he answered imperturbably.

He marked the mistakes in my drawing with a red pencil and gave me another piece of paper.

"Try it again. You'll go on drawing this until you get it right."

My second attempt was better, except that one of the windows landed on the door of the porch. But I did not like to see the house empty, so I populated it with all sorts of people. At the windows sat young women fanning themselves, young men smoking cigarettes, and one nonsmoker just sitting and thumbing his nose at the others. On the porch stood a cabby with a dog lying at his feet.

"Why did you mess it all up again?" asked my master angrily.

I explained that the picture was very dull without any people in it, but he began to scold.

"Damn it all, if you want to learn, you've got to get down to business. That's just a lot of nonsense."

He was very much pleased when I finally managed to make a copy that resembled the original.

"See what you can do when you try? If you continue like this, you'll advance quickly."

And he assigned me a new task:

"Make a plan of our flat showing how the rooms are arranged, where the doors and windows are, and where everything is placed. I won't show you how. You must do it all yourself."

I went into the kitchen and tried to make up my mind where to start.

But at that point my lessons in draughting came to an end.

The old mistress came up to me and said viciously:

"So you want to be a draughtsman, do you?"

Grabbing me by the hair, she knocked my head against the table with such force that I cut my nose and lip. She jumped up and down, tore up my drawing, threw my instruments on the floor, then stood with her hands on her hips and shouted triumphantly:

"You just try it! You'll see what'll happen! So he wants to have somebody else work for him, does he, and get rid of his brother, his own flesh and blood!"

My master came running in with his wife pattering at his heels, and a wild scene ensued. All three threw themselves at one another, spluttering and howling; it ended by the women going off to cry and my master saying to me:

"For the present you'd better drop all that. Stop studying. You yourself can see the result."

I felt sorry for him, so crushed and helpless, forever being squelched by the shouts of these women.

Even before this I had realized that the old woman did not want me to study and did everything in her power to interfere. I had always asked her before sitting down to draw:

"Is there anything else you want me to do?"

"I'll tell you when there is," she would answer testily. "That's all you're good for —to sit there fooling away your time at the table."

And in a few minutes she would be sure to send me on some errand or say:

"The way you swept those entrance stairs! The corners are full of dust and rubbish! Get out and sweep them again!"

I would go to look, but never would I find any dust.

"So you want to argue with me, do you?" she would cry.

One day she poured kvass over all my drawings; another time she upset a bottle of icon oil on them. She did her mischief like a child, with childish cunning and a childish inability to hide it. Never had I seen a person who became irritated so quickly and easily as she did, or who had such a passion for complaining about everything and everyone. People in general enjoy complaining, but she did it with the delight of a singer in his song.

Her love for her son was a sort of madness. I was amused and frightened by the force of it, which I could describe only as a frenzied force. Sometimes after her morning prayers she would climb up on the stove, place her elbows on the edge of his bunk, and whisper ardently:

"My blessed child, blood of my blood, pure as a diamond, light as an angel feather! He's asleep. Sleep, my love, sleep; clothe your heart in happy dreams. Dream a bride for yourself, the fairest of the fair, a rich princess, or a merchant's daughter. And may your enemies die before they're born, and may your friends live a hundred years, and may the maids follow you in flocks, like ducks after a drake."

I found this excruciatingly funny. The coarse, lazy Victor resembled a woodpecker more than anything else, with his long nose and flamboyant clothes, his obstinacy and stupidity.

Sometimes his mother's whispering would wake him up, and he would mutter sleepily:

"I wish you'd go to hell, ma. What are you standing here spitting all over me for? There's no living with you!"

Usually she would climb down meekly and say with a laugh:

"Go ahead and sleep—sleep, you boor."

But sometimes her legs would give way under her, she would slump down on the edge of the stove with her mouth open, panting as if she had burned her tongue, and gasp out stinging words:

"Wha-a-at? It's your mother you're sending to hell, you bastard? Ugh, you stain on my soul, you accursed splinter stuck in my heart by the devil himself! If only you'd rotted before ever you was born!"

She used the filthy words of the drunken streets; it was frightful to listen to them.

She slept little and restlessly. Sometimes she would climb down off the stove several times in the course of the night, lunging against the couch where I was sleeping and waking me up.

"What's the matter?"

"Hush," she would whisper, crossing herself and gazing at something in the dark. "Oh Lord. . . . Elijah the Prophet. . . . Varvara the Blessed Martyr . . . save us from an untimely death. . . ."

With a shaking hand she would light a candle, her round face with its enormous nose puffy with strain and her grey eyes blinking nervously as she studied the objects distorted in the half-light. The kitchen was large, but a superabundance of trunks and cupboards made it seem small. Here the moonlight rested quietly, and an undying fire flickered before the holy images. Kitchen knives gleamed on the walls like icicles, while the dark skillets hanging from the shelves resembled hideous blind faces.

Always the old woman would climb cautiously off the stove, as though she were letting herself down a riverbank into the water. Then she would shuffle in her bare feet to the corner where a flap-eared water can hung like a severed head above the slop bucket. There too stood a tub of clean water.

After a noisy drink, she would peer through the blue filigree of frost on the window-pane.

"Have mercy on me, oh Lord; have mercy on my soul," she would plead under her breath.

Sometimes she would put out the candle and get down on her knees to mutter bitterly:

"Nobody loves me, God; nobody wants me."

Once back on top of the stove, she would make the sign of the cross over the chimney door, then thrust her hand inside to see that the damper was in place. Her hand would become covered with soot, causing her to swear roundly, after which she would immediately fall asleep, as though mesmerized. Whenever she offended me I would think what a pity it was that grandfather had not married her. She would have made him hustle all right! But she too would have met her match. I was constantly suffering from her spleen, but there were days when her puffy, cottony face grew sad, her eyes filmed with tears, and she would say:

"You think I have an easy time of it? I gave birth to my children, took care of them, gave them a start in life, and what do I get for it? Working as cook in their kitchen. Is that an easy thing to bear? And my son bringing in that woman to take my place— the place of his own flesh and blood! Is that right?"

"No, it isn't," I said sincerely.

"Ah, you see?"

And she began a shameless tirade against her daughter-in-law.

"I've been to the bathhouse with her and seen all there is to see. Whatever could have tempted him? Is it with tidbits like hers a man's to be lured?"

She always spoke in the filthiest possible way about the relationship between men and women. At first I was revolted by what she said, but soon I began to listen attentively and with the greatest interest, sensing some bitter truth behind her words.

"It's a great strength woman wields; she managed to deceive even God Himself," she insisted, slapping the table with her palm. "Eve's the one causes all people to go to Hell, and don't you forget it."

She could harangue endlessly about the power of woman, and it always seemed to me that she was trying to frighten someone with such talk. I especially remembered her saying that Eve had deceived God.

In our yard stood another house as large as ours. In four of the eight apartments of these houses lived officers. The regiment priest lived in another. The yard was always filled with batmen and their lady friends— cooks, laundresses, and parlourmaids. The kitchens were constantly the scenes of dramas and romances, with accompanying tears, fights, and quarrels. The soldiers fought with each other, with the ditchdiggers, or with workmen in the house. The women were always being beaten. Our yard seethed with what is called profligacy and dissipation— the bestial, uncurbed hunger of healthy youn ʊ men. At dinner, tea and supper I heard my master and mistress discuss in cynical detail this life filled with coarse sensualness, meaningless brutality, and the filthy braggadocio of conquest. The old woman always knew everything that happened in the yard and retold it gloatingly.

The young wife would listen to the tales with a smile on her full lips. Victor roared with laughter, but my master would make a wry face and say:

"Enough of that, mother."

"Good heavens, you don't even let me open my mouth!" complained the storyteller.

"That's all right, ma. Nothing to stop you here. It's just the family," encouraged Victor.

The elder son felt a squeamish pity for his mother. He always avoided being left alone with her, and if by chance this happened, his mother would shower him with complaints about his wife and then be sure to ask him for money. He would hastily thrust two or three rubles into her hand and some loose change.

"It's foolish of you to take this money, mother. Not that I begrudge it, but you shouldn't take it."

"Just for the beggars—and to buy myself some altar candles."

"Beggars! You'll be the ruin of Victor."

"You don't love your brother, sin on your soul!"

He would walk off with an impatient wave of his hand.

Victor was rude and scornful with his mother. He was an insatiable glutton. On Sundays the old woman made pancakes and always put aside an extra portion for him, hiding them in a jar under the couch on which

I slept. On returning from mass, Victor would make a dive for the jar and mutter:

"Couldn't you have left more, you old skinflint!"

"Hurry up and gobble those down before someone sees you."

"If anyone saw me I'd say you stole the pancakes for me, you old stitch-in-the-side."

One day I took out the jar and ate a couple myself. Victor beat me for it. He disliked me as much as I did him. He teased me, made me polish his boots three times a day, and on lying down on his bunk, would push away the slats and spit through them, aiming at my head.

Perhaps in imitation of his brother, who was always calling people "roaring chickens" he too had set phrases he loved to repeat. But they were amazingly stupid and inept.

"Mama, attention! Where's my socks?"

He tortured me with senseless questions, such as:

"Alexei, maybe you can tell me why it's written 'blue,' and pronounced 'glue'?

Why do they say 'catacombs' instead of 'cats and combs'? Why is it 'to decry' instead of 'to de-weep'?"

I hated the manner in which they all spoke. Brought up as I had been on the beautiful language of my grandmother and grandfather, at first I did not understand combinations of such uncombinable words as "terribly funny," "dying to eat," "awfully gay." It seemed to me that the funny could not be terrible, the gay could not be awful, and I found nothing suggesting death in the appetites of these people.

"Is it correct to speak like that?" I asked them.

"Just look who's set himself up as our teacher!" they replied angrily. "He needs to have his ears plucked!"

I found that "to pluck ears" was also wrong. You could pluck plants and flowers and fruit, but not ears.

They pulled my ears, trying to demonstrate that ears could indeed be plucked, but I remained unconvinced, and cried triumphantly:

"But my ears aren't plucked just the same!"

All about me I saw heartless mischief-making and filthy shamelessness—incomparably more than on the streets of Kunavino, which had no lack of brothels and streetwalkers. Behind the filth and mischief in Kunavino one was aware of something explaining the inevitability of such filth and mischief: drudgery, and a miserable, half-starved existence. Here people lived in ease and comfort, and work was substituted by senseless commotion. And upon everything lay the shadow of an insidious, irritating boredom.

I was extremely unhappy, but I felt even worse whenever Granny came to see me. She always entered the kitchen through the back door, and after crossing herself before the icons, would bow to the waist to her younger sister. This bow crushed me like a many-pood weight.

"Ah, so it's you, Akulina?" my mistress would say in a cold, offhand manner.

I did not recognize Granny. She humbly bit her lips in a way that changed her whole expression. Quietly taking a seat on the bench at the door beside the slop bucket, she would remain as silent as though guilty of some crime. To her sister's questions she replied softly and meekly.

I resented this, and said angrily:

"Why are you sitting there?"

"Hold your tongue. You're not the master here," she replied impressively, giving me an affectionate wink.

"He's always poking his nose in where it don't belong, no matter how you scold him or flog him," said my mistress, beginning her complaints.

Sometimes she would say to her sister malignantly:

"So it's a beggar you've become, eh, Akulina?"

"That's not so bad."

"Nothing's baneful, lest it's shameful."

"They say Christ Himself went begging."

"It's only dolts and heretics say such things, and you listen to them, old fool that you be! Christ was no beggar. He was the

Son of God and He's coming, as is written, to judge the quick and the dead—even the dead, mind you! There'll be no hiding from Him, not even if you burn yourself to ashes. He'll be paying you and Vasili back for being so proud; for turning me down when I came to ask help of you, my fine rich relatives."

"I always did what I could for you," replied Granny unperturbed. "But the Lord has seen fit to chastise us, as you all—"

"It's not enough for you—not enough!"

Her sister went on and on, lashing Granny with her indefatigable tongue, and as I listened to her yelping I wondered how Granny could stand it. I did not love her at such moments.

The young mistress entered the room and nodded condescendingly.

"Come into the dining room. That's all right—come right along."

"Wipe your feet, you rickety ramshackle!" cried the old woman as Granny went out.

My master greeted her cheerfully:

"Ah, the sage Akulina! How are you? Is old man Kashirin still alive?"

Granny gave him one of her most cordial smiles.

"Still sweating? Working away?"

"Working away. Like a convict."

Granny spoke warmly and affectionately with him but in the tone of the elder. Sometimes he would mention my mother.

"Hm—Varvara Vasilyevna. What a woman! A regular Amazon!"

"Remember I gave her that cloak—black silk, with jet beads on it?" put in his wife, turning to Granny.

"Yes indeed."

"Good as new it was."

"Hm—cloak, croak—life's a joke," muttered my master.

"What's that?" asked his wife suspiciously.

"Oh nothing—nothing at all. Happy days are passing, and so are fine people. . . ."

"Why in the world should you say such things?" said his wife anxiously.

Later they took Granny to see the new baby, while I remained to clear away the tea things. "A fine old woman, that grandmother of yours," said my master softly and dreamily.

I was deeply grateful to him for these words. When I found myself alone with Granny I said to her with an aching heart:

"Why do you come here? Can't you see what they're like?"

"Alas, Alyosha, I see everything," she replied, gazing at me with a kind smile on her wonderful face, and at once I felt ashamed: of course she saw everything and knew everything—even what was going on within me at that moment.

After she had glanced cautiously about to see that no one was near, she embraced me and said with great feeling:

"Indeed I would never be coming here but for you—what do I want with them? And then grandfather's been ailing and I've been fussing about with him and not working, so I have no money. And son Mikhailo put out his Sasha, so it's him I've been having to give food and drink as well. They promised to pay you six rubles a year and I thinks to myself—maybe they'll give at least one ruble now. It's most half a year you've been working, isn't it?" She leaned over and began to whisper in my ear. "They said I was to scold you—said you was disobedient. If you'd only live here for awhile, pigeon-widgeon—try to stand it for a year or two till you're stronger on your feet. . . . Will you try?"

I promised to. But that was very hard. I was weighed down by this miserable, boring existence, bustling about from morning to night for the stomach's sake. I lived as in a bad dream.

Sometimes I was tempted to run away. But the accursed winter was at its height. At night the blizzard blew, the wind wailed in the attic, the rafters creaked in the grip of the cold. How could I run away?

I was not allowed to go out to play, and indeed I had no time to. The short winter days flashed by in a whirl of odd jobs.

But I was obliged to go to church—on Saturdays to vespers, on Sundays to late mass.

I enjoyed going to church. I would select some dark, empty corner and stand there admiring the iconostasis, which from a distance seemed to melt in the candlelight flowing in wide golden streams over the stone floor. The dark figures of the icons stirred softly, and gay scintillations were reflected from the gold filigree of the King's Gates. The candles hung in the blue air like golden bees, the heads of the women and girls their flowers.

Everything merged harmoniously with the singing of the choir; everything lived a strange fairy-tale existence; the entire church swayed slowly, like a cradle rocking in darkness as thick as pitch.

Sometimes it seemed to me that the church was submerged in a lake, hidden from the world so that it could live a life apart, different from all other life. Probably this idea sprang from Granny's tale about the fabulous city of Kitezh; often as I rocked drowsily in my surroundings—lulled by the singing of the choir, the hushed prayers, the sighs of the worshippers—I would repeat to myself the sad, melodious tale:

Came then the Tatars in heathen-hordes,
Came on their steeds, armed to the teeth,
And surrounded the beautiful Kitezh-grad
At the sacred hour of the matin prayers.

Oh, dear Lord of the Universe,
Oh, dear Virgin Immaculate,

Come to the aid of the slaves-of-God,

That they finish their prayers in tranquility
And imbibe of Thy Word in humility,

Let not Thy temple be desecrated,
The honour of maidens be violated,
Innocent babes be slain,
The old and infirm be maimed.
Then were the great God Jehovah
And the blessed Virgin Immaculate

Stirred by these dire lamentations,
Roused by these sad supplications,

And spake then the great God Jehovah
To Michael, the blessed Archangel:
"Descend to the human-land, Michael,
And shake up the earth beneath Kitezh-grad,

That the waters shall close over Kitezh-grad.
Then shall the slaves-of-God
Pray to their hearts' content,
Pray without ceasing, pray without wearying,
From Matins to Vespers, through all of the
*   Services*
Year after year, world without end!"

At that time I was saturated with my grandmother's verse, like a comb with honey; it seems that even my thoughts assumed her verse patterns.

I never prayed in church—I hesitated to repeat grandfather's spiteful prayers and lugubrious psalms to Granny's God. I was certain that Granny's God must dislike them as much as I did. Furthermore, they were all printed in a book, which meant that God must know them by heart, like any literate person.

For that reason, whenever my heart contracted with some sweet sadness, or was stung by the day's little hurts, I would try to compose my own prayers. And I had only to think of my unenviable fate to find the words taking form of themselves, without any effort on my part:

> Oh Lord, oh Lord, how unhappy I am!
> I wish to God I were already a man!
> Forgive me, Lord, if I kill myself,
> I have borne as much as anyone can.
> They will never teach me anything here;
> Granny's sister, the ugly witch,
> Does nothing but scold and pull my ear,
> And life itself is a horrid bitch.

I remember many of my "prayers" to this day; the workings of a child's mind leave such deep imprint on the soul that sometimes they remain until death.

It was lovely to be in church, and I now found respite there as formerly I had found it in fields and forest. My childish heart, already so often wounded, and already tainted by life's coarseness, was soothed by vague but ardent dreams.

I went to church only when it was bitterly cold, or when a blizzard raged through the city, freezing the very sky and veiling it in snow clouds, while the earth, also frozen beneath the snowdrifts, seemed incapable of reviving, or of ever again showing signs of life.

On quiet nights I preferred walking through the city, up one street and down another, seeking out the most remote corners. I would hurry along as if on wings, lonely as the moon in the sky, my shadow going before, extinguishing sparks of light on the snow and amusingly slithering over posts and fences. Down the middle of the street would come the night watchman in a huge sheepskin with a rattle in his hand and a dog at his side. His bulky form reminded me of a dog kennel which had crawled out of a yard and set off down the street for some unknown destination, the perplexed dog following at its heels.

Occasionally I met laughing young girls and their swains, and I concluded that they too had run away from vespers.

Sometimes strange odours would pour through openings in lighted windows—delicate, unfamiliar odours, suggesting a different sort of life. And I would stand under the windows, sniffing and straining in the effort to guess what sort of people lived there and what their life was like. At an hour when all respectable people should have been at vespers, here were they, laughing and talking and playing some special kind of guitar which sent sweet notes through the window.

I was particularly intrigued by a low, one-storeyed house on the corner of two quiet streets named Tikhonovskaya and Martynovskaya. I chanced upon it one moonlight night during the thaw preceding Shrovetide. Along with the vapour which streamed through the opening in the window came an amazing sound, as though someone very strong and good were singing through closed lips; the words were indistinguishable, but the song seemed remarkably familiar and comprehensible, though I was prevented from hearing it properly by some string music which kept annoyingly interrupting the flow of the song. I sat down on a stump and concluded that the music must be made by a violin possessing wonderful, even unbearable, power. Listening was almost painful. Sometimes it sang out with such force that the entire house seemed to tremble, making the glass in the windows vibrate. Melting snow dripped off the roof, and tears stole down my cheeks.

I was unaware of the approach of the night watchman until he pushed me off the stump.

"Why are you loafing here?" he asked.

"The music...." I explained.

"What of it? Be off!"

I quickly ran around the block and returned to the house, but now no one was playing. Through the window came a confusion of gay sounds so little resembling the sad music that it seemed I must have dreamed it.

Almost every Saturday I returned to that house, but only once in the spring did I again hear the 'cello. It played without ceasing until almost midnight; on returning home I was given a beating.

I was greatly enriched by these nocturnal wanderings beneath the wintry stars, along the empty streets of the city. I purposely chose streets on the outskirts; the main streets were lighted by many lanterns, and if I were seen by friends of my employers, they would find out I was not attending vespers. Furthermore, on the main streets my walks would be marred by drunkards, policemen, and streetwalkers. And on remote streets it was possible to look through the windows of the first floor, if they were not curtained, or frosted.

I had glimpses of many scenes through those windows. I saw people praying, kissing, fighting, playing cards, carrying on serious, soundless conversations. Before my eyes passed a mute, fishlike panorama, like those seen in the slot-machines.

Through a basement window I observed two women—one very young, the other slightly older—sitting at a table. Across from them sat a long-haired student gesturing extravagantly as he read a book to them. The young girl leaned back in her chair, listening intently, her brows drawn together in a severe line. The older one—very slender, with fluffy hair—suddenly covered her face with her hands and sobbed. The student threw down the book, and when the young girl jumped up and ran out of the room, he fell on his knees before the one with the fluffy hair and began kissing her hands.

Through another window I saw a large, bearded man holding a woman in a red blouse on his knees and rocking her like a little child. Apparently he was singing, for he opened his mouth wide and rolled his eyes. She shook with laughter and threw herself back in his arms, kicking her feet in the air. He pulled her back and went on with his singing, she with her laughing. I watched them for a long time, and went away feeling that their gaiety would last the night.

Many such scenes impressed themselves on my memory for all time. Often the culling of these impressions brought me home late, and made my employers suspicious.

"What church did you go to?" they would ask. "What priest read the service?"

They knew all the priests in town and what chapter of the Bible was being read. It was easy for them to catch me in a lie.

Both women worshipped the wrathful god of my grandfather—a god who demanded being held in fear and awe. His name was ever on their lips, even when they quarrelled.

"Just you wait! God will punish you. He'll make your flesh shrivel, you hussy!" they would shout at each other.

On the first Sunday of Lent, the old woman made pancakes which kept sticking to the frying pan.

"The devil take you!" she shouted angrily, her face inflamed by the fire.

Suddenly, on sniffing the pan, her face darkened, she flung the pan onto the floor and shrieked:

"Lordie God! The skillet's got fat on it! I forgot to burn off the foul thing on Pure Monday! Oh Lord!"

She fell on her knees and began to implore tearfully:

"Dear Lord, forgive me, sinner that I be, for Thy mercy's sake. Don't go punishing an old fool like me, dear God—"

The spoiled pancakes were fed to the dog and the pan was scorched, but thereafter the young mistress kept reminding the older one of this incident.

"You even fry pancakes on an unpurged skillet during Lent!" she would say whenever they quarrelled.

They dragged God into all domestic affairs, into every dark corner of their petty lives. This seemed to give significance and importance to their miserable existence, as though every minute were devoted to the serving of some higher power. I was infected by their habit of identifying God with every trifle, and involuntarily would glance into corners, conscious of some invisible eye on me, while at night I would be gripped by cold fear. This fear emanated from the corner of the kitchen where a lamp was kept ever burning before the sombre images.

Next to the icon shelf was a large window with two frames separated by an upright. Beyond the window stretched a vast blue emptiness, making it seem that the house, the kitchen, and everything else, including myself, hung on the very edge of that emptiness, and that the slightest movement would send us careering into the cold blue abyss, past the stars, into the dead silence, like a stone thrown into water. I would lie motionless in bed for long stretches, afraid to stir, awaiting the fearful end of the world.

I no longer remember how I recovered from this fear, but recover I did, and very soon. Naturally enough my grandmother's kind God came to my aid, and it seems that even then I was conscious of a simple truth: I had done nothing wrong; there was no law by which I could be punished if I was innocent, and I could not be held to account for the sins of others.

I played truant from morning mass too, especially in the spring. The irresistible force of nature's renascence kept leading me away from the church. If, in addition, I had been given a few kopeks for an altar candle, I was indeed lost. I would buy knucklebones with the money and play throughout mass, inevitably coming home late. One day I managed to squander the ten kopeks given me to pay for communion bread and a prayer for the dead, as a result of which I helped myself to someone else's bread from the tray the deacon brought from the altar.

I had a passionate love of games, and would play unwearyingly. I was strong and agile and soon won fame in our district for playing ball, knucklebones, and skittles.

During Lent I was made to prepare for Communion. I went to our neighbour, Father Dorimedont Pokrovsky, for confession. I considered him a stern person and was aware of all the sins I had committed against him: I had damaged his summerhouse by throwing stones at it, had fought with his children, and committed many other crimes which might well have put me in his bad graces. All this was on my mind as I stood in the dingy little chapel awaiting my turn to confess, my heart thumping uncomfortably.

But Father Dorimedont met me with good-natured querulousness.

"Ah, our neighbour!" he exclaimed. "Well, get down on your knees. Tell me your sins."

He covered my head with a piece of heavy velvet. The odour of wax and incense stifled me and made it all the more difficult to say the words I had no wish to say.

"Do you obey your elders?"

"No."

"Say: 'Sin on my soul.'"

To my own surprise I blurted out:

"I stole the host at Communion."

"What's that you say? Where?" asked the priest unhurriedly, after brief consideration.

"At the Church of the Three Saints, at Pokrov Cathedral, at Nikola—"

"Come, come, now. Do you mean to say at all the churches? That's a bad thing, son; a sin. Do you understand?"

"Yes."

"Say: 'Sin on my soul.' You silly boy— did you steal it to eat?"

"Sometimes I ate it, but sometimes I lost my money at skittles, and had to bring the Communion bread home, so I stole it."

Father Dorimedont mumbled something under his breath, asking me a few more questions, then suddenly demanded in a stern voice:

"Have you ever read books printed by the underground press?"

I did not understand the question.

"What?" I asked.

"Forbidden books—have you ever read any?"

"No I haven't."

"All right. Your sins are remitted. Get up."

I looked in some surprise into his face. The expression was kind and thoughtful and I felt ashamed. On sending me to confession, my mistresses had told me many awe-inspiring things to frighten me into confessing everything.

"I threw stones at your summerhouse," I said.

The priest raised his head.

"That was also bad. Run along now."

"And at your dog."

"Next!" said Father Dorimedont, looking past me.

I went away feeling hurt and deceived. The anticipation of this confession had set all my nerves aquiver, and it turned out to be nothing at all, not even interesting. The only interesting thing was the question about those mysterious books. I recalled the book the student had been reading to the women in the basement, and I recalled "That's Fine." He too had owned many thick black books containing unintelligible illustrations.

On the next day I was given fifteen kopeks and sent to Communion. Easter came late that year; the snow had already melted and little puffs of dust curled above the dry streets. The weather was sunny and gay.

Some workmen were having an exciting game of skittles near the church wall. I thought I would have time to take Communion later.

"Will you let me play?" I asked.

"A kopek a game," proudly announced a redheaded, pock-marked fellow.

I replied just as proudly:

"I'll put three under the second skittle from the left."

"Let's see the money."

And the game was on!

I changed my fifteen-kopek piece and put three under my skittle: whoever knocked it down would get the money; whoever missed would owe me three kopeks. I was lucky: two aimed at my skittle and both of them missed, which meant that I had won six kopeks—from grown-up men! This caused my spirits to soar.

"Watch him, fellows, or he'll be running off with his winnings," said one of the players.

This offended me.

"Nine kopeks under the last skittle to the left!" I rapped out sharply.

My bravado seemed to make little impression on the players, but another boy my age cried out a warning:

"Keep your eye on him! He's a lucky devil! I know him!"

"A devil you say? Hm-m-m, we'll see!" replied a lean workman who smelled like a tanner.

He took careful aim and knocked down my skittle.

"How do you like that?" he said, bending over me.

"Another three under the last skittle on the right," I retorted.

"I'll get them too," boasted the tanner, but he missed.

The rules forbid placing stakes under a skittle more than three times running. I began to play for other people's money and won another four kopeks. But when it was again my turn to put up money I lost everything I had. This happened just as mass ended; the bells began ringing and the people came out of the church.

"Burn your fingers?" asked the tanner making to grab me by the hair, but I dodged and ran away. I caught up with a young man dressed in his Sunday clothes and said to him politely:

"Have you just taken Communion?"

"What if I have?" he replied, eyeing me suspiciously.

I asked him to tell me how Communion was taken, what the priest said and what the person taking it was supposed to do.

The young man lowered his head and roared at me like a bull:

"So you ran away from Communion, did you, you heretic? Well I won't tell you a thing. Let your father give you a good trouncing for it!"

I ran home, certain that they would begin to question me and find out that I had not taken Communion.

But after congratulating me, the old woman asked me only one question:

"How much did you give the deacon?"

"Five kopeks," I said at random.

"Three'd have been more than enough, and seven left over for yourself, blockhead."

It was spring. Each day appeared in new raiment, brighter and more lovely than that which preceded it. An intoxicating fragrance came from the young grass and the fresh green of the birches; I had an unbearable longing to go out to the fields where I could lie on my back on the warm earth and listen to the larks. And here I was, brushing winter clothes and helping pack them away in trunks, pulverizing leaf tobacco, beating the dust out of the upholstering—busy from morning to night with duties which I found both hateful and needless.

And there was nothing for me to do in my leisure hours. Our dreary street held no charms, and I was not allowed to go beyond it. Our yard was full of tired, irritable ditch-diggers, dishevelled cooks and laundresses;

every evening the most flagrant mating went on, and I found this so disgusting and offensive that I wished I were blind.

I took a pair of scissors and some coloured paper and climbed up into the attic, where I cut out lacy patterns with which I decorated the rafters. At least it was something to ease my boredom. I was possessed by a fierce desire to go away somewhere where people slept less, quarrelled less, did not so insistently pour out their complaints to God or so often offend people with their harsh opinions.

On the Saturday before Easter they brought the miracle-working icon of the Vladimirskaya Virgin from the Oransky Monastery to our town. The Virgin was to be the guest of the town until the middle of June, during which time she would visit the home of every single parishioner.

She was brought to the home of my employers on a weekday morning; I was in the kitchen shining the brassware when I heard the young mistress cry in a frightened voice from the other room:

"Go open the front door! They're bringing the Oranskaya Virgin!"

Dirty as I was, my hands covered with grease and ground brick, I rushed downstairs and opened the door. On the doorstep stood a young monk with a lantern in one hand and a censer in the other.

"Takes you a long time," he grumbled. "Come help."

Two of the townsmen carried a heavy icon frame up the narrow stairway. I helped them, thrusting my shoulder under one corner and holding it with my dirty hands. Behind us pattered some fat monks who were reluctantly chanting in thick voices:

"Holy Virgin, we beseech Thy intercession—"

"She'll probably cause my arms to wither for carrying Her with dirty hands," I thought miserably.

They placed the icon in the corner on two chairs covered with a clean sheet. On either side it was held by two young and handsome monks whose bright eyes, fluffy hair, and happy faces made them look like cherubs.

The service began.

"Blessed Mother of God . . ." a large priest chanted shrilly as he fingered one puffy red ear lobe hidden in a mass of hair.

"Holy Virgin, bestow on us Thy mercy," sang the monks wearily.

I loved the Virgin. According to Granny's tales, it was She who strewed the earth with flowers and joy, with all that was good and beautiful, as consolation for the poor. And when the time came to kiss Her, I tremblingly pressed my lips to Her mouth, not noticing how the grownups did it.

Someone's strong arm hurled me into the corner by the door. I do not remember the monks carrying out the icon, but I remember only too well my master and mistresses standing around me where I sat on the floor, and anxiously discussing what would happen to me.

"We must speak to the priest—he understands such things better than us. You simpleton!" said my master to me in mild rebuke.

"Don't you know you mustn't kiss the Virgin on the lips? A lot of good your schooling did you!"

For several days I waited like one condemned. First I had grasped the Virgin with dirty hands, then I had kissed Her in the wrong way. Oh, I would be called to account for this! I would surely be called to account!

But apparently the Virgin forgave my involuntary sins, inspired as they were by love. Or perhaps Her punishment was so light that it passed unnoticed among the frequent chastisements meted out to me by these good people.

Occasionally, in order to irritate the old woman, I would meekly remark:

"Looks like the Virgin forgot to punish me."

"You just wait," she would answer. "It's not too late yet."

... While decorating the rafters up in the attic with pink tea wrappers, tin foil, leaves, and other trifles, I would make up verse about anything that came into my

head and chant it to church tunes, like
the Kalmyks do while journeying on horseback.

> Here I sit once more,
> On the attic floor,
> Cutting bits of paper,
> Melting bits of taper;
> I wish I was a dog,
> So I could run away.
> Here all they ever say
> Is: Shut your face, you dolt,
> And learn how to obey!

When the old woman saw my decorations
she grunted and shook her head.

"Why don't you fix up the kitchen like
that?" she said.

One day my master came up into the attic, looked at my handiwork, and said with a
sigh:

"Damn it all, you're a funny one, Peshkov; what'll you ever turn out to be? A magician, eh? No telling—"

And he handed me a five-kopek piece
from the time of Nicholas I.

I made a setting for the coin out of fine wire and hung it like a medal in the most conspicuous spot among my colourful gewgaws.

But on the following day the money disappeared along with the setting. I was certain that the old woman had stolen it.

V

In the spring I finally ran away. One morning while I was buying the bread for breakfast, the baker had a quarrel with his wife and struck her on the forehead with a heavy weight. She ran out into the street, where she collapsed. A crowd gathered, the woman was placed in a cart and taken to the hospital, I ran after the cart, and then somehow, without my being aware of it, I found myself on the bank of the Volga with twenty kopeks in my hand.

The spring day smiled tenderly, the Volga was flooded to a great breadth, the earth was vast and vibrant, while I—until that day I had been living like a mouse in a hole. I decided that I would not return to my master and I would not go to Granny in Kunavino; I had not kept my word, and was ashamed to face her. And besides, grandfather would only gloat on my return.

For two or three days I wandered along the riverbank, fed by the good-natured stevedores and sleeping with them on the piers at night. Finally one of them said to me:

"No good will come of your hanging around like this, boy. Why don't you go aboard the 'Dobry'? They need a dishwasher there."

I went. A tall, bearded steward in a black silk cap looked at me with cloudy, spectacled eyes.

"Two rubles a month," he said quietly. "Passport?"

I had no passport. The steward thought for a moment and then said:

"Bring your mother."

I ran for Granny. She approved of the step I had taken and talked grandfather into going to the Board of Trade to get me a passport. She herself went to the boat with me.

"Very well," said the steward with a glance at us. "Come along."

He led me to the stern of the boat where an enormous cook in a white coat and white cap was sitting at a table sipping tea and smoking a fat cigarette. The steward pushed me toward him.

"Dishwasher."

He immediately left. The cook snorted and his black moustaches bristled as he called after him:

"You'd hire the devil himself, long as he was cheap!"

He angrily threw back his large head covered with close-cropped black hair, glared at me with his dark eyes, blew out his cheeks and shouted at me:

"Who are you?"

I did not like this man at all. In spite of his being dressed all in white, he looked dirty. His fingers were overgrown with hair and long hairs stuck out of his big ears.

"I'm hungry," I said.

He blinked. Then all of a sudden his fierce face changed. A broad smile sent his red cheeks receding in waves to his ears, exposing large, horsy teeth. His moustaches drooped gently, and he came to resemble a fat, good-natured housewife.

He tossed the remains of his tea overboard, poured out a fresh glass and pushed it toward me along with an untouched loaf of bread and a large slice of sausage.

"Go to it. Got a mother and father? Know how to steal? Don't worry, they're all thieves here—teach you soon enough."

He barked out his words. His enormous cheeks were bluish from shaving, and the flesh near his nose was covered with a fine network of veins. His red and swollen nose impinged upon his moustaches, his thick lower lip hung down contemptuously, and a cigarette smoldered in the corner of his mouth. Apparently he had just come from the bathhouse, for he emanated an odour of birch branches and pepper brandy and his neck and his temples were beaded with sweat.

When I had lunched, he slipped me a ruble.

"Go buy yourself two aprons with bibs. Wait! I'll buy them myself."

He adjusted his cap and set off down the deck, rocking from side to side and shuffling his feet like a bear.

. . . Night. A bright moon is scurrying away from the steamer to the meadows on the left. Our antiquated brown steamer with its white-ringed smokestack lazily slaps its paddles through the silvery water; slowly the dark riverbanks rise to meet the boat, casting shadows spangled with the reflections of lights in cottage windows; a sound of singing comes from the village—the girls are having their song-promenade, and the refrain of "ai-luli" sounds like "hallelujah."

Our boat is drawing a barge on a long cable. The barge is also painted brown. On the deck is a large iron cage, and in the cage are prisoners sentenced to exile and hard labour. The bayonet of the sentry standing in the bow shines like a candle, and the stars in the deep blue sky are also like tiny candles. Everything is quiet on board the barge, and flooded with moonlight. Round grey shadows can be seen behind the iron bars of the cage.

They are the prisoners, sitting and gazing at the Volga. The water goes gurgling by—perhaps weeping, perhaps laughing timidly. There is something churchlike about everything, even the smell of oil, suggesting incense.

As I gaze at the barge I recall my early childhood: the trip from Astrakhan to Nizhni; the masklike face of my mother; my grandmother, the person who led me into this hard but interesting life. Whenever I think of my grandmother I forget the hateful and offensive aspects of life. Everything changes, becoming more interesting and pleasant, while people seem better and more lovable.

The beauty of the night moves me almost to tears; I am fascinated by the barge, which resembles a coffin and seems so out of place on the broad bosom of this flowing river, in the meditative silence of this warm night. The uneven contours of the banks, now rising, now falling, cause my heart to quicken, making me want to be good, and to be of service to mankind.

There is something unique about our passengers. It seems to me that all of them—

old and young, men and women—are alike. Our boat moves slowly; people with pressing affairs travel by post-boat, leaving to us the quiet passengers with nothing to do. From morning to night they eat and drink, dirtying a multitude of dishes, knives, forks, and spoons. It is my job to wash these dishes and polish the knives and forks, and I am busy at it from six o'clock in the morning until midnight. In the afternoon from two to six, and in the evening from ten to twelve, I have less work, since the passengers only drink tea and beer and vodka after their meals.

During those hours all the waiters are free. A group of them usually gather for tea at a table near a funnel. Among them are Smury, the cook; Yakov Ivanovich, his assistant; Maxim, the kitchen dishwasher; and Sergei, the waiter serving the passengers on deck, a humpback with a broad, pock-marked face and oily eyes. Yakov Ivanovich tells them dirty stories, laughing his sobbing laughter, baring his mouldy teeth. Sergei stretches his froglike mouth in an ear-to-ear grin, while the sullen Maxim listens in silence, watching the others with hard eyes of uncertain colour.

"Cannibals! Mordovians!" the elder cook interpolates from time to time in his booming voice.

I dislike all these people. The fat, bald Yakov Ivanovich speaks only of women, and always in an obscene way. He has an expressionless face covered with blue blotches. One cheek is marked by a wart sprouting red hairs which he twists to a point. Whenever a sociable, approachable female appears on board, he meekly follows her about like a beggar and talks to her in sugared, plaintive tones, his lips flecked with froth which he keeps licking with quick little movements of his foul tongue. For some reason it seems to me that public executioners should be just that fat and oily.

"Have to know how to warm up a woman," he once informed Sergei and Maxim, who listened attentively, swelling up and turning red.

"Cannibals!" boomed Smury scornfully. Slowly he pulled himself to his feet and said to me: "Peshkov! Come along!"

When we reached his cabin, he handed me a little book in a leather binding, and stretched out on his bunk, which was against the wall of the cold storage room.

"Read to me!"

I sat down on a crate of macaroni and obediently began to read.

"The umbraculum, strewn with stars, means a convenient point of contact with heaven, which they have freed themselves from ignoramuses and prophets—"

Smury emitted a cloud of cigarette smoke and snorted:

"The camels! To write stuff like that!"

"A bared left breast means an innocent heart."

"Whose bared left breast?"

"It doesn't say."

"Then it means a woman's. Ekh, the strumpets!"

He closed his eyes and lay back with his arm behind his head. He shifted the smouldering cigarette stuck in the corner of his mouth and took such a deep draw that something whistled inside his chest and his face became veiled in smoke. At times it seemed to me he had fallen asleep, and I would stop reading and sit staring at the accursed book.

"Read!" he would bark.

"The Venerable replied: behold, my good Frère Suverian—"

"Severian."

"It's written: Suverian."

"To hell with it! There's some poetry at the bottom. Bang off from there."

So I banged off:

Oh, ignorant creatures, presuming to
  probe our affairs!
Never shall your poor minds so much
  as approach them!
Even the chants of the friars shall
  remain beyond your ken!

"Stop!" cried Smury. "Do you call that poetry? Give me the book."

He angrily leafed through the thick blue volume and tossed it under the bunk.

"Try another one."

To my great grief, there were many books in his black trunk with iron fixings. Among them were *Omir's Precepts; Artillery Remembrances; Letters of Lord Sedengaly; Concerning the Bedbug, a Noxious Insect, How to Exterminate It and How to Combat Its Ravages*. There were books without beginnings and endings. Sometimes the cook made me go through them and read out their titles. As I did so, he would mutter angrily:

"The things they write, the rapscallions! Like slapping you in the face for no good reason. *Gervassi!* What the hell do I want with Gervassi? *Umbraculum!*"

The strange words and unfamiliar names stuck annoyingly in my memory, making my tongue itch to repeat them, as though the sounding of them would reveal their meaning. Beyond the window the river kept up a ceaseless song and splash. I longed to go up on deck, where the boat-hands and stokers sat about on packing cases, singing or spinning yarns or winning the passengers' money away from them at cards. How nice it would be to sit with them and listen to their simple, comprehensible words while gazing at the banks of the Kama, at the pine trunks stretching upwards, taut as copper wires, and at the meadows where receding waters had left little lakes reflecting the blue sky like bits of broken mirror. Our boat was apart from the land and kept its distance, but in the quiet of evenfall the ring of an invisible church bell would be wafted from shore, bringing thoughts of towns and people. A fisherman's boat rocked on the water like a crust of bread; a village drew into sight; some little boys were splashing about in the water, and a muzhik in a red blouse came walking down a yellow ribbon of sand. Seen from a distance, everything looked attractive. Objects were reduced to toylike proportions, amusingly tiny and colourful. I was tempted to shout something kind and affectionate to the riverbank—to the riverbank and the barge.

I was fascinated by that brown barge. I could sit spellbound for hours at a time watching it push its blunt nose through the turbid water. The steamer pulled it along like a pig on a rope. On becoming lax, the cable would slap the water, only to be drawn tight again, streaming water as it yanked the barge by the nose. I longed to get a look at the faces of the people sitting like animals in that iron cage. At Perm, when they were taken ashore, I climbed onto the gangplank. Dozens of grey creatures went clumping past me, clanking their chains, bending under the weight of their knapsacks. They were male and female, old and young, ugly and beautiful, just like other people, except that they were dressed differently and were disfigured by having had their heads shaved. To be sure they were outlaws, but Granny had told me so many nice things about outlaws!

Smury looked more like a desperate outlaw than any of them.

"Heaven spare me such a fate!" he muttered, glancing at the barge.

One day I happened to say to him:

"How is it that you are a cook while others are thieves and murderers?"

"I'm not a cook. I'm a chef. Only women are cooks," he said with a snort; then, after a moment's consideration:

"The difference between people lies in their heads. Some people are clever, some dull, still others just dunces. You get clever by reading the right books—black magic and the like. You've got to read all the books, that's the only way to find the right ones."

He was always saying to me:

"Read. If you don't understand a book, read it seven times. If seven don't help, read it twelve."

Smury was curt with everyone on board, including the taciturn steward; when he spoke to anyone he would thrust out his lower lip disdainfully, wriggle his moustaches, and spit out the words like pebbles. But with me he was gentle and attentive, though there was something in his attentiveness which frightened me. Sometimes I felt that the cook, like granny's sister, was not quite normal.

"Stop reading!" he would say, and for a long time would lie with his eyes closed, breathing hoarsely through his nose, his huge belly heaving, his hands crossed on his breast like a corpse's, his scarred, hairy

fingers twitching as though he were knitting
an invisible sock with invisible needles.
Then all of a sudden he would begin to mutter.

"Brains, for example! Here, take them
and see what you can do with them! Brains
are given sparingly and unequal. If only everybody had the same amount—but they don't.
This fellow understands, that one don't, and
the other has no wish to."

Stumbling over the words, he would tell
me stories from his life as a soldier. I could
never discover any point to his stories and
always found them uninteresting, especially
since he never began from the beginning, but
from wherever his fancy dictated.

"So the regiment commander calls up
that soldier and says to him: what was it
the lieutenant told you? And he answers
everything, just like it was, because a soldier's obliged to tell the truth. The lieutenant looks at him like he was a stone wall,
then turns away and drops his eyes. Hm."

The cook inhaled viciously and muttered:

"As if I knew what a person's supposed to say and what he's not! They put

the lieutenant in prison, and his mother. . . . Oh, Lordy me! Nobody ever taught me anything!"

It was hot. Everything shook and hummed gently. Beyond the metal walls of the cabin the paddle wheel thumped and the water splashed. The river flowed in a wide stream past the porthole, a strip of meadowland was visible in the distance, trees loomed into sight. My ear became so used to all the sounds that I was conscious only of the silence, though in the bow of the boat a sailor kept monotonously repeating:

"Se-ven! Se-ven!"

I wished to remain aloof from everything—not to listen, not to work—only to sit somewhere in the shadow, beyond range of the hot, greasy smell of the kitchen—to sit and gaze drowsily at this quiet, weary life slipping over the water.

"Read!" commanded the cook testily.

Even the waiters in first class were afraid of him, and it seemed that the meek, close-mouthed steward also harboured a dread of Smury.

"Hey, you pig!" Smury would shout at the barmen. "Come here, you thief! Cannibals! Umbraculum!"

The boat-hands and stokers treated him with respect, and even curried his favour. He would give them the meat from the broth, ask them about their families and about life in the village. The grimy, greasy Byelorussian stokers were considered the scum of the boat. The Russians called them yaks and teased them by saying:

"Yak, yak, give him the sack."

This infuriated Smury. He would bristle and get red in the face and yell at the stokers:

"Why the hell do you let them walk all over you like that? Smash their mugs for them, the damned katsaps!"*

Once the boatswain, a surly, handsome fellow, said to him:

"Yaks and khokhols? ** One's just about as good as the other."

* *Katsap*—a derogatory name for a Russian. —*Tr.*

** *Khokhol*—a derogatory name for a Ukrainian.—*Tr.*

The cook grabbed him by the belt and the nape of the neck, lifted him up in the air and began to shake him.

"Want me to grind you to a pulp?" he shouted.

There were often quarrels which ended in fights, but no one ever beat up Smury. He was inhumanly strong for one thing, and for another, he was on good terms with the wife of the captain, a tall, handsome woman with a mannish face and straight hair cut like a boy's.

He drank tremendous quantities of vodka, but never got drunk. He began drinking in the morning, finishing off a bottle in four installments, while he sipped beer all day long. Gradually his face flushed and his dark eyes dilated as if in surprise.

Sometimes in the evening he would sit on deck for hours, a huge white figure gazing sullenly into the receding distance. Most people were particularly in awe of him at such moments, but I pitied him.

Yakov Ivanovich would emerge from the kitchen, red-faced and sweating, scratch his bald pate, then disappear with a hopeless wave of his hand. Or he would call from a distance:

"The sterlet stinks."

"Make a salad out of it."

"What if somebody orders fish soup or boiled sterlet?"

"Make it. They'll eat anything."

Sometimes I plucked up the courage to approach him.

"What do you want?" he would say, turning to me with an effort.

"Nothing."

"Good."

Once I said to him:

"Why do you frighten everybody so? You're so good."

To my great surprise, the question did not anger him.

"It's only with you I'm good," he answered, adding presently in a thoughtful, good-natured tone: "Or maybe I'm good with everybody. I just don't show it. You mustn't show people you're good or they'll finish you off. People climb up on a good man like he was a clump of dry ground in a bog and trample him down. Go fetch me some beer."

When he had drunk the beer, glass by glass, he licked his moustaches and said:

"If you was a bit bigger of a birdie, there's lots of things I could teach you. I know a thing or two worth hearing—I'm no fool. You must read books; books'll tell you everything you ought to know. A book's a rare thing. Want some beer?"

"I don't like it."

"Good. Don't start drinking. Drinking's a great grief. Vodka's the work of the devil. If I was rich I'd send you to school. An unlearned fellow's nothing but an ox. Put him between the shafts or make meat out of him—all he does is switch his tail."

The captain's wife gave him a volume of Gogol. I read *Fearful Vengeance* to him and liked it immensely, but Smury shouted angrily:

"Stuff and nonsense. A fairy tale. I'm certain there's other kinds of books."

He took the book away from me and brought another from the captain's wife.

"Here, read *Taras*—what's his other name?" he ordered moodily. "Find the story. She says it's a good one. Who's it good for? Maybe good for her and bad for me. See how she cut off her hair? Why didn't she cut off her ears?"

When we reached the point where Taras challenged Ostap to fight, the cook laughed raucously.

"How do you like that?" he said. "One's got brain, the other's got brawn! What stuff they write, the camels!"

He listened attentively, but often grumbled.

"Humph, idiocy! You can't slice a person from the shoulder to the waist in one blow. Can't be done. And you can't lift a person on a pike; it'd break. Aren't I a soldier myself?"

He was shocked by Andrei's betrayal.

"The scum, eh? For the sake of a woman! Humph!"

But when Taras shot his son, the cook slipped his legs over the side of his bunk, gripped the edge with his hands, and wept. Slowly the tears rolled down his cheeks, dripping onto the floor. He sniffled and muttered:

"Oh Lord, Oh Lord!"

Suddenly he yelled at me:

"Go on reading, you devil's spawn!"

He wept harder and more bitterly when the condemned Ostap cried to his father: "Father! Do you hear me?"

"Everything's done for," whimpered Smury. "Everything. So that's the end? Ah, what an accursed business! They was real men those days. That Taras, eh? A real man, by God!"

He took the book out of my hand and studied it attentively, bathing the cover in his tears.

"A good book is a regular holiday!"

After that we read *Ivanhoe*. Smury liked Richard Plantagenet.

"There's a king for you!" he said impressively. But I found the book boring.

In general our tastes differed. I was fascinated by *The Tale of Thomas Jones*, the old translation of *The History of Tom Jones, a Foundling*.

"Nonsense!" muttered Smury. "What's that Thomas to me? What do I want with him? There must be other books."

One day I told him I knew there were other books—forbidden books, underground books, which were to be read only in cellars at night.

His eyes widened, his moustaches bristled.

"What's that? What lies you telling?"

"I'm not telling lies. The priest once asked me about them during confession, and before that I saw people reading them and crying."

The cook looked at me dully.

"Who cried?" he asked.

"A lady who listened. Another one even ran away in fright."

"Wake up, you're dreaming," said Smury, slowly narrowing his eyes. After a moment's pause he added:

"Sure enough, there must be something secret somewhere. Couldn't help being.... But I'm too old.... And not the sort.... Still, when you come to think of it...."

He could speak with such eloquence for hours at a time.

Quite unconsciously I formed the habit of reading, and read with pleasure. What the books told about was delightfully unlike life, and this made life more onerous than ever.

Smury's interest in books also grew. Often he would call me away from my work:

"Peshkov! Come on and read."

"There's a pile of dishes to be washed."

"Maxim'll wash them."

He roughly drove the elder dishwasher to do my work and the latter took revenge by smashing glasses.

"I'll put you off the boat," the steward warned me calmly.

One day Maxim purposely left some glasses in a basin of dirty water, so that when I emptied the basin overboard, the glasses went too.

"It's my fault," Smury told the steward. "Charge them up to me."

The waiters began to look askance at me.

"Well, you bookworm, what do you think you get paid for?" they would say.

They piled work onto me, purposely dirtying dishes. I sensed that this would end badly, nor was I mistaken.

One evening a red-faced woman accompanied by a girl in a yellow kerchief and a new pink blouse boarded our steamer. Both of them had had a drop. The woman kept smiling and bowing to everyone and chanting her phrases like a deacon.

"Forgive me, my dears, it's a wee sip I've taken. They took me to court and set me free, and I tippled a bit in celebration."

The girl giggled and cast hazy glances at everyone and kept poking the woman in the ribs.

"Get on with you, you hussy! Get along!"

They settled themselves near the second-class section, opposite the cabin where Yakov Ivanovich and Sergei slept. The woman soon disappeared, and Sergei took up his post next to the girl, his froggish mouth stretched in a loose grin.

After work that night, when I had already climbed up on to the table where I slept, Sergei came over to me and grabbed me by the hand.

"Come along, we're going to mate you."

He was drunk. I tried to wrench my hand away, but he struck me.

"Come on, you!"

Maxim rushed up, also drunk, and the two of them dragged me along the deck, past the sleeping passengers, to their cabin. But Smury was standing near the door, while in the very doorway stood Yakov Ivanovich in front of the girl, who was pummelling him in the back.

"Let me go!" she kept crying in a drunken voice.

Smury snatched me out of the grasp of Sergei and Maxim, grabbed the two of them by the hair and banged their heads together, then sent them sprawling on the deck.

"Cannibals!" he said to Yakov, slamming the door in his face. He gave me a shove and barked:

"Get out of here!"

I ran to the stern. The night was cloudy, the river black. In the wake of the ship extended two grey paths diverging to invisible shores; between these paths rode the barge. Now to the left, now to the right would appear red lights illuminating nothing and vanishing quickly behind bends in the river. When they were gone the night seemed even darker than ever, and more oppressive.

The cook came and sat down next to me with a deep sigh as he lighted a cigarette.

"Did they drag you to that trollop? The swine! I heard them rush at you."

"Did you rescue her from them?"

"Her?" He cursed the girl and continued in a pained tone: "They're all pigs here. This boat's worse'n the village. Have you ever lived in the village?"

"No."

"The village is rotten to the core. Especially in winter."

He threw the stub of his cigarette overboard and continued:

"You'll get lost among all these pigs. I feel sorry for you, little mouse. I feel sorry for everyone. Sometimes I don't know what I wouldn't do—get down on my knees and say to them: 'What you doing, you bastards? Are you blind, or what?' Camels!"

The steamer gave a prolonged whistle, the cable slapped the water, the light of a lantern swung through the darkness, locating the pier, while minor lights emerged from the dusk.

"'Drunken Forest,'" muttered the cook. "And there's a river—'Drunken River.' Once there was a rations officer named 'Drunkov.' And a clerk—'Sothead.' I'm going ashore."

Sturdy women from the Kama region were hauling wood on long handbarrows. With springy little steps, bending under their load, they would come in pairs to the black opening in the stoker's hold through which they tossed four-foot logs, calling out in ringing voices:

"Hi-i-i!"

As they hauled their logs the boathands would grab at their legs and breasts and the women would squeal and spit at them. On the return trip the women would defend themselves from slaps and pinches by striking back with their handbarrows. I had observed this dozens of times—on every trip. The same thing occurred at every landing where we took on wood.

It seemed to me that I was an old man who had been living on that boat for many years and knew everything that would happen tomorrow and next week and next autumn.

Now it began to grow light. A big pine woods became visible on a sandy promontory above the pier. The women were climbing the hill to the woods, laughing and singing and screeching. They looked like soldiers, armed with their long barrows.

I wanted to weep; tears seethed in my breast, pressing against my heart, and this hurt.

But I was ashamed to cry, so I helped the boat-hand Borin swab the deck.

Borin was an inconspicuous fellow. He was pale and colourless and would seek out secluded corners where he would sit blinking his little eyes. Once he said to me:

"My honest-to-goodness nickname's not Borin, but Whorin, seeing's how my mother was a whore. I have a sister, and she is too. Looks like it was their fate, the both of them. Fate, brother's, a stone around your neck. You'd like to rise, and there you are."

Now as he mopped up the deck, he said in his quiet voice:

"See how they pick on the girls? Just think! You can set even a wet log to burning if you try hard enough. I don't like that, brother; can't stomach it. If I was a girl I'd drown myself in some dark pool, so help me God! Hard enough to do what you ought as it is, and them stirring up your feelings like that! I'm telling you the *skoptsi* are no fools. Ever heard of the *skoptsi*? Eunuchs. Very smart people—they guessed the right way to live. Away with all the nasty little things in life and just serve God, purelike."

The captain's wife walked past, holding up her skirts as she picked her way among the puddles. She always rose early. She was tall and majestic, with a face so frank and simple that I wanted to run after her and say with all my heart:

"Tell me something—do!"

Slowly the steamer pulled away from the pier.

"We're off," said Borin, crossing himself.

VI

At Sarapul Maxim left the boat. He left
silently, saying goodbye to no one, calm
and serious. Behind him went the jolly
woman, still laughing, and the crumpled
girl, her eyes swollen. For a long time Sergei
kneeled before the captain's cabin, kissing
the panels of the door and knocking his
forehead against it.

"Forgive me, it wasn't my fault," he
wailed. "It was all that Maxim."

The boat-hands, the barman, and even
some of the passengers knew he was lying,
but they kept encouraging him.

"Keep it up, keep it up! He's sure to
forgive you."

And the captain did forgive him, though
he gave him a kick that sent him sprawling.
The next minute Sergei was running about
the deck with breakfast trays, glancing at
people fawningly, like a whipped pup.

In place of Maxim they took on an ex-
soldier from Vyatka, a puny fellow with a

tiny head and red-brown eyes. The second cook immediately sent him to kill some chickens. The soldier killed two and the others ran loose on deck. The passengers tried to catch them and three of the fowls flew overboard. In despair, the soldier sat down on the woodpile near the kitchen and began to cry bitterly.

"What's the matter, you fool?" asked Smury in astonishment. "Who ever heard of a soldier crying?"

"I was a noncombatant," said the soldier softly.

That was his ruin. In half an hour everybody on board was laughing at him. They would come up one at a time, stare at the soldier, and ask: "Him," then go off into peals of coarse, offensive laughter.

At first the soldier did not notice them or their laughter; he just sat there wiping his tears on the sleeve of his old cotton shirt as though hiding them up his sleeve. But soon his red-brown eyes began to glow angrily and he rattled off in the chirping Vyatka manner:

"Why fix your peepers on me? Go to the devil and stay there for good!"

That tickled the public more than ever. They began to poke their fingers into his ribs, pull at his shirt and his apron, teasing him mercilessly until dinnertime. After dinner somebody stuck a lemon rind on the end of a wooden spoon and tied it to the strings of his apron. The spoon swung back and forth as the soldier walked about, making everybody laugh, while he fretted like a mouse in a trap without guessing the cause of their mirth.

Smury watched him without a word, very seriously, his face going soft like a woman's.

I began to feel sorry for the soldier.

"May I tell him about the spoon?" I asked Smury.

He nodded.

When I told the soldier what everyone was laughing at, he snatched at the spoon, tore it loose, threw it on the floor, stamped on it, and grabbed me by the hair with both hands. We began to fight, to the delight of the onlookers who immediately pressed about us.

Smury scattered them and tore us apart, first tweaking my ears and then catching the soldier by the ear. On seeing this tiny fellow twist and caper in an effort to tear himself loose, the people roared and whistled and stamped their feet, doubling over with laughter.

"Hoorah for the garrison! Butt the cook in the belly!"

The mad joy of this herd of humans roused in me a desire to pick up a log and smash their heads.

Smury let go of the soldier and turned on the people like a wild boar, his hands behind his back, his teeth bared, his moustaches bristling.

"Every man to his place—march! Cannibals!"

Once more the soldier threw himself at me, but Smury lifted him up with one hand and carried him to the pump, where he stuck his head under the water and gave him a dousing, twisting the soldier's puny body about as though he were a rag doll.

Some boat-hands, the boatswain and the first mate came running up, and once more a crowd gathered. Above the heads of everyone else towered the steward, as meek and speechless as ever.

The soldier sat down on the woodpile and pulled off his boots with trembling hands. He began to wring out the rags in which his feet had been wrapped, but they were dry. The water dripped off his straggly hair, and this again set the public to laughing.

"You just wait," said the soldier in a thin, high voice. "I'll kill that boy yet!"

Smury held me by the shoulder and said something to the first mate. The boat-hands scattered the public.

"What we going to do with you?" said Smury to the soldier when everyone had gone.

The soldier said nothing; he kept looking at me with wild eyes while his whole body twitched strangely.

"'Ten-shun, you blubberer!"

"Fiddlesticks! This isn't the army!" answered the soldier.

I could see that this took the cook off his guard. His bloated cheeks deflated, he spat and walked away, taking me with him. Shocked, I kept looking back at the soldier, but Smury muttered:

"A cocky fellow, eh? Come along now."

Sergei caught up to us and whispered:

"He wants to cut his throat!"

"What!" shouted Smury, and ran back.

The soldier was standing in the door of the barman's cabin holding the large knife used for chopping off the heads of chickens and splintering firewood. The blade was dull and nicked like a saw. A crowd had gathered in front of the cabin to watch this funny little man with the dripping hair. His snub-nosed face was trembling like jelly, his mouth hung open, his lips twitched, and he kept muttering:

"Fiends. F-i-e-n-d-s!"

I jumped up on something and looked over the heads of the people into their faces. They were smiling and snickering and saying to one another:

"Look, look!"

When he began to push his shirt back into his trousers with his skinny, childlike hand, a handsome man standing next to me said with a sigh:

"What's he hitching up his pants for if he's going to kill himself?"

The public laughed all the louder. It was clear that no one believed him capable of killing himself. Neither did I, but Smury, after a brief glance at him, began to push people about with his belly, admonishing:

"Get away from here, you fool!"

He liked to use this word as a collective noun. He would approach a crowd of people and include all of them when he said:

"Be off, you fool!"

This was amusing, but it seemed true that today, from early morning, all people had been just one big fool.

When he had scattered the crowd, he went up to the soldier and held out his hand.

"Give me that knife."

"It's all the same," said the soldier,

handing over the knife. The cook passed it on to me and pushed the soldier into the cabin.

"Lay down and go to sleep. What's wrong with you, anyway?"

The soldier sat down on the bunk without a word.

"He'll bring you something to eat and some vodka. Do you drink vodka?"

"A little."

"See that you don't touch him. It wasn't him laughed at you, hear? I'm telling you it wasn't him."

"What did they have to torture me like that for?" asked the soldier softly.

Smury said nothing for a minute.

"Think I know?" he answered at last.

He and I went back to the kitchen.

"Hm—they sure picked on a poor specimen," he muttered on the way. "Did you see that? People can drive you crazy, brother; that they can. Stick fast to you like a bedbug, and there you are! What am I saying—a bedbug? They're a thousand times worse than any bedbug!"

When I brought the soldier some bread, meat, and vodka, he was sitting on the bunk rocking back and forth and crying softly like a woman. I put the plate on the table.

"Eat it," I said.

"Close the door."

"It'll be dark."

"Close it, or they'll be coming back."

I went out. I disliked the soldier. He did not rouse my sympathy or pity, and this made me feel uneasy. Granny had always said to me:

"People are to be pitied— poor unfortunates, struggling along—"

"Did you give it to him?" asked the cook when I returned. "Well, how's he feeling?"

"He's crying."

"Humph, the rag! Call him a soldier?"

"I don't feel sorry for him."

"What's that?"

"And a person ought to pity people."

Smury took me by the hand and drew me over.

"You can't make yourself feel sorry, and lying's no good, hear?" he said impressively. "Don't start getting sloppy; know your own mind."

He pushed me away and added gloomily:

"This is no place for you. Here, have a smoke."

My feelings had been deeply stirred by the behaviour of the passengers. I sensed something inexpressibly humiliating in the way they had teased the soldier and laughed with glee when Smury had held him by the ear. How could they enjoy anything so loathsome and pitiable? What could they find so hilariously funny about it?

Once more they were sitting and lying on deck, chewing and drinking and playing cards, talking calmly and respectably and watching the river as though they were not the same people who had hooted and whistled so boisterously an hour ago. Again they were as quiet and lazy as ever. From morning to night they milled slowly about the steamer like gnats or dust motes in a ray of sunlight. Now dozens of them were crowding at the top of the gangplank, crossing themselves before descending to the pier, while dozens of others just like them, wearing the same sort of clothes, bowed in the same way under a weight of sacks and packs, came climbing up onto the boat.

This constant exchange of people brought no change to the life on board the steamer. The new passengers would discuss the same things the others had discussed: land, work, God, women; they would even use the same words:

"It's the will of God that we should endure, so we'll go on enduring. There's nothing to be done about it; that's our fate."

It was dull and irritating to hear them say such things. I could not endure dirt, and I had no desire to endure being treated cruelly and unjustly. I was sure I had done nothing to deserve such treatment. Nor had the soldier deserved it. Certainly he had not wished to look ridiculous.

They put the serious, kindhearted Maxim off the boat, while they kept the despicable Sergei. And why did these people who were capable of torturing a person to madness, meekly. obey the rough orders of the boat-hands and accept the coarsest upbraiding without taking the slightest offence?

"Get away from the rails!" shouted the boatswain, narrowing his wicked, handsome eyes. "Can't you see the boat's listing? Beat it, you devils!"

The devils obediently rushed to the other side of the deck, from which they were again chased like a herd of sheep.

"Ugh, you rats!"

On hot nights it was unbearable under the metal awning which became heated during the day. The passengers crawled over the deck like roaches, sleeping wherever they pleased. At every landing the boat-hands would wake them up with kicks and blows.

"Hey, clear the road! Get back to your places!"

They would get up and sleepily wander off in any direction.

The boat-hands differed from the passengers only in their clothes, yet they ordered them about like policemen.

The most striking thing about people is their shyness and timidity and sad resignation, and it is strange and terrible when this crust of resignation is suddenly broken through in moments of brutal merrymaking that are rarely diverting. I felt that people did not know where they were being taken, and it made no difference to them where the steamer put them off; wherever they landed, they would remain on shore for only a brief space before boarding this or some other steamer, which would again take them somewhere; all of them were homeless wanderers, all lands were alien, and all people the veriest cowards.

Once, shortly after midnight, one of the machines broke down with an explosion like a cannon shot. The deck was immediately enveloped in white steam which rose from the engine room, curling thickly through all the cracks. Someone shouted deafeningly:

"Gavrilo! A piece of felt and some red lead!"

I slept next to the engine room on the table where I washed the dishes. When I was awakened by the explosion and the shock, everything was quiet on deck; the machinery was hissing with steam and the hammers were knocking quickly. But the next minute all the deck passengers were yelling and howling in the most terrifying way.

In the white fog which was quickly dispersing, uncombed women and dishevelled, fish-eyed men were rushing about, knocking each other down; all of them were tugging at bundles and sacks and suitcases, stumbling and falling, striking at each other, appealing to God and St. Nikolai. The sight was fearful, but interesting. I kept running after the people to see what they would do.

This was my first experience of a night alarm, and for some reason I sensed that it was all a mistake. The boat kept up its normal speed; along the right-hand bank, very close, burned the campfires of the haymakers; the night was bright, lighted by a high, full moon.

But the people kept rushing about ever more frenziedly. The cabin passengers put in their appearance. Somebody jumped overboard; others followed. Two muzhiks and a monk snatched up some logs with which they uprooted one of the benches screwed to the deck; a large cage of chickens was thrown over the stern; in the centre of the deck near the steps leading to the captain's bridge kneeled a muzhik who kept bowing to those who rushed past and howling like a wolf:

"Oh true believers, I'm a sinner!"

"A boat, you devils!" shouted a fat gentleman in nothing but a pair of trousers as he beat his breast with his fist.

The boat-hands rushed here and there, grabbing people by the nape of the neck, punching them in the head, tossing them aside. Smury strode about heavily with a coat thrown over his night clothes.

"Have some shame!" he urged everyone in a thundering voice. "Have you gone clean crazy? The boat's sound, not sinking. There's the riverbank a stone's throw away. The haymakers fished out all the fools who threw themselves overboard—there they are, see?—two boatloads."

He brought his fists down on the heads of third-class passengers, so that they folded up like sacks all over the deck.

Before the excitement had calmed down a fine lady wearing a cape and brandishing a tablespoon rushed at Smury and shouted:

"How dare you!"

A perspiring gentleman held her back.

"Leave him alone, the blockhead," he said irritably, sucking at his moustaches.

Smury shrugged his shoulders, blinked in perplexity, and turned to me.

"How do you like that?" said he. "What does she want with me anyway? Never saw her before in my life!"

A little muzhik snuffled back the blood flowing from his nose and shouted:

"What people! What bandits!"

During that summer I twice witnessed panic on the steamboat, and both times it was the result not of actual danger, but of the fear of it. A third time the passengers caught two thieves, one of them disguised as a pilgrim. They took them out of sight of the boat-hands and beat them for almost an hour. When the boat-hands finally rescued the thieves, the crowd flew at them:

"Thieves hiding thieves, we know you!" they shouted.

"You're brigands yourselves, and that's why you want to spare them!"

The thieves had been beaten unconscious. They were still unable to stand on their feet when they were handed over to the police at the next landing.

Many such incidents occurred, so distressing that one wondered whether people were inherently good or bad, meek or menacing. Why were they so cruelly, ravenously vicious, and so shamefully servile?

If I asked the cook about this, he would only wrap his face in cigarette smoke and reply irritably:

"What's it to you? People are just people. One's clever, another's a fool. Read books and stop racking your brains. You'll find all the answers in the books, if they're the right ones."

He had no use for religious books and the *Lives of the Saints*.

"They're just for priests, or sons of priests," he would say.

Wanting to do something nice for him, I decided to present him with a book. On the pier at Kazan I paid five kopeks for the *Legend of How Peter the Great Was Rescued by a Soldier*. But the cook was drunk and formidable at that moment, so I decided to read the *Legend* myself before giving it to him. I liked it immensely—everything was so simple and clear, concise and interesting. I was certain that the book would give him much pleasure.

But when I handed it to him, he crumpled it into a ball without a word and threw it overboard.

"There's your book for you, you fool!" he said sullenly. "Here I am, training you all the time like you was a hunting dog, and still you go eating the birds."

He stamped his foot and shouted at me.

"What kind of a book do you call that? I've read all that nonsense! Is it the truth that's written there? Come now, tell me!"

"I don't know."

"Well I know! If they chopped off that first fellow's head, he'd have fallen off the ladder and the others wouldn't have climbed up into the hayloft. Soldiers are no fools! They'd have set fire to the hay and that's the end of it! Hear?"

"Yes."

"So there you are! I know about that tsar Peter—nothing like that ever happened to him! Be off with you!"

I realized that the cook was right, but still I liked the book. Once more I bought the *Legend* and read it a second time, discovering to my surprise that the book really was worthless. This shamed me, and I came to look upon the cook with even greater respect and trust, while for some reason he kept saying:

"Ekh, you should be studying! This is no place for you!"

I too felt that this was no place for me. Sergei treated me abominably. Several times I caught him taking tea-things from my table and selling it to the passengers when the steward was not looking. I knew this was called thieving.

"Careful! See you don't let the waiters take knives and forks from your table!" Smury had warned me more than once.

There were many other things that boded ill for me, and often I was tempted to abandon the boat at the next landing and run off to the woods. I was kept from doing so by Smury, who seemed to grow ever more attached to me, and by the fascination of the boat, with its constant motion. I disliked the stops at the piers and kept waiting for something to happen that would take us off the Kama River into the Belaya, far up to Vyatka, or into the Volga, where I would see new shores and towns and people.

But nothing happened. My life on the steamer came to an abrupt and shameful end. One evening when we were travelling from Kazan to Nizhni, the steward sent for me. When I reported to him, he closed the door and said to Smury, who was sitting gloomily on a carpet-covered stool:

"Here he is."

"Do you give Sergei spoons and things?" he asked me roughly.

"He takes them himself when I'm not looking."

"You don't see him, but you know about it," said the steward quietly.

Smury brought his fist down on his knee, then scratched the spot.

"Wait a bit. There's no hurry," he said, and fell to thinking.

I looked at the steward and he at me, but I was aware of no eyes on the other side of his glasses.

He lived quietly, walked noiselessly, spoke in lowered tones. Sometimes his faded beard and vacuous eyes glinted out of some corner, only to vanish at once. Before going to bed he would kneel for a long time in front of the icon with the lamp ever burning above it. No matter how long I watched him through the diamond-shaped window in the door, I could never detect him praying; he simply knelt and gazed at the lamp and the icon, sighing and stroking his beard.

"Did Sergei give you any money?" asked Smury after a pause.

"No."

"Never?"

"Never."

"He wouldn't lie," said Smury to the steward, but the latter answered softly:

"It makes no difference. There you are."

"Come along," cried the cook, coming over to my table and giving me a fillip on the back of the head. "Fool! And I'm a fool too! I should have kept an eye on you."

At Nizhni the steward settled accounts with me. I received something like eight rubles—the first sizable sum I had ever earned.

As he took leave of me, Smury said dismally:

"Hm. Keep your eyes open in the future, hear? Mustn't go flycatching."

He slipped a bright beaded tobacco-pouch into my hand.

"Here, take it. Fine work—my godchild made it for me. Well, goodbye. Read books—that's the best thing you can do!"

He took me under the arms and lifted me into the air to kiss me, then set me firmly down on the pier. I felt sorry for him and for myself. Indeed, I could scarcely keep back the tears as I watched this huge, lumbering, lonely man push his way through the stevedores back to the boat.

How many similar people—as kind, as lonely, and as divorced from life—did I meet in later years!

VII

Granny and grandfather had again moved into town. I returned to them in an angry, belligerent mood. My heart was heavy. Why had they branded me a thief?

Granny greeted me affectionately and immediately went to heat the samovar. Grandfather spoke with his usual sarcasm.

"Save up much gold?"

"All I saved belongs to me," I replied, sitting down by the window. I proudly took a pack of cigarettes out of my pocket and lighted up.

"Oho!" said grandfather, following my every movement. "You don't say! So you've taken to the devil's weed, have you? Isn't it a bit early?"

"I even have a pouch," I boasted.

"A pouch!" squealed grandfather. "What you doing—trying to tease me?"

He rushed at me, his thin, strong arms outstretched, his green eyes flashing. I jumped up and butted him in the stomach. The old man collapsed on the floor and for a few tense seconds remained sitting there blinking at me in surprise, his dark mouth hanging open.

"So it's me you knocked down—your grandfather," he said at last in a strained voice. "The father of your own mother?"

"I've taken enough beatings from you," I mumbled, realizing that I had done something loathsome.

With a light, agile movement grandfather got up and sat down next to me. He snatched the cigarette out of my hand and threw it out of the window.

"You dunderhead! Don't you know God will never forgive you for such a thing as long as you live?" he asked in a frightened voice; then, turning to Granny: "Just think, mother! It was him struck me. Him. Struck *me*. Ask him if it wasn't."

Without bothering to ask me she came over and began to shake me by the hair.

"Here's what he gets for it! Take this! And this!" she said.

She did not hurt me physically, but my feelings were deeply injured, especially by grandfather's spiteful laughter. He jumped up and down on his chair, slapping himself on the knees and croaking:

"That's it! That's the way!"

I wrenched myself free, ran out into the entranceway, and threw myself down in a corner, where I lay, wretched and despairing, listening to the hum of the samovar.

Granny came out and leaned over me to whisper in a scarcely audible voice:

"Forgive me; I didn't really hurt you, did I? I just did it for the looks. There was nothing else to do. After all, grandfather's an old man and you must be respecting him. He too has his bones all broken and his heart brimming with grief. You mustn't go hurting him. You're not a little one any more; you can understand. You must understand, Alyosha. He's just a big baby—no more nor less."

Her words flowed over me soothingly, like warm water. The friendly rustle of her speech eased my pain and made me feel ashamed; I embraced her tightly and we kissed.

"Go in to him; go ahead, it'll be all right. Only don't smoke in front of him all of a sudden, just like that. Give him time to get used to it."

When I entered the room and glanced at grandfather I could hardly keep from laughing. He was indeed as gleeful as a baby. His face was shining, he stamped his feet and pounded the table with paws all overgrown with red fuzz.

"Well, little billy-goat, have you come back to do some more butting, eh? You little brigand you! Just like your father! Coming into the house like that, without so much as crossing yourself, and reaching for a fag first thing; phooh, you little two-kopek Bonapart!"

I made no reply. He ran out of words and became wearily silent, but during tea he began to lecture me:

"The fear of God's as needful to a person as reins to a horse. There's no one to befriend us but God; man is man's worst enemy."

I was struck by the truth of his words, that men were enemies, and remained untouched by the rest of what he said.

"You must go back to work for your Aunt Matryona now, and in the spring you can return to a boat. But spend the winter with them. And don't tell them you'll be leaving in the spring."

"Why fool people?" put in Granny, who had just fooled grandfather with the sham shaking she had given me.

"You can't live without fooling people," insisted grandfather. "Nobody does."

That evening when grandfather sat down to read the Psalter, Granny and I went through the gate and out to the fields. The tiny, two-windowed hut in which grandfather now lived was situated at the very edge of town, at the end of Kanatnaya Street, where he had once owned a house.

"Just see where we've moved to!" laughed Granny. Grandfather can't find himself a place for his soul's ease, so he keeps moving about. And this don't suit him, but it suits me."

For some three versts in front of us extend-

ed a meagre turfy stretch cut up by gullies
and ending in a line of birches marking the
Kazan road. Above the gullies protruded the
bare wands of bushes looking like blood-stained
whips in the cold glow of the sunset.
The grass was stirred by a light evening
breeze, and this movement was repeated beyond the nearest gully by the shadowy forms
of strolling couples from the town. Off to the
right stood the red wall of the dissenters' cemetery known as the "Bugrovsky Hermitage",
while a dark clump of trees to the left marked
the Jewish cemetery. Everything looked desti-
tute; everything clung silently to the lacerated
earth. The windows of the little houses here
at the edge of town seemed to be winking
timidly at the dusty road, along which wandered
undersized, underfed hens. A herd of lowing
cows passed the Devichy Convent. From a
nearby camp came the sound of martial
music, trumpets blaring, horns hooting.

A drunkard stumbled along, pulling brutally at an accordion and muttering:

"I'll reach you yet—for sure."

"Who'll you reach, you simpleton?" said

Granny, squinting into the red sunlight. "You'll be falling down and going to sleep and while you sleep they'll strip you bare—even take away that accordion of yours—your heart's joy."

I kept glancing round as I told Granny all about life on the boat. After what I had seen, I found my present surroundings depressing, and felt miserable. Granny listened with wrapt attention, as I always listened to her, and when I told her about Smury she crossed herself fervently and said:

"Ah dear, a good man; may the Blessed Virgin help him! Mind you don't forget him! Always hold the good things tight in your memory, and as for the bad—just toss them away."

It was very difficult for me to confess to her why I had been dismissed from the boat, but I grit my teeth and managed it somehow. The story made not the slightest impression on her.

"You're still too young; haven't learned how to live yet," she remarked indifferently.

"People keep telling each other they haven't learned how to live—the muzhiks, the boat-hands, Aunt Matryona kept telling her son. What's there to learn?"

Granny compressed her lips and shook her head.

"That I don't know," she replied.

"But you keep saying it too!"

"Why shouldn't I?" answered Granny calmly. "But don't let it hurt you. You're still too little; you're not expected to know how to live. And who does? Only the thieves. Take your grandfather—he's smart and book-learned, but it hasn't helped him a bit."

"Have you had a good life?"

"Me? Ah, yes, a good one. And a bad one. Changeable."

People strolled past us, dragging long shadows after them, and the dust rose like smoke from under their feet to bury the shadows. The sadness of eventide increased. From the window came the grumbling voice of grandfather:

"Spare me the fullness of Thy wrath, Oh God. Punish me according to my strength—"

Granny smiled.

"God must be sick and tired of him," she said. "Every evening he whines like this, and what for?—old as he is, beyond all wants, to keep growling and complaining so! God must have a good laugh when he hears this voice every evening: 'There's that Vasili Kashirin at it again!' Humph. Well, come on, let's get to bed."

I decided to go in for catching songbirds. It seemed to me a good means of gaining a livelihood. I would catch the birds and Granny would sell them. So, having bought a net, a ring, and some snares, and made some cages, here I am at dawn, hiding in the bushes of a gully while Granny roams the woods nearby with a sack and a basket in search of the last mushrooms, berries and nuts.

The tired September sun has just ascended. Its pale rays now expire in the clouds, now spread their silver fan down into my retreat. Shadows still linger at the bottom of the gully, and a white mist rises. One steep, clayey bank is dark and bare; the other, sloping gently, is overgrown with grass and thick bushes bright with red, yellow and brown leaves which the wind rips off and scatters through the gully.

In the burdocks at the bottom the goldfinches are chirping; through the ragged foliage I catch glimpses of the crimson caps on their perky little heads. The titmice are twittering inquisitively all about me, blowing out their white cheeks and fussing noisily like Kunavino lasses on a holiday. Quick, clever, and saucy, they must know and touch everything, so one after another they fall into the snare. It is painful to watch them struggle, but I must be callous—I am in business. I remove the birds to a cage kept for that purpose and cover it with a sack, to make them grow quiet.

A flock of siskins alights on a hawthorn bush radiant with sun. The birds are overjoyed by the sun and twitter all the more gaily, like a pack of schoolboys. A frugal, thrifty shrike, late for the flight south, sits on a waving wand of sweet briar trimming its wings with its beak and turning a beady black eye in search of quarry. Suddenly soaring like a lark, it catches a bumblebee, which it spikes on a thorn, and then takes up watch alongside, twisting and turning its thievish grey head. Silently a pine-finch flies past—my heart's desire—if only I could catch one! A bullfinch, red and cocky as a general, leaves the flock and comes to rest on an alder bush, where it chirps testily, swinging its black bill up and down.

The higher the sun, the more the birds and the gayer their song. The entire gully becomes filled with the music, to which the rustle of the bushes in the wind forms a constant accompaniment. The insistent voices of the birds cannot drown out this soft, sweet-sad rustle. I hear in it the farewell song of summer; it whispers telling words that line themselves up into a poem, while my memory involuntarily brings back old scenes.

From somewhere up above Granny cries: "Where are you?"

She is sitting on the edge of the gully with her kerchief spread out beside her, and on the kerchief are bread, pickles, turnips and some apples. Among all these blessings sparkles a beautiful little cut-glass decanter with a crystal stopper representing the head of Napoleon. The decanter contains some vodka flavoured with St. John's wort.

"Oh Lord, how good it all is!" breathes Granny gratefully.

"I've made up a song!"

"Have you really?"

I repeat some lines like:

Winter is coming, the flowers are done,
Farewell to summer, with its warming sun! . . .

Without hearing me out, she says:

"There's already a song like that, only it's better."

And she recites in a singsong voice:

Ah, the summer sun is setting
And the nightingales have left,
Here am I, a lonely maiden,
Of my summer's joy bereft.

I go walking in the morning
And recall that happy May
When you led me, ah, so blissful,
Under skies now cold and grey.

Kindly maidens, dearest sisters,
When the winds of winter blow,
Take my heart, consumed by sorrow,
Bury it beneath the snow.

My pride as a poet is not injured in the least. I like her song exceedingly and feel sorry for the maid.

"That's how grief is sung," says Granny. "It was the maid sang it. She walked with her swain in the summertime, but came winter and he left her alone, perhaps to go to another one. And she wept in grief. What you've never felt you never can sing. But just see how fine she made the song!"

Granny was greatly amazed the first time she sold some birds for forty kopeks.

"Fancy that! I thought nothing would come of it—just a little boy's whimsy. But look how profitable it turned out!"

"You sold them cheap at that."

"Did I now!"

On market days she would earn a ruble or even more, and could not get over it. How much money could be made on trifles!

"Why, a woman washes clothes all day long or scrubs floors for twenty-five kopeks! It makes no sense at all. It's wrong. And it's wrong to keep birds in cages. You must drop this business, Alyosha."

But I was greatly taken up by birdcatching. I enjoyed it and retained my independence without causing anyone but the birds the slightest inconvenience. I armed myself with good equipment; I had learned much from talking with experienced birdcatchers. I began going alone almost thirty versts away—to the Kstovsky Woods or to the banks of the Volga where in the tall pines I could catch crossbills, or a special variety of titmouse highly prized by bird lovers—a long-tailed white specimen of rare beauty.

Sometimes I would set out in the evening and trudge along the Kazan road all night long, frequently in the autumn rain, through deep mud. On my back I carried an oilcloth sack containing my snares and cages and bait for the birds, and in my hand a thick chestnut staff. It was cold and fearful in the autumn darkness—very fearful. Along the side of the road stood old, lightning-struck birches, their wet branches converging above my head; at the foot of the hills to my left, on the Volga side, occasional lights floated past on the masts of late steamers and barges, and they seemed to be receding into a bottomless abyss. I could hear the hooting of their horns and the slapping of paddle wheels through the water.

Out of the cast-iron earth rose the huts of the villages I passed. Vicious, hungry dogs rushed at my legs; the night watchmen wound their rattles and shouted in frightened voices:

"Who goes there? Who's been brought by the devil—a name not to be mentioned in the night-tide?"

I dreaded having my snares taken away, and for that reason always carried five-kopek pieces to bribe the watchmen. I became friendly with the night watchman in the village of Fokino. He was filled with amazement by my exploits.

"You again?" he would say. "What a fearless, restless night bird, eh?"

His name was Nifont; he was small and grey and looked like one of the saints. Often he would take a turnip or an apple or a handful of peas out of his pocket and thrust them into my hand, saying:

"Here you are, friend. I saved this little treat for you. I hope you enjoy it."

And he would accompany me to the edge of the village.

"Farewell. God be with you."

I would reach the woods at dawn, set my snares, hang up the bait, and lie down at the edge of the woods to await the day. Silence. Everything about me lay in the grip of deep autumnal slumber. At the foot of the dusky hills I caught a faint glimpse of broad meadows segmented by the Volga, the farthest reaches dissolving in mist. Far away, beyond the woods bounding the meadows, the sun rose slowly, setting fire to the black manes of the forest. Then began a strange, soul-stirring movement. Ever faster mounted the mist, shining silver in sunlight, while beneath it, bushes and trees and haystacks rose slowly off the earth. It was as though the meadows were melting in the sun's warmth and pouring in a golden-brown stream in all directions. Now the sun touched the quiet waters at the river-bank, and it seemed that the whole river flowed to the spot where it had dipped its golden fingers. As the golden disc climbed ever higher it shed a joyful blessing all about, warming the cold, shivering earth, which in gratitude breathed forth the sweet fragrance of autumn. Seen through the transparent air, the earth looked enormous, endlessly magnified. Everything aspired to the distance, luring one to the blue ends of the earth. Dozens of times I watched the sunrise in that place, and each time a new world was born before me—a world uniquely beautiful.

Somehow I bear a particular love for the sun. I like its very name, the sweet sound of it, the rich resonance of it. I love to close my eyes and turn my face to a warm ray, or to catch it on the palm of my hand, when it thrusts like a sword through a crack in a fence, or the branches of a tree. Grandfather had the greatest respect for "Prince Mikhail Chernigovsky and Boyarin Feodor, who refused to bow to the Sun." But I visualized them as vicious men, morose and dark as gypsies, with the sore eyes of Mordovian peasants. When the sun rose over the meadows, I involuntarily smiled with joy.

Above me rustled the evergreens, shaking the dew off their boughs. In the shadows under the trees I glimpsed the silver brocade of hoar-frost upon lacy fern fronds. The brown grasses, felled by the rain, lay motionless upon the earth, yet when a ray of sunlight struck them, one could detect a slight stirring, perhaps a last effort to survive.

The birds awoke. From branch to branch bounced fluffy grey balls—the titmice; fiery crossbills pecked at the cones atop the pines; at the end of a bough swung a nuthatch preening its feathers and cocking a suspicious eye at my nets. And suddenly I realized that the entire forest, which only a moment before had been steeped in solemn meditation, was now articulate with hundreds of bird voices, was filled with the bustle of these purest of living creatures, in whose likeness Man, father of earthly beauty, had created for his own delight the elves and seraphims and cherubims and all the angelic choir.

It was a pity to capture the birds, and shameful to imprison them in cages; I received boundless pleasure from just watching them. But a hunter's zeal and the desire to earn money outweighed my pity.

I was amused by the cunning of the birds. A blue titmouse studied the snare with the utmost attention, and on realizing the danger it held, approached cautiously from one side, deftly snatching the seed from between the wooden bars. The titmice are clever birds, but too inquisitive, and this is their ruin. The staid bullfinches are stupid; whole flocks streamed into my net, like well-fed burghers going to church. When I clamped on the cover they were greatly surprised, rolling their eyes and pecking at my fingers with their thick bills. The crossbill would walk calmly and imposingly into the net. The finch, a unique bird, would perch for a long time in front of the snare, leaning back on its broad tail and slowly swinging its long bill from side to side. Its habit was to run up and down the tree trunks like a woodpecker, always in the wake of the titmice. There was something appalling about this grey little bird, so lonely, unloved by all and loving no one. Like the magpie, it stole shiny little objects and hid them away.

By noon I would finish my work and go home through the woods and over the fields.

If I took the main road through the villages, other boys or village desperadoes would snatch my cages away from me and break my snares. I had learned this from bitter experience.

I would reach home in the evening, tired and hungry, but filled with the sense that I had gained something, that I had grown in strength and knowledge. This new strength enabled me to listen calmly to grandfather's ridicule. Seeing this, he would begin a grave discourse:

"Enough of this nonsense; enough, I tell you. Nobody ever made his way in the world by birdcatching. Find a place for yourself and set your brains to growing there. A man wasn't made to devote himself to trifles. He's the seed of God, meant to give forth good grain. A man's like a ruble—put it to good use and it will triple its value. Do you think living's easy? It's a hard thing, living. The world's a dark night that every man must light for himself. We're all born with ten fingers, but everyone wants his hands to reach the farthest and grab the most. You have to be strong, and if you're not, you have to be cunning. The

weak and the frail are sure to fail. Live friendly with people, but always remember you're
alone; listen to everyone, trust no one. If
you trust your eye, the measure's awry. Be
closemouthed; it's not the tongue built towns
and cities, but the ruble and the hammer.
You're no Bashkirian or Kalmyk, whose only
wealth is lice and sheep."

He could go on like this all evening; I
knew the words by heart. I liked the sound
of them, but I was suspicious of their meaning.
From what he said I concluded that there were
two forces making life difficult: God and
people.

Granny would be sitting at the window
spinning thread for lace, the spindle humming
in her dexterous fingers. After listening silently
to grandfather's words for awhile, she would say:

"Everything will turn out like the Mother
of God wants it."

"What's that?" grandfather would shout:
"God? I haven't forgotten about God; I know
God all right! Do you think God has peo-
pled our earth with fools, old fool that
you be?"

. . . It seemed to me that no one lived as well as soldiers and Cossacks. Their lives were gay and simple. On fine mornings they would appear beyond the ravine opposite our house, scatter over the field, and begin an exciting, complicated game. These strong, fleet men in white shirts would dash merrily across the field with rifles in their hands, disappear in the ravine, and then suddenly, at the blast of a trumpet, rush out on the field again with shouts of "hurrah!" and an ominous beating of drums, making straight for our street, bayonets bristling, as if they meant to overturn our house like a hayrick.

I also shouted "hurrah" and ran at their heels. The menacing roll of the drums roused in me an irrepressible desire to destroy something—to tear down a fence or beat somebody.

In off moments the soldiers would treat me to a smoke of makhorka and show me their heavy rifles. One or another of them would point his bayonet at my stomach and cry with exaggerated ferocity:

"Spike the cockroach!"

The bayonet would glisten in the sun, seeming to writhe like a live snake about to strike. That was frightening, but pleasurable.

A Mordovian drummer boy taught me to handle the drumsticks. First he took my hands in his and squeezed them till it hurt, then thrust the sticks into my numb fingers.

"Strike it—once, and again—once, and again! Ta-ta-ta-taaaaa! Easy with the left, hard with the right—ta-ta-ta-taaaa!" he shouted hoarsely, staring at me with birdlike eyes.

I kept running with the soldiers until their drill was over, when I would march with them across the whole town to their barracks, listening to their strong singing, gazing into their kind faces, all looking so new and bright, like five-kopek pieces straight from the mint.

This solid mass of men, all alike, swept gaily along the street, filling one with delight and the irresistible desire to plunge into it, as into a river; to enter into it, as into a forest. These people were afraid of nothing, looked at everything boldly, could conquer anything, would achieve whatever they wanted, and, best of all, were simple and kindhearted.

But one day during a pause, a young non-commissioned officer gave me a fat cigarette.

"Have a smoke. This is a very special cig-arette—I wouldn't give it to anybody but you—you're such a fine chap!"

I lit up. He stepped back, and all of a sudden a red flame blinded me and singed my fingers, nose, and brows. Grey, acrid smoke caused me to sneeze and cough. Blinded and frightened, I stood prancing on one spot while the soldiers formed a solid ring about me, laughing in loud merriment. I went home. Behind me I heard their laughter and whistling and a snapping like that of a shepherd's whip. My fingers hurt, my face stung, tears flowed from my eyes; but I was more oppressed by a dull, aching wonderment than by this pain. Why should they have done this to me? Why had such good men found it amusing? On reach-ing home I climbed up into the attic and sat there for a long time recalling all the in-comprehensible cruelty I had witnessed in my short life. Especially vivid was my memory of the little soldier from Sarapul. He stood before me as true as life.

"Well, do you understand?" he asked.

But soon thereafter I was to witness something much more cruel and shocking.

I began to frequent the barracks where the Cossacks lived, near Pecherskaya Sloboda. The Cossacks were different from the soldiers—not so much because they were expert horsemen and dressed better, as because they spoke differently, sang different songs, and were excellent dancers. Sometimes in the evening, after grooming their horses, they would gather in a circle near the stables and a little red-headed Cossack would shake back his wavy hair and begin to sing in a high voice like a clarinet. Standing there straight and tense, he would sing a soft sad song about the quiet Don or the blue Danube. He closed his eyes like the dawn-bird, which often sings until it drops dead to the earth. His blouse was open at the throat, revealing his collarbone sticking out like a bit of bronze accoutrement, and indeed his whole figure seemed cast of bronze. He stood there sightless, waving his arms, rocking on his thin legs as though the earth were heaving under him, and he seemed to have ceased being a man and become a trumpeter's horn, a shepherd's pipe. Sometimes I fancied that he would fall over backwards on the earth and die like the dawn-bird, because he had poured all his soul, all his strength, into his song.

His comrades stood about him with their hands in their pockets or behind their broad backs, gazing sternly at his bronze face and his waving hands, themselves singing calmly and impressively, like the choir in church. At such moments all of them, bearded and unbearded alike, resembled icons—just as dread, just as aloof. And the song stretched out like a highway, broad and even and filled with the wisdom of the years. While listening I forgot whether it was night or day, whether I was a child or an old man. Everything was forgotten. The voices of the singers died down until we could hear the ceaseless movement of the autumn night creeping over the fields, and the sighing of the horses as they dreamed of the freedom of the steppes. My heart swelled to bursting from the fullness of this extraordinary feeling and from a vast, mute love for people and for the land.

It seemed to me that the little bronze Cossack was more than a man—something much more significant—a legendary creature far and above all mortals. I was incapable of speaking to him. If he would ask me a question I would smile happily, but remain silent with embarrassment. I was ready to follow him about like an obedient dog if only I could see him more often and hear him sing.

One day I saw him standing in a corner of the stable studying a plain silver ring on his finger. His fine lips were moving, his little red moustaches were twitching and his face wore a sad, injured expression.

On another dark evening I brought my cages to the tavern on Staraya Sennaya Square. The owner of the tavern was passionately fond of songbirds and often bought them from me.

The Cossack was sitting in a corner near the bar, between the stove and the wall. Beside him sat a plump woman, almost twice his size. Her round face was shining like parchment and she was looking at him with the fond, somewhat anxious gaze of a mother. He was drunk and kept shifting his feet over the floor. He must have kicked her, for she started and frowned and said to him softly:

"Stop your nonsense."

With a great effort the Cossack lifted his brows, but dropped them at once. He was hot, and pulled open his coat and shirt, baring his throat. The woman pushed her kerchief off her head on to her shoulders, and placed her strong white arms on the table, folding her hands so tightly that the knuckles grew white. The more I looked at them, the more it seemed to me that the Cossack was the unruly son of a loving mother. She reproved him affectionately while he remained meekly silent; there was nothing he could say to her just remonstrances.

Suddenly he got up as though stung, pulled his cap low over his forehead, slapping it down, and went toward the door without buttoning his coat. The woman also got up.

"We'll be back in a minute, Kuzmich," she said to the tavern keeper.

Their going was accompanied by the laughter and jests of the patrons.

"When the pilot returns he'll give it to her!" said one of them solemnly.

I followed them out. They moved through the darkness about a dozen paces ahead of me, crossed the muddy square, and made straight for the high bank of the Volga. I could see the woman lurch in her effort to support the Cossack, and I could hear the mud squashing under their feet.

"Where are you going? Where are you going?" the woman kept asking softly.

I followed them through the mud, though my road lay in another direction. When they reached the edge of the embankment the Cossack stopped, took a step back, and suddenly struck her full in the face. She cried out in fright and surprise:

"Oh, why should you?"

I too was frightened and ran up to them, but the Cossack grabbed the woman about the waist, threw her over the railing, jumped down after her, and both of them went rolling in one dark mass down the grass of the embankment. Stunned, I stood stock-still listening to the tussle and the ripping of clothing and the hoarse breathing of the Cossack down there below. The woman kept muttering in a low voice:

"I'll scream. I'll scream."

Then she gave a loud, painful groan, and everything grew still. I felt for a stone and threw it over the embankment. Nothing but a rustle of weeds. The glass door of the tavern banged, somebody grunted as though he had fallen, and again there was silence, filled with latent terror.

Halfway up the embankment appeared something large and white. Slowly and unsteadily it climbed, sobbing and whimpering. I recognized it as the woman. She was climbing on all fours, like a sheep, and I could see that she was naked to the waist. Her large round breasts glowed whitely, so that she seemed to have three faces. At last she reached the railing and sat down near me, breathing like a winded horse and trying to smooth her dishevelled hair. Dark smudges of dirt were clearly visible on her white body. She wept and brushed away her tears with the movements of a cat washing its face.

"Heavens, who are you! Get away, you shameless boy!" she cried softly on catching sight of me.

I could not go away; I was paralyzed by wonderment and bitter grief. I remembered the words of Granny's sister:

"Woman's a force to be reckoned with. Didn't Eve deceive God himself?"

The woman got up, covered her breasts with the remnants of her dress, thus exposing her legs, and quickly walked away. Up the embankment climbed the Cossack, waving some white garments in the air. He gave a low whistle, listened, and then said in a gay tone:

"Darya! Well, didn't I tell you a Cossack would always get what he wanted? So you thought I was drunk, did you? Oh no, that was just to fool you! Darya!"

He stood firmly on his feet, and his voice sounded sober and mocking. Stooping down, he wiped the mud off his boots with the woman's clothes and went on talking:

"Here, take your blouse! Come on, Darya, no sulking!" and in a loud voice he called her an obscene name.

I remained sitting there on a heap of brush listening to that voice so isolated in the silence of the night, and so crushingly imperious.

Before my eyes danced the lights of the lanterns on the square. From out of a clump of dark trees to the right rose the white School for Daughters of the Nobility. Lazily telling off his filthy words and waving the white garments, the Cossack set out over the square and vanished like a bad dream.

From the water tower down below came the sound of steam hissing through an outlet pipe. A cab clattered down the descent to the river. Not a soul was in sight. Anguished, I walked along the edge of the embankment, clutching in my hand a cold stone which I had intended to throw at the Cossack. Near the church of St. George the Conqueror I was stopped by the night watchman, who angrily asked who I was and what I carried in the sack on my back.

When I told him about the Cossack, he roared with laughter.

"That's something for you!" he cried. "Cossacks don't stand on ceremony, brother! They're no match for us. And the woman was a bitch all right!"

Again he went off into peals of laughter and I continued on my way, wondering what he found to laugh at.

In horror I kept thinking: what if that woman had been my mother, or my grandmother?

VIII

When the first snow fell, grandfather once more took me to Granny's sister.

"It won't do you any harm—no harm," he said.

I felt that during the summer I had lived through tremendous experiences, making me older and wiser, while life at my employers' had become duller than ever. In the same old way these people poisoned themselves by overeating; they talked about their ailments in the same monotonous detail; the old woman prayed to her God with the same fearful vengeance. The younger mistress had grown thinner after giving birth to another child, but while taking up less space, she continued to move about with the same staid importance as when she had been pregnant. As she sewed clothes for the children she would quietly sing one and the same song:

> *Vanya, Vanya, Vanychka,*
> *Brother Vanya, brother dear,*
> *I will sit upon the sled,*
> *You will kneel behind and steer.*

If anyone entered the room she would immediately stop singing and say angrily:

"What do you want?"

I was certain that this was the only song she knew.

In the evenings my mistresses would call me into the dining room and say:

"Tell us about your life on the steamboat."

Sitting on a chair near the lavatory door, I told them everything. I enjoyed recalling that other life in the midst of this life, into which I had been forced against my will. As

I became absorbed in my story, I would forget about my audience, but not for long. The women had never been on a steamer and would ask:

"Weren't you scared?"

I could not understand what there was to be scared of.

"What if the boat had turned over in a deep place and sunk?"

My master laughed, and while I knew that steamers did not turn over and sink in deep places, I was unable to convince the women of this. The older one was sure that steamers did not float on the water, but that their paddle wheels moved along the bottom like the wheels of a cart along a road.

"How can it float if it's iron? An axe don't float, does it?"

"But a dipper does."

"A fine comparison! A dipper's little and empty."

When I told them about Smury and his books, they eyed me suspiciously. The old woman claimed that only fools and heretics wrote books.

"What about the Psalter? And King David?"

"The Psalter's a holy book, and even so King David asked God's forgiveness for the psalms."

"Where's that written?"

"Here on my hand! I'll give you a smart smack on the back of the head to teach you where!"

She knew everything, and made all her remarks—always absurd—with the utmost confidence.

"The Tatar on Pechorka Street died and his soul came pouring out of his throat, black as tar."

"The soul's a spirit," I said.

"I'm talking about a Tatar, you fool," she retorted witheringly.

My young mistress was also afraid of books.

"It's very harmful to read books, especially when you're young," she said. "There was a girl lived on our street—Grebeshok Street—came from a good family too, but she started reading books and she read and read until she fell in love with the deacon! Didn't the deacon's wife go at her though? Tooth and nail! Right out in the street in front of everybody! Something awful!"

Sometimes I would use words from Smury's books, in one of which I had read: "Strictly speaking, no one invented gunpowder; it made its appearance as a result of a long process of minor observations and discoveries."

For some unintelligible reason these words stuck in my mind. I became especially fond of the expression "strictly speaking," which seemed to me very forceful. The use of it cost me much suffering—needless suffering, a rather common variety.

One evening when the family asked me to tell them about my experiences on the steamer I answered:

"Strictly speaking, there's nothing to tell."

They were overwhelmed, and began croaking:

"What's that? What did you say?"

All four of them broke out laughing.

"'Strictly speaking!' Good heavens!" they kept repeating.

Even my master said to me:

"That was a silly thing to say."

For a long time after that they called me "strictly speaking."

"Hey, there, 'strictly speaking'! How about coming over here and wiping up the floor after the baby, 'strictly speaking'?"

This senseless teasing surprised rather than offended me.

I lived in a fog of stupefying misery which I tried to relieve by working as hard as possible. There was plenty of work. There were two infants in the household, and since my carping mistresses were forever dismissing the nurse-maid, the care of the babies fell largely to me. Every day I washed diapers and once a week I went to Gendarme Spring to rinse the clothes. The washwomen there laughed at me.

"What are you doing this woman's work for?" they would say.

Sometimes as a result of their teasing I would lash them with wet clothes; they would pay me back in kind, and I found it jolly and interesting to be with them.

Gendarme Spring flowed at the bottom of a deep gully leading to the Oka River. The gully separated the city from a field named after the ancient Slavonic God Yarilo. To this field the townspeople came to promenade on Semik.* Granny told me that in her youth people still believed in Yarilo and paid him homage. They would tar a wheel, set fire to it, and send it rolling down the hill accompanied by shouts and singing. If it reached the Oka, that meant that Yarilo accepted their tribute; the summer would be fine and would bring happiness to all.

Most of the washwomen lived in Yarilo Field, and all of them were energetic and sharp-tongued. They had a thorough knowledge of the life of the city and it was interesting to listen to their accounts of the merchants, clerks, and officers for whom they worked. Rinsing the clothes during the winter in the icy water of the spring was a cruel task; the women's hands froze until the skin cracked. They stood bending over the wooden trough into which

* The Thursday of the seventh week after Easter.—*Tr.*

the water flowed, barely protected from wind and snow by an old, dilapidated wooden roof. Their faces were flushed and frostbitten, their aching fingers refused to bend, the tears flowed from their eyes, but they kept up an incessant chatter, informing each other of the latest happenings and accepting things and people with exceptional courage.

The one who spoke best was Natalya Kozlovskaya, a woman somewhat over thirty, fresh and strong, with mocking eyes and a particularly sharp and versatile tongue. The other women always listened attentively when she spoke; they sought her advice and respected her for her skill at work, her neat way of dressing, and for the fact that she sent her daughter to study at the Gymnasium. When she made her way down the slippery path, bending under the weight of two basketloads of wet clothes, they would greet her cheerfully:

"How's that daughter of yours?" they would ask.

"She's all right, praise the Lord. Studying."

"She'll be a gentlewoman before you know it."

"That's what I sent her to school for. How did the lady fair come by her golden hair? She got it from us, from the scum of the earth. Where else? The more you know, the finer you grow. God sent us into this world young and foolish, but He wants us to leave it old and wise. So it's up to us to study and learn things."

Everyone became silent when she spoke, listening attentively to her sure, flowing speech. They praised her to her face and behind her back, wondering at her strength and endurance and cleverness. But no one tried to imitate her. She made herself some leather gauntlets out of boot tops in order to protect her arms to the elbow and prevent her sleeves from getting wet. Everyone said it was a clever thing to have done, but nobody else did it, and when I appeared in such gauntlets the women only laughed at me.

"Ho, ho! Learning from a woman!" they chided.

And they would say about her daughter:

"What an important young miss! Well, there'll be one lady the more, and what of it?

Maybe she won't finish her studies—maybe she'll die first."

"Life's not so easy for the learned ones either. Take the daughter of the Bakhilovs— just look how long she studied. And what became of her in the end? A schoolteacher. And once a schoolteacher, that means an old maid."

"Sure enough. A man'll grab you up without any book learning, long as there's something to grab hold of!"

"A woman's brain don't lie in her head!"

It was strange and disturbing to hear them speak so shamelessly of themselves. I knew how soldiers and sailors and ditchdiggers spoke about women and I had heard men boast to each other about their own virility and about the number of women they had fooled. I sensed their hostility to "the skirts," but whenever I heard a man telling about his conquests, his bragging was accompanied by something which led me to think his words contained more exaggeration than truth.

The washwomen did not tell each other about their love affairs, but when they spoke about the men, they did so with a mockery and a vengeance corroborating the statement that women were a force to be reckoned with.

"However you try to pass them by, you're sure to come back to the women," said Natalya one day.

"The veriest truth," shouted an old hag in a hoarse voice. "Don't the monks and the hermits abandon God Himself to come to us?"

This talk to the accompaniment of the sobbing of the suds and the slapping of the wet clothes here in this filthy hole at the bottom of the gully where not even the cleansing snow could lie for any length of time—this shameful, vicious talk about a great mystery, about the source from which spring all peoples and all tribes, roused in me a timorous revulsion, making my thoughts and sensibilities recoil from all the "love affairs" pressing so insistently about me; for long the conception of "love" was closely associated in my mind with these filthy, obscene affairs.

Yet in the gully among the washwomen, or in the kitchens among the officers' batmen, or in the cellars among the labourers, I found life incomparably more interesting than at home, where the frozen patterns of speech, concepts, and events roused nothing but a dull, chafing boredom. My employers' lives moved in a vicious circle of eating, sleeping, being ill, and of fussily getting ready to eat and sleep. They were forever talking about sin and death, clustering about these fears like grain about the millstone, in dreadful expectation of being crushed.

In off hours I would go out into the shed and chop wood so as to be alone. But I rarely found solitude, for the officers' batmen would be sure to come and begin talking about the people in our yard.

Most often I was joined by Yermokhin or Sidorov. The first was a tall, stoop-shouldered man from Kaluga. He had a small head and filmy eyes and seemed woven entirely of thick, strong sinews. He was lazy, and exasperatingly stupid. His movements were slow and clumsy, and whenever he set eyes on a woman he would mumble and slump forward as though about to fall at her feet. None of the men in our yard could understand the speed with which he conquered cooks and chambermaids;

they all envied him and stood in awe of his bearish-like strength. Sidorov was a thin, bony fellow from Tula. He was always sad of mien, spoke softly, coughed timidly; his eyes burned with a faltering light, and he kept glancing into dark corners. Whether speaking in his hushed voice or sitting silent, he kept his eyes glued to the darkest corner.

"What are you looking at?"

"Perhaps a mouse will run out. I love mice— such quick, quiet little things."

I wrote letters for the batmen—to their sweethearts, or to their families in the village. I enjoyed doing this, especially for Sidorov. Every Saturday he wrote to his sister in Tula.

He would invite me into his kitchen and sit beside me at the table, rubbing his shaved head briskly and whispering into my ear:

"Well, let's begin. First—like you're supposed: 'Most respectful sister! May you enjoy good health for years on end'—and all the rest of it. Finished? Good. Now write: 'I got your ruble, but you mustn't do that and I thank you very much. I don't need anything, we live fine.' We don't live fine at all. We live

262

like a pack of dogs, but you don't have to tell her that. Write: 'We live fine.' She's still too little; she's only fourteen years old. Why should she know everything? And now go on writing like they taught you."

He hung over my left shoulder, breathing hotly and odoriferously into my face and whispering insistently:

"Tell her not to let the boys hug her or touch her breasts or anything else. Write: 'If somebody talks gentle to you, don't believe him. He just wants to fool you and ruin you.'"

He made a great effort not to cough. His grey face became crimson, his cheeks billowed out, the tears came to his eyes, and he bent double on his chair, knocking against me.

"You're pushing my arm!"

"That's all right; you go ahead and write: 'Be wary of the fine gentlemen most of all; they'll fool a girl the very first time. They know how to talk and can say anything, and once you believe them, there's nothing for you after that but a brothel. If you save up a ruble, give it to the priest; he'll keep it for you if he's a good man. But better to bury it in the ground somewhere—be sure nobody sees you and remember where.'"

It was very painful to listen to his whispering, drowned out by the screeching of the hinges on the little window overhead. I glanced about at the sooty stove and at the cupboard, covered with fly-spots. The kitchen was indescribably dirty, full of bedbugs, reeking of smoke and kerosene and fried grease. Roaches rustled on the stove and among the kindling. My soul was desolate, and I could have wept for that poor soldier and his sister. How was it possible to live like that?

I went on writing, disregarding Sidorov's whispering. I wrote about how dull and hurtful life was, while he sighed and said to me:

"You've written a lot. Thanks. Now she'll know what to be afraid of."

"You mustn't be afraid of anything," I retorted angrily, though I myself was afraid of many things.

The soldier laughed and cleared his throat.

"Stupid! How can you help being afraid? What about the fine gentlemen? What about God? And lots of other things?"

On receiving a letter from his sister he would say anxiously:

"Please hurry and read it to me."

Three times he would have me read the almost indecipherable note, so disappointingly brief and dull.

He was kind and softhearted, but his attitude toward women was like that of everyone else—coarse and primitive. As I voluntarily and involuntarily witnessed the affairs which swiftly developed before my very eyes, I observed that Sidorov would rouse a woman's pity with his complaints about the hard life of a soldier and turn her head with feigned affection, while later, when telling Yermokhin about his conquest, he would spit and make a face, as if he had just swallowed a bitter dose. This wounded me to the quick, and I asked the soldier why they all lied and deceived and made sport of the women, passing them on from one to the other, often even beating them.

He only laughed softly and said:

"Don't pay any attention to such things. They're bad—even sinful. You're too young. It's too early for you to know."

But one day I succeeded in getting a more definite answer and one which I never forgot.

"Do you think she don't know I'm fooling her?" he said with a wink and a cough. "She knows all right! She wants me to fool her. Everybody lies about such things. They're ashamed, because nobody really loves anybody else—they just do it for fun. That's very shameful. Just wait a bit and you'll learn for yourself. You have to do it at night, or if it's daytime, hiding away in some dark corner like a lumber-room. It's for this God drove Adam and Eve out of Paradise, and it's for this all people are unhappy."

He said this so well, so sadly, so remorsefully, that it somewhat compensated for his "affairs." I was more friendly with him than with Yermokhin, whom I hated and whom I tried in every way to plague and ridicule. My efforts were successful, and often he would chase me through the yard with violent intentions, usually thwarted by his clumsiness.

"It's forbidden," said Sidorov.

I knew it was forbidden, but I did not believe it was the cause of human unhappiness because I had often observed an extraordinary expression in the eyes of those who were in love, and I sensed the exceptional benevolence of lovers. It was a joy to witness the heart's holiday born of love.

But as I remember it, life at that time seemed to grow ever more dull and cruel, congealed irrevocably in the forms and relationships which I observed from day to day. I never even considered the possibility of anything better than that which existed, than that which confronted me, unchanging, day after day.

But once the soldiers told me something that stirred me deeply. In one of the flats lived the cutter from the best tailor shop in town. He was a quiet, modest man, not a Russian. His wife was a small woman without any children, who read books all day long. In the midst of the noise of our yard, among all the drunkards living in our house, these two remained unseen and unheard. They did not entertain, and they themselves never went anywhere except to the theatre on holidays.

The husband was away at work from early morning till late at night; his wife, who looked like a girl in her teens, went to the library twice a week in the afternoon. I often saw her walking along the lane with tiny steps and a slight limp, her little hands neatly gloved, swinging her books from a strap like any school-girl—so simple and fresh and new and clean. She had a birdlike face with quick little eyes, and she was as pretty as a china doll on a mantel. The soldiers said that one of her ribs was missing on the right side, and that was why she limped, but I liked her limp; it imme-diately set her apart from the officers' wives in our yard. In spite of their shrill voices and loud clothes and high bustles, these women looked old and worn, as though they had long been lying forgotten in some dark closet among other discarded things.

The little wife of the cutter was consid-ered not quite normal by the neighbours. They said her mind had become so touched by reading that she was no longer capable of looking after the house. Her husband did the marketing himself and gave orders to the cook, a huge, sullen, foreign woman with one inflamed eye that was always running, and a tiny pink slit in place of the other. The mistress herself, as they said, was unable to tell beef from veal, and one day disgraced herself by buying horse-radish instead of parsley.

Just imagine the shame of it!

All three of them were out of place in that house; they seemed to have fallen there by chance, like birds who have sought protection from wintry blasts by flying through the window of a dirty, stuffy, human habitation.

And then the batmen told me that the officers were playing a low and churlish game with the cutter's little wife. Almost every day one of them would send her a note telling of his love and heartache and extolling her beauty. She would reply by asking to be left in peace, expressing her regret that she had caused them suffering and praying God to free them of their attachment. On receiving such a note, the officers would read it collectively, have a good laugh, and collectively compose another letter to her signed by any one of them.

As they told me this, the batmen also laughed and upbraided the woman.

"The stupid, lame little fool," said Yermokhin in his deep bass.

"All women like to be fooled," chimed in Sidorov. "They understand all right."

I did not believe that the cutter's wife realized they were making fun of her, and I made up my mind to inform her. One day, seeing her cook go down into the cellar, I ran up the back stairs to the little woman's flat, entered the kitchen, found it empty, and went into the dining room, where the cutter's wife was sitting at the table holding a heavy gold cup in one hand and a book in the other. In her fright she pressed the book to her breast and cried in a low voice:

"Who is it? Augusta! Who are you?"

I poured out a confusion of words, expecting her to throw the book or the cup at me. She was sitting in a large maroon armchair, and was dressed in a blue dressing gown with fringe at the hem, and lace at the throat and wrists, while her wavy brown hair cascaded about her shoulders. She looked like an angel from the King's Portal in church. Leaning back in the chair, she fixed her round eyes on me angrily at first, but soon her expression softened into a wondering smile.

When I had told her everything, I turned to leave.

"Wait!" she cried.

She put the cup on a tray, tossed the book on the table, folded her hands, and said in the full voice of a grown person:

"What a strange boy you are! Come here."

I approached hesitantly. She took my hand and stroked it with cold little fingers.

"No one sent you to tell me that, did they?" she asked. "Very well, I believe you—you thought of it yourself."

Letting go of my hand, she covered her eyes and said in a soft, pained voice:

"So that's what those filthy soldiers say about me!"

"You better move away," I advised solemnly.

"Why?"

"They'll be the ruin of you."

She laughed pleasantly.

"Have you ever studied?" she asked. "Do you like to read books?"

"I have no time to read."

"If you liked to read, you'd find time. Well, thank you very much."

She held out her little hand with a silver coin between thumb and forefinger. I was ashamed to take this cold gratuity, but I dared not refuse. On leaving I placed it on the post of the stairway.

I carried away with me a profound and wholly new impression. It was as though day had suddenly dawned for me, and for some time thereafter I lived in the joy of remembering that spacious room and the cutter's little wife dressed in blue like an angel. Everything there had been unfamiliarly beautiful; a thick golden rug had lain under her feet and the wintry day had glanced through the silvery window to warm itself in her presence.

I wanted to have another look at her. What would happen if I went and asked her for a book?

I went, and found her in exactly the same place, again with a book in her hands. But this time her face was tied up in a brown kerchief and one eye was swollen. She handed me a book in a black binding and mumbled something unintelligible. Sadly I took away the book, which smelled of creosote and aniseed drops. On reaching home I wrapped it in paper and a clean blouse and hid it up in the attic, lest my employers find it and destroy it.

They subscribed to the *Niva* for the sake of the dress patterns and the souvenirs which came with it. They never read the magazine, but after looking at the pictures, put it up on top of the wardrobe in the bedroom. At the end of the year they had it bound and hid it under the bed along with three volumes of the *Picture Review*. Whenever I washed the bedroom floor the books became soaked with dirty water. My master subscribed to the newspaper, *The Russian Courier*.

"The devil only knows why they write such stuff," he would say when reading it in the evenings. "What a bore!"

On Saturday, while hanging up the clothes in

the attic, I remembered the book. I took it out, unwrapped it, and read the first line:

"Houses are like people, in that each one has its own physiognomy."

I was struck by the truth of this statement. I read on, and continued reading there at the dormer window until the cold drove me away. That evening, when my employers went to vespers, I took the book into the kitchen and lost myself in the worn pages, as yellow as autumn leaves. They transported me into another world, with different names and relationships, where I met noble heroes and base villains unlike any of the people I knew. It was a long novel by de Montépin depicting a strange, dynamic life crammed with people and events. Everything in the novel was amazingly lucid, as though some light hidden between the lines illuminated the good and the bad, helping the reader to love and to hate, and led him on and on through the tangle of circumstances in which all these people were caught. An insistent desire was born to help this one and hinder that. The reader utterly forgot that all this life, so unexpectedly revealed, existed only on paper. In fact, everything was forgotten in the fluctuations of the conflict, one minute filling him with joy, the next with despair.

So utterly absorbed did I become in my reading that when the doorbell tinkled, I could not at first comprehend who was ringing it and why.

The candle had almost burned out, and the candlestick I had polished that morning was coated with wax. The icon lamp, which it was my duty to tend, had slipped out of its frame and gone out. I rushed about the kitchen trying to hide the traces of my crime by shoving the book under the stove and mending the lamp.

"Are you deaf? Can't you hear the bell?" cried the nurse, running out of the bedroom.

I hurried to the front door.

"Snoozing?" asked my master severely; his wife complained that she had caught her death of cold all because of me, while his mother began to harangue me. As soon as she entered the kitchen she noticed the burnt candle and asked me what I had been doing.

The fear that she would find the book stunned me, as though I had just fallen from a great height, robbing me of speech. The old woman shouted that if they didn't watch out I would be setting the house on fire, and when my master and his wife came in to have supper she said:

"Just see, he's burned up a whole candle, and he'll burn down the house yet."

During supper the four of them kept scolding me, recalling all my voluntary and involuntary crimes and warning me that I would come to a bad end. But I knew their words were prompted neither by malice nor benevolence, but simply by boredom. And it was strange to see how silly and insignificant they looked in comparison with the people in the book.

When they had finished eating and were heavy with food, they turned wearily to their beds. The old woman, after first directing some vicious complaints to God, crawled up on the stove and became quiet. Whereupon I took my book from under the stove and went to sit by the window. The night was bright, with a full moon shining, but even so the print was too small to be made out. My longing to read was irrepressible. Taking a copper pan off the shelf, I deflected the moonlight on to the book, but this was worse—even darker. Then I stood up on the bench in the corner and began to read by the light of the icon lamp. In my weariness I slipped down on to the bench and fell asleep and was awakened by the cries and blows of the old woman. She stood there barefoot, in nothing but her shift, angrily tossing her head, her face flushed with anger, holding my book and striking me with it across the shoulders.

"Oh come, mom, stop your shouting," wailed Victor from his bunk. "There's no living with you."

"That's the end of the book—she'll tear it up," thought I.

At breakfast the next morning I was called to account.

"Where did you get that book?" asked my master sternly.

The women competed in shouting at me, while Victor picked up the book and sniffed it.

"Smells of perfume, honest to goodness," he said.

When I told them the book belonged to the priest, they examined it in wonder, indignant that the priest should read novels. This, however, caused them to calm down a bit, though my master still warned me it was dangerous and harmful to read.

"It was them—the readers—who blew up the railroad, in an attempt to kill—"

"Have you gone crazy!" interrupted his wife in fright. "What ideas are you putting into his head!"

I carried de Montépin to the soldier and told him what had happened. Without a word Sidorov took the book, opened up a little chest, found a clean towel, wrapped the book in it, and hid it in the chest.

"Don't mind them. Come here and read; I won't tell anyone," he said. "And if you come when I'm not home, you'll find the key behind the icon. Open up the chest and read to your heart's content."

Thanks to my employers' attitude toward the book, I came to cherish it as a vastly important and awe-inspiring secret. The fact that certain "readers" had blown up a railroad in the attempt to kill someone interested me little, though I had not forgotten the priest's question during confession, nor the student reading in the basement, nor Smury's references to "the right books," nor yet what grandfather had said about "freemasoners" who read black books and dealt in black magic:

"And during the blessed reign of Tsar Alexander Pavlovich, the fine nobles conspired with the black-bookers and the freemasoners to give over the entire Russian people into the hands of the Roman Pope, the Jesuits. Here General Arakcheyev steps in, catches them all and sends the whole lot to Siberia, regardless of title or position. There they worked like ordinary convicts until they rotted away like any filth."

I also remembered "umbraculum, dotted with stars," and "Gervassi," and the solemn, mocking words: "Oh ignorant creatures, presuming to probe our affairs! Never shall your poor minds so much as approach them!"

I felt that I was on the threshold of some great mystery, and this feeling made me live like one possessed. I longed to finish the book, dreading that it would become lost or damaged in the batman's kitchen. How could I ever explain such a thing to the cutter's wife?

The old woman kept a sharp eye on me to see that I did not visit the soldier, and was constantly nagging at me.

"Bookworm! It's only loose living the books teach. Look at her who spends all her time over books—she can't even go to market any more. Always having affairs with the officers! Don't I know how she lets them come to see her in the daytime?"

I wanted to cry out:

"That's a lie! She doesn't have affairs with them!"

But I dared not defend the cutter's wife lest the old woman should guess the book was hers.

For several days I lived in an extremity of misery. I became absent-minded and could not sleep, filled with anxiety over the fate of de Montépin. One day the cook from the cutter's house stopped me in the yard and said:

"Bring back the book."

I chose the hour after dinner, when my employers were taking their nap, to appear before the cutter's wife in a state of dejection and embarrassment.

I saw her now as I had seen her that first time, excepting that she was dressed differently. She was wearing a grey skirt and a black velvet bodice with a turquoise cross at her throat. She reminded me of a bullfinch.

When I told her I had not had time to finish the book and that I was forbidden to read, the hurt of it and the joy of seeing her once more caused my eyes to fill with tears.

"What stupid people!" she said, raising her fine brows. "And I thought your master had an interesting face. Don't let it upset you so; I'll think of a way out. I'll write to him."

This frightened me, and I told her that I had lied to my master by saying the book belonged to the priest.

"Please don't write," I begged. "They'll only laugh at you and scold you. Nobody in our house likes you; they all make

fun of you and call you a fool and say you
have a rib missing."

My words came out all in a rush, and as
soon as they were spoken I realized they were
offensive. She bit her upper lip and slapped
herself on the hip as though she were on
horseback. I hung my head and wished the
earth would open to swallow me up, but presently she sank down on a chair and burst out
laughing.

"Oh how stupid, how very stupid! But
what can I do about it?" she asked herself as
she gazed fixedly at me. Then with a sigh she
added: "You're a very strange boy—very."

I glanced into the mirror next to her and
saw a high-cheekboned, broad-nosed face with
a large bruise on the forehead and untrimmed
hair sticking out in all directions. Was this
what you called "a very strange boy"? Certainly there was no resemblance between this
strange boy and that dainty china doll.

"You didn't take the money I gave you
last time. Why not?"

"I didn't need it."

She sighed.

"Well, it can't be helped. If they permit you to read, come back and I shall give you books."

There were three lying on the mantel; the one I had just returned was the thickest. I gazed at it sadly. The cutter's wife held out a little pink hand and said:

"Well, goodbye."

I cautiously touched her hand and hurried away.

Perhaps it was true what they said of her: that she did not understand anything. Had she not just called twenty kopeks money, like a small child?

But I liked this in her.

IX

It is both sad and amusing to recall how much insult and injury and trepidation my sudden passion for reading caused me.

It seemed to me that the books belonging to the cutter's wife were terribly expensive, and in the fear that my old mistress would burn them up, I tried to put them out of my mind and began to take little bright-coloured books from the shop where I bought the bread for breakfast.

The shopkeeper was a most unpleasant fellow—thick-lipped and sweaty, with a flabby, pasty face spotted and scarred with scrofula, with pale eyes and puffy hands ending in stubby fingers.

In the evenings his shop became a rendezvous for young boys and girls of easy virtue from our street. My master's brother went there to drink beer and play cards almost every evening. I was often sent to call him for supper and more than once I caught glimpses of the florid, foolish wife of the shopkeeper sitting on the knees of Victor or some other young man in the crowded little room behind the shop. Apparently the owner took no offence; nor did he take offence when his sister, who helped him wait on the customers, was embraced by soldiers and singers and anyone else who so desired. There was very little to sell in the shop, and the owner explained this by saying that the enterprise was a new one, and he had not yet had time to get going properly, though he had opened up in the autumn. He showed his customers filthy pictures and allowed anyone who wished to copy smutty verses.

I read the vapid books of Misha Yevstigneyev, paying a kopek a piece for the privilege; I found this expensive, and the books gave me no pleasure at all. *Guak, or True to the Death; Francil, the Venetian; The Battle of the Russians With the Kabardinians, or The Fair Mohammedan Who Died on the Coffin of Her Spouse,* such literature could not satisfy me, and often roused my indignation. It was as though the books were trying to make a fool out of me by relating such improbable things in such clumsy language.

Books like *The Streltsi, Yuri Miloslavsky, The Mysterious Monk,* and *Yapancha, the Tatar Horseman,* pleased me more; at least they left some impression. But most of all I enjoyed the *Lives of the Saints.* Here was something serious and convincing, at times even deeply moving. For some reason all the men martyrs reminded me of "That's Fine," all the women martyrs reminded me of Granny, while the prelates reminded me of grandfather in his best moments.

I did my reading up in the attic or out in the shed when I went to chop wood. Both places were equally cold and uncomfortable. If the book was particularly interesting or if I had to finish it in a hurry, I would get up at night and read by the light of a candle. But the old woman noticed that the candles diminished during the night and took to measuring them with a splinter of wood which she hid away. I usually discovered the splinter and evened it down to the size of the burnt candle, but if I failed to do so, and in the morning she discovered a discrepancy between the length of the candle and the splinter, she would raise such a hullabaloo in the kitchen that Victor once shouted indignantly from his bunk:

"Quit your barking, mom! There's no living with you! Of course he burns the candles, because he reads books—gets them down at the store. I've seen him. Go search the attic."

The old woman rushed up into the attic where she found a little book which she tore to shreds.

Naturally this was a blow, but it only fanned my desire to read. I was certain that if one of the saints should land in this house, my mistresses would begin to teach him how to behave, and in general to make him over as they saw fit; and they would do this only for lack of something better to do. If they should ever stop shouting and passing judgment on people and making fun of them, they would turn into mutes, unable to speak at all, and quite unaware of themselves. In order to be aware of oneself, a person must bear some conscious relationship to others. The only relationship my employers knew was that of teacher and judge, and if a person brought himself to live according to their pattern, they would judge him even for that. Such was their nature.

I resorted to various subterfuges in order to read. Several times the old woman destroyed my books so that I finally found myself in debt to the shopkeeper to the enormous amount of forty-seven kopeks! He demanded immediate payment and threatened to take it out of my employers' money when I came for bread.

"What'll happen then?" he asked teasingly.

I found him unbearably repugnant; apparently he sensed this, for he took special delight in torturing me with all sorts of threats. Whenever I entered the shop his blotched face would smear in a smile.

"Have you brought the money you owe me?" he would ask mildly.

"No."

This seemed to disconcert him, and he would frown.

"No? What am I supposed to do with you? Set the law on you, so's they'll ship you off to some reformatory?"

I had no means of getting the money, for my pay was given to my grandfather. I did not know what to do. When I asked the shopkeeper to wait for his money, he extended his hand, as puffy and greasy as a pancake, and said:

"Kiss it. I'll wait."

I picked up a weight from the counter and aimed it at his head; he ducked and shouted:

"Hey, what are you doing? I was just fooling!"

I felt that he was not fooling, and decided to steal the money in order to be rid of him. I often found loose change in my master's pockets when I brushed his clothes in the morning; sometimes it would fall out on the floor, and once a coin rolled into the woodpile under the stairs. I forgot to tell my master about it until some time later, when I chanced to come upon a twenty kopek piece among the wood. When I returned it, his wife said to him:

"See? You must count your money when you leave it in your pockets."

"Oh, he wouldn't steal anything," he replied, smiling at me.

Now that I had resolved to steal the money I recalled his words and his trusting smile. That made it hard for me. Several times I took some change out of his pockets, counted it, and—put it back. I struggled with myself for three days, and then all of a sudden things were settled very simply.

"What's the matter with you these days, Peshkov?" asked my master unexpectedly. "You're not yourself. Feeling bad?"

I told him frankly what was worrying me.

"Just see what books lead to," he said with a frown. "In one way or another they're sure to bring you to harm."

But he gave me fifty kopeks with the warning:

"Mind you don't let my wife or my mother know or there'll be trouble."

Then he added with a good-natured laugh:

"You're a persistent little devil, damn it all! That's all right—not a bad trait. But give up the books! With the new year I'll subscribe to a good newspaper and then you'll have something to read."

He did so, and every evening between tea time and supper I would read to my employers *The Moscow Leaflet*, which published novels by Vashkov, Rokshanin, Rudnikovsky, and other authors whose books were designed for people dying of boredom.

I disliked reading out loud; it hindered my understanding of the contents. But my audience listened attentively, with a sort of reverent enthusiasm, gasping and exclaiming over the villainy perpetrated, and proudly remarking to each other:

"And here we are living along so calm and peaceful, without knowing a thing of what goes on outside, praise the Lord!"

They mixed everything up, attributing the deeds of the famous highwayman Churkin to the coachman Foma Kruchina; they were constantly confusing the names, and when I would straighten them out they would say in amazement:

"What a memory the boy has!"

Quite often *The Moscow Leaflet* would publish verse by Leonid Grave. I liked it immensely and copied it into my notebook, but my mistresses would say of the poet:

"Just think of it—an old man writing poetry!"

"It's all the same to him, drunk and feeble-minded as he is!"

I enjoyed the poetry of Struzhkin, and Count Memento-Mori, but both the old and the young woman insisted that poetry was sheer nonsense.

"It's only clowns and actors talk poetry."

How tedious were those winter evenings in that stuffy little room with the eyes of my employers fixed on me! Night, still as death, reigned beyond the window; now and then came a crackling of frost, but the people sat about the table without a word, like frozen fish. Or else the wind would claw at walls and windowpanes, shrieking down the chimneys, banging the dampers, while from the nursery came a wailing of infants. It made me want to slink off into some dark corner and howl like a wolf.

At one end of the table sat the women, sewing or knitting socks; at the other, Victor leaned reluctantly over some drawing he was copying, shouting every once in a while:

"Stop shaking the table! There's no living with you, you shike-pikes, you hammer bills!"

Off to one side my master sat in front of an enormous frame, embroidering a tablecloth in cross-stitch. From beneath his nimble fingers emerged red crabs, blue fish, yellow butterflies and brown autumn leaves. He himself had made up the design and had been executing it for three winters. Now he was thoroughly sick of it and often in the daytime, if I was not busy, he would say to me:

"Well, Peshkov, have a go at the table-cloth."

So I would pick up the heavy needle and have a go. I felt sorry for my master and was always anxious to help him in any way possible. It seemed to me that one day he would stop his drawing and embroidering and card playing, and begin to do something else, something interesting, the something of which he dreamed when, suddenly laying down his work, he would stare at it wonderingly, as though seeing it for the first time. Standing there with his hair falling over his brows and cheeks, he had the look of a novice in a monastery.

"What are you thinking about?" his wife would ask.

"Nothing special," he would reply, resuming his work.

I would marvel in silence. How could you ask a person what he was thinking about? And how could he answer such a question? A person thinks about many things at once—about what his eyes are beholding now, or what they beheld yesterday or last year, all the impressions vague and confused, in constant movement, constant change.

The articles from *The Moscow Leaflet* did not last out an evening, and I suggested reading the magazines piled under the bed in the bedroom.

"What's there to read in them?" asked my young mistress sceptically. "Nothing but pictures."

But the *Picture Review* was not the only periodical stored under the bed. There was also *The Flame*, from which we began reading Salias' *Count Tyatin-Baltiisky*. My master was delighted with the foolish hero of this story, laughing till the tears rolled down his cheeks at the sad adventures of that young gentleman.

"Oh, how funny!" he would cry.

"It's all just made up," his wife would say in order to demonstrate the independence of her opinion.

The volumes from under the bed rendered me a great service. Because of them I won the right to take magazines into the kitchen and read at night.

Fortunately for me, the old woman went to sleep in the bedroom after the nurse went on a drinking bout. Victor did not object to my reading; when everyone was asleep, he would quietly dress himself and vanish until morning. My mistress always took the candle into the other room, so that I was left without a light. Since I had no money to buy a candle, I began to secretly gather the wax off the candlesticks and put it into an empty sardine tin, covering it with iconlamp oil and twisting a wick out of thread. In this way I obtained a smoky sort of lamp which I placed up on the stove.

Whenever I turned a page of these enormous volumes, the little red tongue of flame would flicker and threaten to go out; the wick kept sinking in the smelly wax, and the smoke stung my eyes; but all these handicaps were as nothing compared to the delight with which I studied the illustrations and read the explanations beneath them.

Ever broader grew my view of the world, adorned with fabulous cities, lofty mountains and beautiful seashores. Life became wonderfully expanded, and the earth waxed fairer as I was made aware of its multiplicity of towns and peoples and interests. Now as I gazed at the expanses beyond the Volga, I realized that they represented more than empty space. I had always felt particularly depressed when looking out upon this hinterland: the meadows lay flat upon the earth, relieved only by dark patches of thickets; beyond the meadows rose a jagged rim of forest surmounted by a cold, cloudy sky, the earth was empty and lonely. My heart too was empty, and disturbed by a soft sadness; all desire vanished; there was nothing to think of, and I wanted only to close my eyes. No hope dwelt in this desolate wilderness, which drained the heart of every wish.

The texts to the illustrations told in simple language about other lands and other people; they spoke of various events of the past and the present, many of which I did not understand, and this irked me. Sometimes my brain would be pierced by strange words like "metaphysics," "chiliasm," "Chartist."

They would worry me to death, growing in my mind until they overshadowed everything else, and it seemed to me that I would never understand anything if I failed to discover the meaning of these words. It was just they which stood guard at the threshold of all mysteries. Often whole sentences would remain in my memory, like splinters in the flesh, keeping me from thinking of anything else.

I remember reading some strange lines:

O'er the desert rides Attila,
Steel-clad leader of the Huns,
Dark and silent as the grave,

Behind him rode a black cloud of warriors, shouting:

Where is Rome, Rome the mighty?

I knew that Rome was a city, but who were the Huns? This I had to find out.

When a convenient moment presented itself, I asked my master.

"The Huns?" he asked in some surprise. "The devil only knows who they were. Probably just some beggars."

He shook his head disapprovingly.

"Your head's packed full of rubbish, Peshkov, and that's very bad."

Good or bad, I had to know.

I assumed that Solovyov, the regiment priest, must know who the Huns were, and on meeting him in the yard, I asked him.

He was pale and ailing and always irritable, with red eyes, no eyebrows, and a little yellow beard.

"What do you care?" he queried, poking his black staff into the dirt.

When I put the question to Lieutenant Nesterov, he only replied fiercely:

"Wha-a-at?"

I decided I must go to the chemist's shop and ask the friendly chemist; he had an intelligent face and wore gold-rimmed spectacles on his big nose.

"The Huns," said Pavel Goldberg, the chemist, "were a nomad people like the Kirghiz. They don't exist any more—they all died out."

I was disappointed and annoyed, not because the Huns had died out, but because the meaning of this word which had tortured me so, proved to be so simple and of so little significance for me.

But I was very grateful to the Huns. After my experience with them, words ceased to harass me, and thanks to Attila I made the acquaintance of chemist Goldberg.

This man knew the simple meaning of all the learned words, and he had the key to every secret. He would adjust his glasses with two fingers, look fixedly into my eyes through the thick lenses, and speak to me as though he were driving tacks into my head:

"Words, my little friend, are like leaves on a tree, and in order to know why the leaves are such as they are, you must know how the tree grows. You must study. Books, my little friend, are like a lovely garden, in which you will find everything that is pleasant and beneficial."

I often ran to the chemist's shop for soda and magnesia for the adults, who were always suffering from heartburn, and for bay oil and physics for the infants. The terse teachings of the chemist inspired me with a more serious attitude toward books, until without my noticing it they became as indispensable to me as vodka to a drunkard.

They showed me a different life, a life filled with great desires and emotions, leading people to crime or to heroism. I observed that the people about me were incapable of crime or heroism; they lived apart from all that the books wrote about, and it was difficult to discover anything interesting in their lives. One thing I knew—I did not want to live as they did.

From the texts below the illustrations I learned that in Prague and London and Paris there were no garbage-filled dams and gullies in the centre of the city. There the streets were straight and wide, the buildings and churches entirely different. And the people were not locked indoors by a six-month winter, nor was there a Lent during which one could eat nothing but salted cabbage, salted mushrooms, oat flour, and potatoes served with loathsome linseed oil. During Lent it was forbidden to read books. The *Picture Review* was taken away, and I was forced to become a part of this empty, lenten life. Now that

I was in a position to compare it with the life described in books, it seemed even more drab and ugly. Under the influence of my reading I felt stronger, and I worked with a will and a vengeance because I had an aim: the sooner I finished, the more time I would have for reading. Deprived of my books, I became lazy and listless, and possessed of a morbid forgetfulness I had never known before.

I remember that it was during these dull days that a mysterious event occurred. One evening, when everyone had gone to bed, the cathedral bell suddenly began to boom. Immediately everyone woke up and rushed to the windows half dressed.

"An alarm? A fire?" they asked each other.

We could hear people in other flats moving about and banging doors. Someone ran through the yard leading a horse by the bridle. My old mistress shouted that the cathedral had been robbed, but my master hushed her.

"Quiet, mother, anyone can tell that's no alarm!"

"Well then, the bishop's died."

Victor climbed down off his bunk.

"I know what's happened, I know," he muttered as he pulled on his clothes.

My master sent me up into the attic to see if the sky were glowing. I ran upstairs and climbed through a dormer window out on to the roof. There was no glow, but the big bell continued to toll in the quiet, frozen air. The snow crunched under the running feet of invisible people and there was a screeching of sleigh runners. Ever more ominous sounded the big bell. I returned downstairs.

"There's no fire."

"Tut, tut!" said my master who was already in hat and coat. He pulled up the collar and began uncertainly to push his feet into his galoshes.

"Don't go, don't go," pleaded his wife.

"Nonsense."

Victor, who was also in hat and coat, kept teasing everyone by saying:

"I know what it is!"

When the brothers had left, the women ordered me to heat the samovar, while they stationed themselves at the windows; but almost immediately my master rang the bell, ran silently up the stairs, opened the hall door, and announced in a thick voice:

"The Tsar's been assassinated!"

"Not assassinated!" exclaimed the old woman.

"Yes, assassinated. An officer told me. What'll happen now?"

Presently Victor rang the bell and said testily as he pulled off his things:

"And I thought it was war!"

After that everybody sat down to drink tea and talk in hushed, guarded voices. It had become still outside; the bell had stopped tolling. For two days people continued to whisper and to go visiting and to receive visitors and to recount everything in detail. I tried hard to understand just what had happened, but my employers hid the newspapers from me, and when I asked Sidorov why they had killed the Tsar, he answered softly:

"It's forbidden to talk about it."

The whole affair was quickly forgotten, eclipsed by the cares of daily life, and soon I lived through a most unpleasant experience.

One Sunday when the family had gone to early mass and I had set about tidying up the flat, after first heating the samovar, the baby entered the kitchen, pulled the tap out of the samovar, and crawled under the table to play with it. The samovar pipe was filled with live coals, so that when the water ran out, the whole thing came unsoldered. From the other room I could hear it rumbling with strange fury. I rushed into the kitchen and saw to my horror that it had turned black and was shaking as though with the ague. The unsoldered pipe to which the tap had been fastened was dangling dejectedly, the lid had careened, melted pewter was dripping from under the handles, and the blue-black samovar looked for all the world as if it were drunk. When I threw cold water over it, it hissed and collapsed sadly on to the floor.

At that moment the bell rang. When I opened the door, the old woman's first question was whether the samovar had boiled.

"Yes, it has," I answered briefly.

This answer, no doubt dictated by fear

and shame, was looked upon as a bad attempt at humour, and my punishment was increased accordingly. I was given a beating. The old woman administered it with a bundle of pine laths; the operation was not very painful, but it left innumerable splinters deeply imbedded in my flesh. By evening my back had swelled up like a pillow, and by noon of the next day my master had to take me to the hospital.

When the doctor, who was comically tall and thin, had examined me, he said in a deep, calm voice:

"I must draw up an official testimony to cruelty."

My master blushed and shifted his feet and began to mumble something to the doctor, but the latter gazed over his head and answered tersely:

"Can't do it. Have no right."

Then he turned to me and said:

"Do you wish to file a complaint?"

My back hurt so much that I said:

"No I don't. Just hurry and do something for me."

They led me into another room, laid me on a table, and the doctor pulled out the splinters with some delightfully cold pincers, joking the while:

"A fine job they made of this hide of yours, youngster. You'll be waterproof from now on."

When he had finished his work, tickling me unbearably, he said:

"I pulled out forty-two splinters, youngster! That's something for you to boast to your pals about! Come back to have the bandage changed tomorrow at this same time. Do they beat you often?"

"Used to beat me oftener," I replied after a moment's consideration.

The doctor laughed in his deep voice.

"Everything's for the better, youngster; everything's for the better!"

When he took me back to my master, he said to him:

"Here he is, good as new. Send him back tomorrow, we'll bind him up again. Lucky for you he has a sense of humour."

While we were riding back in the droshky, my master said to me:

"They used to beat me too, Peshkov. What's to be done about it? And how they beat me, brother! At least you have me to feel sorry for you, but nobody ever felt sorry for me. Nobody at all. Mobs of people everywhere, and not a single bastard to show you any pity! Ah me, such roaring chickens!"

He went on this way throughout the journey; I felt sorry for him and was grateful to him for speaking to me so kindly.

When we reached home I was greeted like a conquering hero. The women made me tell them how the doctor had taken out the splinters and what he had said. They interrupted my tale with oh's and ah's, smacking their lips and frowning over the gory details. I was amazed by their morbid interest in illness and pain and all sorts of unpleasantness.

Seeing how pleased they were that I had refused to file a complaint against them, I asked permission to borrow books from the cutter's wife. They dared not refuse under the circumstances, but the old woman exclaimed in surprise:

"Aren't you a little devil though!"

On the following day I was standing in front of the cutter's wife, hearing her say to me:

"But they told me you were ill and had been taken to the hospital! Just see how false rumours are!"

I did not deny it. I was ashamed to tell her the truth—why should she be troubled with anything so coarse and sad? I was happy that she did not resemble other people.

I began to read the thick volumes of Dumas-the-Elder, Ponson du Terrail, Montépin, Zaccone, Gaboriau, Aimard, and Bois-Robert. I read these books quickly, one after another, and they made me happy. I felt that I was part of an extraordinary life, and this stirred sweet emotions, filling me with energy. Once more my homemade lamp was set to smoking, for I read the night through, until the very dawn. My eyes grew inflamed, and my old mistress would say gloatingly:

"Just wait, you bookworm, your pupils will burst and you'll go blind!"

Very soon I perceived that all these interesting books, despite variety of plot and differences of setting, said the same thing, namely:

good people are always unhappy and persecuted by bad people; bad ones are always more lucky and clever than good ones, but in the end some inexplicable factor conquers evil, and virtue inevitably triumphs. I became sick of the "love" about which all the men and women spoke in exactly the same words. Besides being boring, this banality roused vague suspicions.

Sometimes, I would begin to guess after reading a few pages who would triumph in the end and who would be defeated; as soon as the tangle of the plot became evident, I would set myself to unravelling it. Putting aside the book, I would ponder over it like a problem in mathematics, and ever more often would be correct in my solutions as to which of the characters would land in paradise, which would be condemned to purgatory.

But beyond all this I became aware of a fact of vast importance to me; I glimpsed the contours of another sort of life with other relationships. It was clear to me that in Paris the cabbies, workmen, soldiers, and all the "rabble" were not like those in Nizhni-Novgorod, Kazan, and Perm. They spoke more boldly to the gentles, conducting themselves in their presence with greater ease and independence. Here was a soldier, but he did not resemble a single soldier of my acquaintance—neither Sidorov, nor the soldier on the steamer, nor yet Yermokhin; he was more of a human being than they. He had something in common with Smury, while being less crude and bestial. Or here was a shopkeeper, but again he was better than any of the shopkeepers of my acquaintance. Nor were the priests in the books like the priests I knew. They had more love and sympathy for people. In general, life abroad as depicted in the books was better, easier, and more interesting than the life I knew. In foreign countries people did not fight so often and so brutally, did not make the vicious sport of a man the passengers had made of that soldier on the steamer, and did not pray to God as vindictively as my old mistress.

I noticed especially that when describing villains, people of base and greedy character, the books did not show them possessed of that inexplicable cruelty and that passion to mock others which was so familiar to me. The villains in the book were cruel in a practical way; their cruelty was almost always comprehensible. But I had seen senseless, purposeless cruelty, cruelty merely for the sake of amusement, without any other purpose.

Every new book emphasized the difference between life in Russia and life in other countries, rousing in me a vague dissatisfaction and increasing my suspicion that these thumbed yellow pages were not entirely truthful.

Then Goncourt's novel *The Brothers Zemganno* fell into my hands. I read it in one night, and my wonder at the novelty of it led me to reread the sad, simple tale. It contained no complicated plot, no superficial attractions; at first it even seemed as dry and serious as the *Lives of the Saints*. The language, so exact and unembellished, at first disappointed me, but the laconic words and strong phrases went so directly to my heart and gave such a convincing account of the drama of these acrobat brothers, that I trembled with joy. I cried till I thought my heart would break when the poor acrobat with the broken legs climbed up into the attic to his brother, who was secretly practising their beloved art.

When I returned this wonderful book to the cutter's wife I asked her to give me another just like it.

"What do you mean by another just like it?" she asked with a laugh.

Her laugh embarrassed me, and when I could not explain what I wanted, she said:

"That's a dull book. Just wait and I'll find a better one for you, something more interesting."

In a few days she gave me Greenwood's *True Story of a Little Ragamuffin*. I winced self-consciously at the title of the book, but the very first page brought a smile of delight which continued until I had read it from cover to cover, rereading certain passages two and three times.

So even abroad little boys found life difficult! Indeed, my life seemed easy in comparison; in other words, there was no reason to lose heart.

I received great encouragement from Greenwood, and soon thereafter I came upon one of the really "right" books—*Eugénie Grandet*.

Old man Grandet reminded me vividly of my grandfather. I was sorry that the book was so short, and amazed at the amount of truth it contained. Life had made this truth only too familiar to me, but the book revealed it in a new light, the light of calm, dispassionate observation. All the authors I had read except Goncourt passed judgment on people in the stern, vociferous manner of my employers, often making the reader sympathize with the villain and become exasperated with the virtuous characters. I had always been vexed to see that no matter how much thought and effort a person expended, he was always thwarted in his searchings by these same virtuous people, who stood in his path from the first page to the last, implacable as a stone wall. To be sure, the evil intentions of vice were sure to be dashed to pieces against this wall, but stone is not a substance to rouse one's affections. However strong and beautiful a wall,

if you are intent on reaching the apples growing behind it, you have little inclination to
admire its stones. And it always seemed to me
that whatever was most true and most important remained hidden behind those virtuous
people.

There were neither villains nor heroes in
Goncourt, Greenwood, and Balzac. There were
only simple people who were marvellously
alive. No one could doubt that everything they
said and did was said and done in just that way
and could not possibly have been said or done
in any other.

In this way I learned to know the great joy
of reading a "good book, a right book." But
how was I to find such books? The cutter's
wife could not help me.

"Here are some good books," she said,
offering me Arsène Houssaye's *Hands Full of
Roses, Gold, and Blood,* along with the novels
of Belleau, Paul de Kock, and Paul Féval.
But now it cost me an effort to read such
books.

She enjoyed the novels of Marryat and
Werner; I found them boring. Nor did I like

Spielhagen, but I took enormous pleasure in the stories of Auerbach. I preferred Sir Walter Scott to Sue and Hugo. I wanted books that would stir my emotions and make me happy; books like those of the wonderful Balzac. The china doll also came to please me less.

Whenever I went to see her I would put on a clean blouse, comb my hair, and in every way try to make myself look presentable. I doubt that I was successful, but I hoped that on observing my respectability she would speak to me in a more simple, friendly manner, without that brittle smile on a face so shiningly clean that it always seemed to have been specially donned for the occasion. But she would be sure to smile and ask in a sweet, tired voice:

"Did you read it? Did you like it?"

"No."

She would raise her fine brows slightly, and say with a sigh, in a familiar nasal tone:

"Why not?"

"I've already read about that."

"About what?"

"About love."

She would frown and give an affected laugh.

"Dear me! But all the books write about love!"

Sitting there in the large armchair, she would swing her little feet in fur slippers, yawn, pull her blue dressing gown closer about her shoulders, and tap the binding of the book in her lap with rosy finger tips.

I wanted to say to her:

"Why don't you move away from here? The officers still write notes to you and make fun of you."

Lacking the courage to voice my thoughts, I would go away, taking with me another fat volume about "love," and a heartful of disappointment.

Down in the yard the gossip about this woman became more mocking and malicious. It was painful for me to hear this filthy talk, which no doubt was false. When I was not with her, I pitied her and feared for her. But when I was in her presence and saw her sharp eyes, the feline grace of her little body, and her "company" face, my fear and pity vanished like mist.

In the spring she suddenly went away, and a few days later her husband moved out.

While their flat was still unoccupied, I went to look at the bare walls marred by twisted nails and nail-holes and discoloured patches where pictures had hung. The painted floors were strewn with paper, bits of bright material, empty pillboxes and perfume bottles, among which glittered a large brass pin.

I felt sad; I longed to see the cutter's little wife once more and tell her of my gratitude.

X

Even before the cutter and his wife moved out, the flat below ours had been occupied by a black-eyed young woman with her little girl and her mother, a grey-haired old lady who was always smoking a cigarette in an amber holder. The young woman was very handsome. She was also proud and imperious, with a deep, pleasant voice and a manner of throwing back her head and narrowing her eyes when speaking to people, as though they were too far away to see distinctly. Almost every day her soldier-servant Tufyayev would lead a slim-legged brown horse to the porch of her flat, and the woman would appear in a long, steel-grey velvet riding habit, white gauntlets and brown boots. Holding her long train and an amethyst-set riding crop in one hand, she would stroke the nose of her horse with the other. The creature would bare its teeth, roll its eyes and paw the hard earth, its whole body trembling with excitement.

"Robby, Robby," she would murmur softly, patting the horse's finely arched neck.

Then she would place her foot on Tufya-yev's knee, lightly spring into the saddle, and set the horse prancing down the length of the dam. She sat her mount as though she had been born in the saddle.

She was beautiful with that rare beauty that always seems new and unique, and always fills the heart with intoxicating joy. As I looked at her I thought that such must have been Diane de Poitiers, Queen Margot, La Valliere, and other enchanting heroines of historical novels.

She was constantly surrounded by officers from the division stationed in our city. In the evenings they came to her home and played the piano, the violin, and the guitar, and sang and danced. Major Olesov outdid everyone else in prancing before her on his short little legs. He was a fat fellow with grey hair and a red face as greasy as an oiler's. He played the guitar well and behaved like the young woman's humble, devoted servant.

Her chubby, curly-haired, five-year-old daughter was just as radiantly beautiful. The gaze of her enormous blue eyes was calm and serious and expectant, and there was something unchildlike in her gravity.

From dawn to dark the grandmother was busy with household affairs, aided by the sullen, silent Tufyayev and a plump, cross-eyed parlourmaid. The child had no nurse and grew up almost without surveillance, playing all day long on the verandah or on the woodpile opposite it. In the evenings I often went out to play with her and came to love her very much. She soon grew attached to me and would fall asleep in my arms when I told her fairy tales. When she was asleep, I would carry her to bed. Soon matters reached the point at which she refused to sleep unless I came to bid her good night. On my entering the nursery she would extend a chubby little hand importantly and say:

"Goodbye until tomorrow. What else must I say, grandmuvver?"

"God protect you," replied her grandmother, letting out thin streams of smoke through her teeth and nose.

"God protect you until tomorrow; now I'm going to sleep," repeated the child, cuddling into her lace-trimmed quilt.

"Not until tomorrow, but always," her grandmother corrected.

"Isn't tomorrow always?"

She loved the word "tomorrow" and transferred everything she liked into the future. She would stick a bunch of flowers or twigs into the earth and say:

"Tomorrow this will be a garden."

"Tomorrow I will buy myself a horse and go riding like muvver."

She was a clever child, but not very spirited. Often in the middle of a game she would become pensive and ask unexpectedly:

"Why do priests have hair like women?"

One day she was stung by nettles and shook her finger at them with the warning:

"Watch out or I'll pray to God and He'll do something bad to you. He can do something bad to anybody, even to muvver."

Sometimes she would be possessed of a quiet sadness. Pressing close to me and lifting her blue, expectant eyes to the sky, she would say:

"Sometimes grandmuvver scolds, but muvver never scolds, she only laughs. Everybody loves muvver because she never has any time because people always come to see her and look at her because she's so pretty. Muvver is wonderful. That's what Olesov says: wonderful muvver!"

I was delighted to listen to the child's accounts of a world unfamiliar to me. With eager enthusiasm she spoke about her mother, revealing to me a new life, bringing back to my mind the story of Queen Margot. This increased my faith in books and my interest in what was happening about me.

One evening while I was sitting with the child dozing in my arms, waiting for my employers to return from a walk, her mother rode up on horseback, sprang lightly out of the saddle, and, throwing back her head, asked:

"Is she asleep?"

"Yes."

"Really?"

The soldier Tufyayev came running up and led away the horse. Thrusting her riding crop into her belt, the young woman held out her arms and said:

"Give her to me!"

"I'll carry her myself."

"No you won't!" the lady cried with a stamp of her foot, as though I were her horse.

The little girl woke up, blinked, caught sight of her mother, and also held out her arms. The two of them went in.

I was used to being shouted at, but it was particularly unpleasant to learn that this woman shouted. Anyone would obey her, however softly she voiced her demands.

In a few minutes the cross-eyed maid came and called me: the child had stubbornly refused to go to bed without first saying good night to me.

Not without a feeling of pride, I entered the drawing room where the young woman was sitting with her daughter on her lap, swiftly undressing her.

"Well, here he is; he's come, this monster of yours," she said.

"He's no monster, he's my playmate."

"Really? Very well. Let's give your playmate a present, shall we?"

"Oh yes, do let's."

"All right. You run off to bed and I'll give him something."

"Goodbye until tomorrow," said the little girl, holding out her hand. "God protect you until tomorrow."

"Who ever taught you to say that?" cried her mother in surprise. "Grandmother?"

"Yes."

When the child had left, the woman beckoned to me.

"What shall I give you?"

I replied that I did not want anything, but perhaps she would lend me a book to read.

She lifted my chin with warm, fragrant fingers and said, smiling pleasantly:

"So you like to read, do you? What books have you read?"

She was even lovelier when she smiled; in my embarrassment I named a few novels at random.

"What did you find in them that pleased you?" she asked as she drummed on the table.

She emanated a strong, sweet odour of flowers, strangely mingled with horse sweat. Through her long lashes she studied me thoughtfully. No one had ever looked at me like that before.

The room seemed as small as a bird's nest because of the quantity of handsome upholstered furniture it contained. The windows were hidden by the thick foliage of plants; in the dusk glistened the snowy-white tiles of the stove, next to which stood a shiny black piano; in dull gilt frames on the walls hung darkened scrolls covered with ancient Slavonic lettering, while from each swung a cord with a large seal at the end. All these objects gazed at the lady as humbly and reverently as I did.

To the best of my ability I explained to her that life was very dull and difficult, but that one forgot this when reading books.

"Really?" she exclaimed, getting up. "That was rather well said, and I guess you are right. But I suppose it can't be helped. I shall be only too glad to give you books, only at present I have none. But here, you can take this."

From the couch she picked up a worn volume in a yellow binding.

"When you've finished it, I'll give you the second volume—there are four."

I went out taking with me the *Secrets of St. Petersburg* by Prince Meshchersky, and began to read it assiduously. But it soon became clear that the "secrets" of St. Petersburg were much more boring than those of Madrid or London or Paris. The only thing which interested me in the book was the fable of Freedom and the Club.

"I'm better than you," said Freedom, "because I'm wiser."

"Oh no, I'm better than you because I'm stronger," retorted the Club.

They argued for some time and then began to fight. The Club gave Freedom a trouncing, and as I remember it, the latter subsequently died in hospital of her injuries.

One of the characters in the book was a nihilist. I recall that according to Prince Meshchersky a nihilist is so dangerous a person that one glance from him is enough to strike a chicken dead in its tracks. I came to look upon the word "nihilist" as insulting and indecent, but outside of that, I understood nothing, and this fact depressed me. Apparently I was incapable of understanding good books. Not for a moment did I doubt that this was a good book. Such a beautiful and important lady would never read bad ones!

"Did you enjoy it?" she asked when I returned Meshchersky's novel.

It was hard for me to admit that I did not. I feared to offend her.

But she only laughed and disappeared behind the portieres of the door leading into her bedroom, from which she presently emerged with a little book in a blue morocco binding.

"You'll enjoy this one; be careful not to soil it."

The book was a volume of Pushkin's verse. I read it through at one sitting, gripped by the greed one experiences in finding himself in an incomparably beautiful spot, every corner of which he wishes to explore simultaneously. It was like coming out of a bog and finding oneself in a glade, all sunny and flowering, where one stands enchanted for an instant before rushing from end to end of it, experiencing a thrill of delight each time one's foot touches the soft grass.

I was so amazed by the simplicity and music of Pushkin's verse that for a long time prose seemed unnatural, and I had difficulty in reading it. The prologue to *Ruslan and Ludmilla* was like the quintessence of Granny's finest tales, and some of the lines overwhelmed me with their exquisite perfection:

> *There, on unexplored pathways,*
> *Lie tracks of undiscovered beasts. . . .*

327

As I repeated these wonderful lines, I envisioned those scarcely perceptible paths which I knew so well, and those mysterious tracks with the trampled grass on which the dew still glistened like drops of quicksilver. It was amazingly easy to remember this full-sounding verse which richly ornamented whatever thought it expressed. It filled me with happiness and made living easy and pleasant; indeed, the verse seemed the harbinger of a new life. What a joy to be able to read!

Pushkin's delightful tales in verse were more accessible to my heart and understanding than his other works; I learned them by heart by simply reading them over and over; then when I went to bed I would lie there with my eyes closed, whispering them to myself until I fell asleep. Sometimes I would recite them to the officers' batmen, who would laugh and swear in wonder. Sidorov would pat my head and say softly:

"How fine they are, eh?"

My employers became aware of the state of excitement I was in, and the old woman began to scold.

"He's got so lost in that reading of his the samovar's gone four days without a polish, the scamp! Once I get after him with the rolling pin—"

But what was a rolling pin to me? I defended myself with verse:

> . . . *the old witch,*
> *Her dark soul charged with evil. . . .*

The beautiful lady rose even higher in my esteem. So that was the kind of book she read! She was none of your cutter's china dolls!

When I brought her the book and sadly relinquished it, she said with conviction:

"You liked that book, didn't you? Have you ever heard of Pushkin?"

I said no, for while I had read something about the poet in one of the magazines, I wanted to hear what she would tell me.

When she had given me a brief account of Pushkin's life and death, she asked me with a smile, bright as a summer's day:

"Now do you see how dangerous it is to love a woman?"

According to all the books I had read, this was indeed dangerous, but—good.

"It may be dangerous, but everybody falls in love," I said. "The women also suffer."

She looked at me through lowered lashes, as she looked at everything, and remarked in a serious tone:

"Really? Do you understand what this means? If you do, then I hope you will never forget it."

Then she began to question me as to what poems had especially pleased me.

I began to explain and to recite, gesticulating enthusiastically. She listened in grave silence, then rose and began to pace the floor, saying thoughtfully:

"You should be going to school, my precious little monkey. I must think it over. Are the people you work for your relatives?"

When I said they were, she exclaimed "Oh!," as if I were to blame.

She gave me the *Songs of Béranger* in a fine gilt-edged edition with engravings and a red morocco binding. These songs, with their strange combination of caustic bitterness and unrestrained merriment, filled me with ecstasy.

The blood froze in my veins as I read the bitter words from "The Old Beggarman":

Why do you not crush me underfoot
Like a loathsome insect, good people?
Ah! Had you but taught me
To labour for the benefit of mankind!
Then, sheltered from the wintry blast,
This worm would have become an industri-
  ous ant.
Like a brother would I have loved you,
But now, an old vagabond, I die your
  enemy.

And immediately afterwards I laughed till I cried over the "Weeping Husband." I especially remembered Béranger's remark that

For simple souls it is not hard
To learn the art of being merry. . . .

Béranger roused irrepressible spirits, filling me with the desire to do mischief and make witty, impudent remarks, a desire which I very soon indulged. I memorized his verse too, and whenever I found time for brief visits to the batmen's kitchens, would recite them with the greatest enthusiasm.

But soon I was forced to abandon this, for the lines:

> *And does not any cap become*
> *A maid of seventeen?*

gave rise to a most revolting discussion of women. The insult of it drove me to a state of madness, in which I struck the soldier Yermokhin over the head with a pan. Sidorov and the other batmen rescued me from his bearlike clutches, but I dared not visit the officers' kitchens thereafter.

I was not allowed to go out for walks, and indeed there was no time for walking. My work had increased, for now, in addition to the duties of housemaid and yardcleaner and errand boy, I was given the daily task of nailing calico to a large frame, pasting my master's drawings to it, making copies of his building estimates, and checking contractors' bills. My master worked from morning to night, like a machine.

At that time the public buildings at the fair grounds became the private property of the merchants. Hasty efforts were made to reconstruct the trade rows, and my master signed contracts to repair old booths and build new ones. He drew plans for "reconstructing straight arches, building dormer windows," and similar things. I would take the drawings, along with an envelope containing a twenty-five ruble note, to an old architect who, after receiving the money, would write on the plans: "Plans checked with actual building, and all work carried on under the personal supervision of the undersigned." Naturally nothing was ever checked with the actual building, and he could not possibly supervise building operations since the state of his health permanently confined him to the house.

I delivered bribes to the fair inspector and other people, receiving from them "permits for various violations of the law," as my master termed these documents. As a reward for all this, I was given the right to await my employers in the yard on evenings when they went visiting. This rarely happened, but whenever it did, they would return after midnight, which gave me several hours during which I could sit on the porch or on the woodpile opposite, gazing through the windows of the flat belonging to my lady and listening to the gay music and conversation proceeding therefrom.

The windows would be open. Through the curtains and the screen of vines I could glimpse the fine figures of officers moving about the rooms and the roly-poly major trailing my lady, who was always gowned with amazing simplicity and beauty.

In my own mind I called her Queen Margot.

"So this is that gay life pictured in French novels!" I would think to myself as I gazed up at the window. And always I felt a bit sad. My childish jealousy was roused by seeing all these men hovering about Queen Margot like bees about a flower.

There was one tall, solemn officer with a scarred forehead and deep-set eyes who visited her less often than the others. He always brought his violin and played beautifully, so beautifully in fact, that passers-by would stop to listen and people from our street would come to sit on the woodpile, and even my employers, if they happened to be home, would open the window and praise the musician. I do not remember their ever having praised anyone else except the deacon at the Cathedral, and I know that they enjoyed juicy fish pies much more than this, or any other, music.

Sometimes the officer would sing, or recite poetry in a husky voice, breathing loudly, his hand pressed to his brow. One day when I was playing beneath the window with the little girl, Queen Margot begged him to sing; for some time he refused, then said very precisely:

Only a song has need of beauty—
Beauty has no need of song. . . .

I liked the lines, and for some reason I began to feel sorry for the officer.

The thing I loved best was to gaze at my lady when she sat alone at the piano, with no one else in the room. The music went to my head; I saw nothing but that window, beyond which the graceful figure of the woman was etched in yellow lamplight, her proud profile very delicate, her white hands fluttering like birds over the keys.

I watched her and listened to the sad music and spun fantastic dreams: some day I would discover buried treasure and give it all to her— let her be rich! If I were Skobelev I would again declare war on the Turks, ransom my captives, and build a house for her on the Otkos, the finest site in the city, so that she could move out of our house and away from our street where everyone spread filthy, offensive gossip about her.

All the servants working in our house and all the occupants—especially my employers— spoke just as maliciously of Queen Margot as they had of the cutter's wife, only they spoke of her more cautiously, in lowered tones, with covert glances.

Perhaps they were afraid of her, because she was the widow of a highborn gentleman. Tufyayev once told me (and he was literate— always reading the Bible) that the documents hanging on her wall were charters granted to her husband's forebears by various tsars, including Godunov, Alexei, and Peter the Great. Perhaps people were afraid that she would beat them with her amethyst-set riding crop; they said she had once lashed an important official with it.

But the whispered words were no better than the loudspoken ones. My lady lived in a cloud of hostility which pained and puzzled me. Victor told us that once, on returning home after midnight, he had peeked through the window of Queen Margot's bedroom and seen her sitting on the couch in negligee, while the major knelt before her, cutting her toenails and bathing her feet with a sponge.

My old mistress spat and scolded while the young one blushed furiously.

"Oh Victor!" she squealed. "Aren't you ashamed? How lewd those fine folks are!"

My master smiled and said nothing. I was very grateful to him for saying nothing, but feared that he might yet add his voice to the din. With much oh-ing and ah-ing the women asked Victor all the details—just how the woman was sitting and how the major was kneeling—and Victor kept throwing them choice morsels:

"His face was all red and his tongue was hanging out. . . ."

I could see nothing shameful in the fact that the major had cut my lady's toenails, but I did not believe that his tongue had been hanging out. This, it seemed to me, was a loathsome lie.

"If it was so indecent, why did you peek through the window?" I said. "You're not a baby any more."

Of course they scolded me, but I did not mind the scolding. I wanted only one thing— to run downstairs and kneel before my lady as the major had done and say to her:

"Do move out of this house—please do!"

Now that I knew there was another kind of life and other kinds of people and feelings and ideas, I was more than ever disgusted by this house and its occupants. It was enmeshed in a web of filthy gossip which not a single person escaped. The regiment priest, a poor, sickly man, was reputed to be a lecherous drunkard; according to the accounts of my employers, all the officers and their wives lived in sin. I came to abhor the tedious talk of the soldiers about women, but most of all I loathed my employers. I knew only too well the true worth of the judgments they were so fond of passing on others. Picking other people to pieces was the only amusement which was free of charge, and so it became their only one. It was as if they were taking vengeance for the piety and boredom and drudgery of their own lives.

When they told smutty stories about Queen Margot I suffered convulsions of emotion beyond my years. My heart was filled to bursting with hatred for the gossipers and I was possessed of an unconquerable desire to plague them and antagonize them, though sometimes I was overwhelmed by a surge of pity for myself and all people. This inarticulate pity was harder to bear than the hatred.

I knew more about my Queen than they, and I was afraid they might learn what I knew.

On Sunday mornings when the family went to the Cathedral for high mass, I would visit my lady. She would call me into the bedroom where I would sit in an armchair upholstered in gold-coloured silk, and the little girl would climb up into my lap while I told her mother about the books I had read. My Queen lay in the wide bed with her two little hands under her cheek, her body hidden by a cover of the same golden hue as everything else in the bedroom, her dark hair lying in a braid over her tawny shoulder, sometimes hanging over the edge of the bed down onto the floor.

As she listened, she would look at me with her soft eyes and say with a faint smile:

"Really?"

It seemed to me that even her smile was the condescending smile of a queen. She spoke in a deep, tender voice, but I felt that she always repeated one and the same thing:

"I know that I am incomparably better and finer than other people, and I have no use for any of them."

Sometimes I found her sitting in a low armchair in front of the mirror combing her hair, which was as long and thick as Granny's;

it lay on her knees and the arms of the chair
and hung over the back almost down to the
floor. In the mirror I saw her firm, dusky
breasts. She would put on her corset cover
and stockings in my presence, but her nakedness did not rouse shameful feelings in me;
I took a joyful pride in her beauty. She always
effused a fragrance of flowers, and this was,
as it were, armour against lecherous thoughts
of her.

I was strong and healthy and knew the
secret of the sex relationship. But I had heard
people speak so filthily and heartlessly and
with such malicious joy about sex that I could
not imagine this woman in the embrace of a
man; I could not believe that anyone had the
right to lay a bold and shameless hand upon
her, the hand of one who owned her body.
I was certain that the love of the kitchens
and the sheds was something alien to Queen
Margot; that she knew some other, more exalted joy, a different kind of love.

But on entering the drawing room one
late afternoon, I was stopped by hearing her
ringing laughter, and a man's voice coming

from the other side of the portieres leading into her bedroom.

"Don't hurry!" pleaded the man. "Good heavens! It's unbelievable!"

I should have left. I realized that, but I was powerless to move.

"Who's there?" she called. "Oh, it's you? Come in."

The air in the room was heavy with the fragrance of flowers. It was dark, for the windows were curtained. Queen Margot lay in bed with the coverlet pulled up to her chin, while next to her, his back to the wall, sat the officer-violinist in nothing but a shirt which was open to reveal a great scar extending from his right shoulder to the nipple, so brightly red that even in the half-light I could see it distinctly. The officer's hair was comically tousled, and for the first time I saw a smile on his sad, scarred face. He smiled strangely, and his large, feminine eyes looked at my Queen as though he were seeing her beauty for the first time.

"This is my friend," said Queen Margot, and I could not tell whether her words were addressed to him or to me.

"What has frightened you so?" Her voice seemed to come from a great distance. "Come here."

When I approached, she put a hot, bare arm about my neck and said:

"When you grow up you too will know happiness. Go away now."

Having placed the book on the shelf, I took another and went out.

Something crunched in my heart. To be sure, not for a moment did I think that my Queen loved like ordinary people, nor could I think such a thing about the officer. I kept seeing his smile; he had smiled as joyfully as a child, with sudden wonder, and his sad face had become transformed. He must have loved her—how could anyone *not* love her? And there was good reason why she should have lavished her love upon him, this man who played so beautifully and recited poetry with such deep feeling.

But the very fact that I sought these consolations indicated that all was not well, that there was something wrong in my attitude toward what I had seen, and toward Queen

343

Margot herself. I felt that I had lost something, and for several days I was profoundly
grieved.

One day I riotously misbehaved, and when
I came to my lady for another book, she said
to me sternly:

"It seems that you are an incorrigible little
ruffian! I had never thought that of you."

This was too much for me to bear, and
I began to tell her how I suffered and hated
life when people said bad things about her.
She stood opposite me with her hand on
my shoulder, and at first she listened with
serious attention, but soon she gave a laugh
and gently pushed me away.

"Enough of that! I know all about it,
do you understand? I know everything, everything!"

Then she took both my hands in hers and
said very tenderly:

"The less attention you pay to all that
rubbish the better it will be for you. You
don't wash your hands very well."

She might have spared her words. If she
had had to polish the brass, scrub the floor

and wash diapers, I think her hands would not have looked any better than mine.

"If a person knows how to live, everybody hates and envies him; if he doesn't know how, everybody has contempt for him," she said thoughtfully. Then, drawing me up and toward her, she looked deep into my eyes with a smile.

"Do you love me?" she asked.

"Yes."

"Very much?"

"Yes."

"But—why?"

"I don't know."

"Thank you. You're a darling. I like to have people love me."

She gave a short laugh and seemed about to say something, but with a sigh she fell silent, still holding my hands.

"Come see me more often; come whenever you can."

I took advantage of this invitation, and profited greatly by her friendship. While my employers were having their after-dinner nap, I would run downstairs, and if she were home, I would sit with her for an hour or even more.

"You must read Russian books; you must learn to know our own Russian life," she taught me as she pushed the pins into her fragrant hair with nimble, rosy fingers.

Then she would go over the names of Russian writers and ask:

"Will you remember them?"

Often she would exclaim thoughtfully and with slight vexation:

"Dear me! You should be studying, and I keep forgetting it!"

After sitting with her I would run back upstairs with a new book in my hands and a sense of having been cleansed.

I had already read Aksakov's *Family Chronicle*, the delightful Russian poem *In the Forest*, the amazing *Notes of a Huntsman*, several volumes of Grebenka and Sollogub, and the verse of Venevitinov, Odoyevsky, and Tyutchev. These books purged my soul, freeing it of the chaff of bitter, beggarly reality. Now I appreciated what was meant by good books and realized how essential they were to me. They filled me with the calm confidence that I was not alone upon the earth and would surely make my way in life.

Granny came to see me and I gave her an ecstatic account of Queen Margot. Taking a generous sniff of tobacco, she said:

"That's a pleasant thing to hear! There's lots of good people on this earth. You've only got to look for them and you'll find them for sure."

One day she said:

"Perhaps I should go to her and say thank you on your account?"

"No, don't."

"All right, I won't. Lordy, Lordy, how nice it all is! I'd be only too glad to live the ages out."

Queen Margot was not given the opportunity to see me placed in school. On Whitsunday an unpleasant incident occurred that was almost my undoing.

Not long before the holidays, my eyelids swelled up, nearly closing my eyes completely. My employers were afraid I would become blind, and so was I. They took me to a doctor of their acquaintance, an obstetrician named Heinrich Rodzevich. He lanced the inside of my lids, and for several days I lay with a bandage over my eyes, pining away in darkness and pain. On the eve of Whitsunday the bandage was removed and I got up off my bed as though rising out of a grave in which I had been buried alive. Nothing could be more horrible than blindness, an unspeakable misfortune, depriving its victims of nine-tenths of the world.

On gay Whitsunday, released from all my duties at noon because of my ailment, I went from kitchen to kitchen visiting the batmen. All but the solemn Tufyayev were drunk. Toward evening Yermokhin struck Sidorov over the head with a log; he fell unconscious in the entranceway and the frightened Yermokhin ran to hide in the ravine.

Rumours that Sidorov had been murdered quickly spread in the yard. A small crowd gathered at the verandah steps to stare at the soldier stretched motionless in the doorway between kitchen and entranceway. People whispered that the police should be called, but no one called them, and no one had the courage to touch the soldier.

The washwoman Natalya Kozlovskaya arrived in a new lavender frock with a white kerchief about her shoulders. Angrily pushing people aside, she stepped into the entrance-way and squatted down beside the body.

"You fools, he's alive!" she called out in a loud voice. "Bring some water!"

"Don't go poking your nose into other people's business!" they warned her.

"Water, I said!" she shouted as though at a fire. Then in businesslike manner she pulled her new frock above her knees, jerked down her petticoat, and placed the bleeding head of the soldier in her lap.

Gradually the timid and disapproving onlookers dispersed. In the half-light of the entranceway I could see the washwoman's brimming eyes glistening in her round white face. I brought a pail of water. She told me to pour it over Sidorov's head and chest.

"But don't wet me—I'm going visiting," she warned.

The soldier came to, opened his glazed eyes and moaned.

"Lift him up," said Natalya, putting her hands under his armpits and holding him at arm's length so as not to soil her dress. We carried him into the kitchen and placed him on the bed. She wiped his face with a wet cloth and went out, saying:

"Keep wetting the cloth and holding it to his head while I go out and hunt for that other fool. The crazy devils, they'll drink themselves into prison yet!"

She let down her stained petticoat, kicked it into the corner, and carefully patted down her crisp new frock. Then she went out.

Sidorov stretched himself, hiccuped and groaned, while the dark blood kept dripping from his head on to my bare foot. This was unpleasant, but fear kept me from shifting my foot.

I was bitterly disappointed. Outdoors, everything bespoke the holiday; verandahs and gates had been decorated with young birches; maple and rowan boughs had been tied to every pillar; merriment rang down the length of the street, and everything was new and youthful. Early in the morning it had seemed to me that the spring holiday had come to stay, and that thereafter life would be more pure and bright and gay.

The soldier vomited, filling the kitchen with the stifling stench of warm vodka and scallions. From time to time vague, flat faces with squashed noses would be pressed against the windowpane, the spread palms on either side looking like hideous ears.

As the soldier's mind cleared he muttered:

"How's that? Did I fall? Yermokhin? There's a friend for you!"

He coughed and wept drunken tears and wailed:

"My little sister, my poor little sister!"

Wet and slimy and stinking, he pulled himself to his feet, reeled, flopped down on the bed again, and said as he rolled his eyes fearfully:

"He murdered me all right!"

This struck me funny.

"What are you laughing at, you devil?" asked the soldier, gazing at me dully. "How can you laugh—me murdered like this—once and for all. . . ."

He began to thrust me away with both hands, muttering:

"First in Tophet, Ilya the Prophet; when in need, George-on-a-steed. Out of my way, fiend!"

"Stop your nonsense," I said.

He roared with anger and shifted his feet.

"Me murdered, and you—!"

He struck me across the eyes with his heavy, dirty, limp hand. With a cry I rushed blindly out into the yard where I met Natalya dragging Yermokhin along by the arm and shouting:

"Get along, you horse!" Then, seeing me: "What's wrong?"

"He's fighting."

"Fighting?" repeated Natalya in surprise; giving Yermokhin a tug, she said to him:

"Well, you have the Lord to thank this time."

I washed my eyes with cold water and came back to glance through the door into the kitchen, where I saw the two soldiers weeping and embracing each other in maudlin reconciliation. Then they tried to embrace Natalya, but she slapped them off and cried:

"Keep your paws off me, you curs! What do you take me for, one of your blowzies? Lie down and have a snooze before your masters come home—lively now, or you'll be in for it!"

She put them both to bed like little children—one of them on the cot, the other on the floor. When they were both snoring, she came out into the entranceway.

"Just look at my frock—all wrinkled, and me setting out to go visiting! Did he strike you? The stupid fool. There's your vodka for you! Don't drink, my lad. Don't ever get the habit."

I sat down beside her on the bench near the gate and asked her how it was she had no fear of drunks.

"I have no fear of sobers either. Here's where I hold them!" she said, showing me a red, tight-clenched fist. "Used to be my husband, him that's dead, would drink himself green. I'd tie him up, hand and foot, and when he slept it off I'd pull his pants off and give him a beating with some good strong rods:

'Stop your toping, stop your tippling! Once you've got a wife, she's the one to turn to for your pleasure, and not your cups!' That's how! I'd beat him till I couldn't beat him no more, and after that he'd be like putty in my hands."

"You're strong," I said, remembering the woman Eve, who had deceived God Himself.

Natalya replied with a sigh:

"A woman needs more strength than a man; she needs strength for the two of them, and the Lord cheated her out of it. You can't count on a muzhik."

She spoke calmly and without malice, sitting there with her arms folded on her large bosom, her back against the fence, her eyes fixed sadly on the rubbage-cluttered dam. I lost all track of time as I sat listening to her wise observations; suddenly I caught sight of my master with his wife on his arm coming along the far end of the dam. They were walking slowly and importantly, like a rooster and a hen, staring at us and exchanging remarks.

I ran to open the front door. As we were climbing the stairs, my mistress said bitingly:

"So you're making up to the washwoman, are you? Is that what you learned from the lady downstairs?"

The remark was too stupid to give offence; it hurt me more to hear my master add with a short laugh:

"Well, it's about time, isn't it?"

The next morning when I went out into the shed for wood, I found an empty purse lying near the cat-hole in the door. I had seen Sidorov with this purse dozens of times, and so I immediately took it to him.

"And where's the money?" he asked, running his fingers inside. "A ruble and thirty kopeks. Hand it over."

His head was wrapped in a towel, his face was yellow and drawn, and he blinked his swollen eyes at me, refusing to believe that the purse had been empty when I found it.

Yermokhin came up and tried to convince him that I was the thief.

"It was him took it," he said, nodding

at me. "Take him to his master. A soldier don't
steal from a brother soldier."

These words suggested to me that he was
the one who had stolen the money and planted
the purse near our shed. So I said to his face,
then and there:

"That's a lie. You stole it!"

I was convinced of the rightness of my
guess when his coarse face became distorted
with fear and rage.

"Prove it!" he shrieked.

How was I to prove it? With a shout, Yermokhin dragged me out into the yard; Sidorov
followed us, also shouting, while heads began
popping out of the windows. Queen Margot's
mother watched us calmly as she puffed on the
inevitable cigarette. Realizing that I was
ruined in the eyes of my lady, I completely
lost my head.

I remember that the soldiers held my hands
and brought me before my employers, who
kept nodding to each other as they listened to
the charge against me.

"Of course it's his doings," said my young
mistress. "I saw him making up to the wash-

woman at the gate last night. He must have had money—can't get anything from her without money."

"That's right!" cried Yermokhin.

My head reeled, I was consumed with wild fury, I roared at my mistress and received a vicious beating.

But I was tortured less by the beating than by thoughts of what Queen Margot would think of me now. How was I to justify myself in her sight? This was a bitter hour for me.

Fortunately the soldiers quickly spread the news of what had happened throughout the yard and down the length of the street. That evening, as I lay up in the attic, I heard Natalya Kozlovskaya shouting below:

"Why should I keep my mouth shut? Come along here, my good man, come right along; come along, I tell you, or I'll go to your master and he'll make you come!"

I immediately sensed that the noise had something to do with me. She was standing and shouting near our entrance, and her voice grew ever louder and more triumphant.

"How much money did you show me yesterday? And where did you get it, eh? Let's hear."

Choking with joy, I could hear Sidorov wailing miserably:

"Oh Yermokhin, Yermokhin!"

"And the boy blamed and beaten!"

I wanted to rush downstairs and dance with joy and kiss the washwoman's hand, but at that moment I heard my mistress shout, probably from the window:

"The boy was beaten for his foul tongue; you're the only one who ever thought he stole the money, you slut!"

"You're a slut yourself, my dear, and a fine fat cow if you don't mind my saying so."

Their quarrelling was music to my ears; hot tears of pain and gratitude to Natalya flooded my heart, and I choked with the effort to restrain them.

My master slowly climbed the attic stairs and sat down on a projecting beam beside me.

"Looks like you have no luck, Peshkov," he said, smoothing down his hair.

I turned away without answering.

"But there's no denying you use the most outrageous language," he continued.

"Soon's I get up I'm going away," I announced quietly.

He sat smoking and saying nothing for awhile, then he remarked, carefully studying the end of his cigarette:

"Well, that's your business. You're not a little boy any more. You know best what to do."

He got up and went downstairs. As usual, I felt sorry for him.

Four days later I left my job. I wanted desperately to say goodbye to Queen Margot, but I lacked the courage to go to see her, and, to tell the truth, I hoped that she herself would send for me.

When taking leave of the little girl I said:

"Tell mother that I thank her very much; very, very much! Will you remember?"

"Yes," she promised, with a tender, affectionate smile. "Goodbye till tomorrow."

Some twenty years later I met her again. She was the wife of an officer of the gendarmes.

Once more I became a dishwasher, this time on the *Perm,* a large, fast steamer, white as a swan. This time I was the under-dishwasher, or "kitchen boy," and received seven rubles a month. It was my task to assist the cook.

The steward was a fat fellow, inflated with arrogance and bald as a rubber ball. With his hands behind his back, he would pace the deck all day long, like a pig searching for shade on a hot day. The buffet was adorned by his wife, a woman past forty, once pretty, but now much the worse for wear. She used so much powder that it flaked off her cheeks, covering her gaudy dress with sticky white dust.

The kitchen was commanded by the cook Ivan Ivanovich, nicknamed Teddybear. Little and chubby, with a hooked nose and mocking eyes, he had dandified manners, always wearing starched collars and shaving every day, so that his cheeks had a bluish tinge. He wore his dark moustaches curled upwards, and in free moments he would twist it with roasted red fingers, viewing it proudly in a little round hand-glass.

The most interesting person on board was the stoker Yakov Shumov, a square, broad-shouldered muzhik. His snub-nosed face was as flat as a spade, his bearish eyes glanced out from under thick eyebrows, his cheeks were covered with curly beard resembling marsh moss, while his head was capped with ringlets so thick that he could hardly run his crooked fingers through them.

He was a successful gambler and an amazing glutton. Like a hungry dog he would hang about the kitchen, begging for meat or bones, and in the evenings he would drink tea with Teddybear and give extraordinary accounts of himself.

In childhood he had assisted the town shepherd in Ryazan, until a passing monk lured him into a monastery, where he remained as a novice for four years.

"And I'd still be a monk, a black star of God," he said in his bantering way, "if it wasn't for a pious woman from Penza as came to our monastery. A taking little thing she was, and she turned my head. 'Oh what a nice one, oh what a strong one,' she says, 'and here's me, an honest widder, all alone; won't you come work for me, as my man-about-house?' says she, 'me with my own house and trading in chicken-feathers and down?'"

"I had no objection, so she takes me for her man-about-house and I take her for my mistress and sit soft for some three years—"

"You're a bold liar," interrupted Teddy-bear as he anxiously studied a pimple on his nose. "If people earned money by lying, you'd be rich."

Yakov chewed on, the grey ringlets moving up and down on his cheeks and his furry ears shifting. After the cook's interruption, he continued in his quick, even way:

"She was older than me, so I got bored, got sick of her, I did, and took up with her niece, and she hears of it and grabs me by the scruff of the neck and throws me out."

"Gives you your pay in a fitting way," put in the cook in the same easy manner as Yakov.

The stoker thrust a lump of sugar in his cheek and went on:

"So I goes shifting around in the wind for some time till I hitches up with an old trader from Vladimir, and him and me goes tramping half round the world—to the mountains called the Balkans we goes, and to them same Turks and Rumanians and Greeks and to various Austriaks—to all sorts of people—buying from one, selling to another."

"Did you steal?" asked the cook in all seriousness.

"Not the old man—not for nothing. And he says to me: walk honest over foreign earth; there it's laid down to take a man's head for the littlest stealing. Oh, I tried stealing, of course, only it didn't work: I tried leading a horse out of a merchant's stable. Well, I didn't manage; they caught me and natural enough began to beat me, and when they got through beating me they dragged me to the police. There was two of us—one a real, honest horse thief, and me mostly to see what would happen. I was working for that merchant then—setting a stove in his new bathhouse. The merchant falls sick and begins to see me in bad dreams. He gets scared and goes to the higher-ups and says: 'let him go'—that'll be me—'let him go,' says he, 'seeing's how I see him in my dreams, and if I don't forgive him I'll probably die, seeing's how he's a magician no doubt'—that'll be me a magician. Well, the merchant was a famous one, so they lets me go."

"Shouldn't have let you go; should've hung a stone around your neck and sunk you in the river for three days till they soaked all the tomfoolery out of you."

Yakov quickly picked up the idea:

"You're right about there's a lot of tomfoolery in me—enough tomfoolery in me for a whole village if the truth's to be told."

The cook poked his finger inside his collar and pulled at it angrily, shaking his head and saying with annoyance:

"Humph! A convict like this goes walking around guzzling and swilling and snoozing, and all what for? Tell me this—what are you living for?"

The stoker smacked his lips and replied:

"That I don't know. I just live along like the rest. Some lie down, others walk around, clerks sit on their backsides all day long, but everybody's got to eat."

This only added to the cook's annoyance.

"You're such a pig there's no putting it in words. You're just swill for the pigs, that's what!"

"What you mad about?" asked Yakov in surprise. "Us muzhiks is all acorns from the same oak. Don't be mad; it won't make me any better."

Soon I became closely attached to this man; I gazed upon him with undiminishing wonder and listened to him openmouthed. It seemed to me that he had built up within himself a strong structure of life experience. He addressed everyone informally, looked at everyone from under bristling brows with the same frank independence, and placed everyone—the captain, the steward, and the important passengers up in first class—on the same level as the boat-hands, the waiters in the dining-room, the third-class passengers, and himself.

Sometimes he would stand before the captain or the chief engineer with his long, apelike arms behind his back, listening in silence as they upbraided him for laziness or for unconcernedly stripping a person at cards. It was clear that the upbraiding did not impress him, and the threats to put him off the boat at the next landing did not frighten him.

There was something different about Yakov, as there was about "That's Fine." Apparently he too was convinced that he was someone apart, not to be understood by others.

I never saw this man pensive or sulky, nor do I remember his being silent for any length of time. Words poured out of his mouth in an unending stream, almost against his will. Whenever he was being scolded or told an interesting story, his lips would move as though he were repeating to himself what he heard; or perhaps he was quietly voicing his own thoughts. Every day when his work was over he would climb out of the hold all sweaty and smeared with oil, barefoot, his wet, unbelted blouse open to expose a chest overgrown with curly hair. Presently we would hear his deep, monotonous voice scattering words over the deck like drops of rain.

"Greetings, mother. Where you going? To Chistopol? I know the place, used to work for a rich Tatar farmer there, Usan Gubai-dulin by name. The old man had three wives; a husky fellow he was, with a red face. One of his young wives was a taking little Tatar woman—I lived in sin with her."

He had been everywhere and lived in sin with nearly all the women he had met. He recounted everything in a calm, kindly manner, as though no one had ever offended or abused him. A minute later his speech would come flowing from somewhere in the stern.

"Anybody want to play cards? Bang-down, or threezies, or bags? A comforting thing, cards; just sit down and haul in the money like a merchant."

I noticed that he rarely used the words "good," "bad," or "wicked," but almost always called things "taking," or "comforting," or "curious." For him a pretty woman was "a taking little thing," a fine sunny day was "a comforting day." His favourite exclamation was:

"Spit on it!"

Everyone considered him lazy, but it seemed to me that he laboured at the furnaces down in that stinking, stifling hold as conscientiously as anyone else, though I never heard him complain of being tired as the other stokers did.

One day an old woman among the passengers had her purse stolen. The evening was clear and quiet, with everyone feeling well-disposed. The captain gave the old woman five rubles and the passengers took up a collection for her. When they handed her the money, she crossed herself and bowed to the waist, saying:

"Ah, my dears, you've given me three-rubles-ten more than the purse had in it."

Somebody shouted gaily:

"Take it, Granny, and be thankful. An extra three rubles always comes in handy."

Someone else made the apt remark:

"Money's not people; it's never unwanted."

But Yakov went up to the old woman with his own suggestion:

"Give me the extra money," said he. "I'll play cards with it."

The people laughed, thinking the stoker was joking, but he insisted in all seriousness:

"Come on, Granny, what do you want with money? You'll be crawling into your grave tomorrow."

They shouted at him and drove him away, and he said to me in wonder:

"What a queer bunch! What do they want to poke their noses into other people's business for? She said herself she didn't need the extra money, and three rubles would be a great comfort to me."

It seemed that he took pleasure in just the looks of money. While talking, he would polish a silver or copper piece on his pants and then hold it up in front of his pug nose to catch the glint of it. But he was not greedy.

One day he invited me to play bang-down. I did not know how.

"Don't know how!" said he in amazement. "How's that? And you knowing how to read! I'll have to teach you. Come on, we'll play just for the fun of it, with sugar as stakes."

He won half a pound of loaf sugar from me and pushed it piece by piece into his cheek. When he felt that I already understood the game, he said:

"Now let's play in earnest—for money. Got any?"

"Five rubles."

"And I've got two-something."

Naturally he soon won everything from me. Wishing to retrieve, I staked my winter coat for five rubles—and lost; I put up my new boots for three—and lost again. Then Yakov said to me irritably, almost in anger:

"You're no player—too hotheaded. Take back your coat and your boots; I don't want them. Here they are, and take your money too—four rubles—one goes to me for the lesson, if you don't mind."

I was very grateful.

"Spit on it!" he said in response to my gratitude. "A game's a game—which means, just for fun. But you go at it like it was a fight. And you don't have to get hot even in a fight—fix 'em with a cool eye. What's there to get hot about? You're young; you've got to hold yourself in tight. Missed once, missed five times, missed seven times—spit on it! Step back. Cool off. Go after it again. That's how to play a game."

I kept liking him more—and less. Some-times when he talked he reminded me of Granny. There was much about him that attracted me, but I was repulsed by a thick crust of indifference to people, which seemed to have formed throughout the course of his life.

One day at sundown one of the second-class passengers, a fat merchant from Perm, got drunk and fell overboard. Frantically waving his arms, he was carried away in the red-gold trail behind the ship. The engines were imme-diately shut down and the ship brought to a standstill, the paddle wheels throwing up a riot of foam, blood-red in the sunset. In this seething blood struggled a dark body, now far astern, while from the water rose heartrending shrieks. The passengers also shouted and pushed and crowded to the stern of the boat. A friend of the drowning man, a bald, ruddy-complexioned fellow who was also drunk, fought his way through the crowd, roaring:

"Clear the way! I'll reach him!"

Two boat-hands were already in the water, swimming to the drowning man, and a lifeboat was being let down. Above the shouts of the boat-hands and the squeals of the women could be heard the calm, husky voice of Yakov:

"He'll drown anyhow because he's wearing a coat. You're sure to drown if you've got long clothes on. Take the women—why is it they always drown before the men? It's their skirts. Soon's a woman hits the water she goes straight to the bottom like a pood weight. Look— he's drowned already. What did I tell you?"

He had indeed drowned. For some two hours they made a futile search for his body. His friend, now sober, sat disconsolately in the stern muttering:

"Just see what's happened! What's to be done now? What'll I tell his folks, eh? If it wasn't for his folks. . . ."

Yakov stood in front of him with his hands behind his back, offering words of comfort:

"Can't be helped, merchant! Nobody knows how he'll meet his end. Happens a fellow eats mushrooms and—phwit!—gone to his grave! Thousands of people eat mushrooms to their health; only one to his death. And what's a mushroom, after all?"

He stood before the merchant, broad and hard as a grindstone, scattering his words like chaff. At first the merchant wept softly, wiping the tears off his beard with a broad palm, but when the meaning of Yakov's words reached him, he broke into a wail:

"Get away, you devil! What you wringing my soul out of me for? True believers, take him away, or I'm not accounting for what'll happen!"

Yakov withdrew calmly, remarking:

"People are funny all right! Try doing good; never understood."

Sometimes it seemed to me that the stoker was simple-minded, but more often I felt that he just pretended to be so. I wanted desperately to hear about the places he had been and the things he had seen, but he gave me little satisfaction. Throwing back his head and half-closing his dark, bearlike eyes, he would stroke his fleshy face and drawl out reminiscences:

"There's people everywhere, brother, like ants. People here, people there—swarms of them. Most of all, of course, are the peasants.

Spread all over the earth, like autumn leaves. Bulgars? Sure I saw Bulgars, and Greeks too, and then there was Serbs and Rumanians and various gypsies—all kinds! What're they like? Hm, what could they be like? In the towns, townspeople; in the country, countryfolk. Just like ours. Ever so much alike. Some as even talk like us, only not exactly, like for instance the Tatars or Mordovians. The Greeks can't talk like us—go babbling anything comes into their heads; sounds like words but no telling what it's all about. You have to talk to them with your hands. That old man of mine, he made believe he could understand the Greeks too—went about muttering kalamará, kalamaróo! He was a sly one all right! Couldn't he get their dander up though! What's that? Asking me again what they were like? Simpleton, what could they be like? Of course they're dark, and the Rumanians are dark too—they're all one faith. The Bulgars are also dark, but they pray like us. As for the Greeks—they're like the Turks."

I felt that he had not told me everything, that there was something he was holding back.

From the magazine illustrations I had learned that the capital of Greece was Athens, an ancient and beautiful city. But Yakov shook his head sceptically and denied Athens.

"They've been lying to you there, brother. There's no Athens; there's only Athon, and that's not a city but a mountain with a monastery on it. That's all. It's called The Holy Mountain of Athon. There's pictures of it; the old man sold them. There's the town of Belgorod on the River Danube, something like Yaroslavl or Nizhni. Their cities aren't much to speak of, but as for their villages —that's different. Their women too—simply too taking for words. I almost stayed back there on account of one such. What was her name, now?"

He briskly rubbed his palms over his face, making his beard crackle softly while from somewhere deep down in his throat came a chuckling like the clatter of cracked bells.

"How a person forgets things! And it used to be that me and her. . . . She cried when I said goodbye, and so did I, believe it or not. . . ."

With calm shamelessness he began to teach me how to treat women.

We sat there in the stern, a warm, moonlit night floating up to meet us, the meadowlands on the left scarcely visible beyond the silvery water, the hillsides on the right sprinkled with winking yellow lights like captive stars. Everything was in movement, wakefully aquiver, living a quiet, but intense life. And his husky words came falling through the sweet, sad silence:

"Happened she would fling out her arms as she came awake. . . ."

Yakov's tale was brazen, but not revolting; it contained no boasting, no cruelty, was artless, and a bit nostalgic. Up in the sky, the moon's nakedness was just as brazen and roused the same sorrowfulness within me. I remembered only the good things, the very best: Queen Margot, and the lines made unforgettable by their truthfulness:

> *Only a song has need of beauty;*
> *Beauty has no need of song.*

Shaking off my meditative mood like a fit of drowsiness, I again pressed the stoker to tell me about his life and what he had seen.

"Queer bird you are," said he. "What'll I tell you? I've seen everything. A monastery? Yes, I've seen a monastery. A pub? And a pub. I've seen the life of the gentles, and the life of the muzhiks. I've had plenty, and I've had nothing."

Slowly, as though he were crossing a shaky bridge over a deep stream, he would recall the past:

"Take this, for instance: here's me sitting in the lockup for horse-thieving. It's Siberia for sure this time, thinks I to myself. And there's the police officer cussing the stoves in his new house for smoking. So I says to him: 'I can put that right for you, your honour.' He goes after me tooth and nail. 'Hold your tongue! The best stove layer in town couldn't mend them!' But I says: 'Sometimes a fool's smarter than a lord.' It was Siberia staring me in the face made me so bold. 'All right, have a try,' says he, 'but if they smoke worse when you're through, I'll pound you to a pulp.' Well, in two days the stoves were mend-ed. He couldn't get over it, that police officer, and flies at me again: 'You dolt! You dunderhead! An expert like you going around stealing horses! How do you account for a thing like that?' So I says: 'Just my stupidness, your honour.' 'You're right,' says he. 'Just stupidness. What a pity. I feel sorry for you,' says he. Hear that? A police officer. His calling give him no right to be soft, but there he was, pitying me."

"Well, and what then?" I asked.

"Nothing. He just pitied me. What else do you want?"

"Why should he pity you? You're strong as a rock."

Yakov laughed good-naturedly.

"What a queer bird you are! A rock, you say? Even a rock's to be respected. A rock's got its own job to do; it's rocks they use to pave streets with. Everything's to be respected. Everything has it's use. Take sand. What's sand? Yet grass grows out of it."

When the stoker said such things, it became particularly clear to me that he had knowledge beyond my understanding.

"What do you think of the cook?" I asked him.

"Who—Teddybear?" asked Yakov indifferently. "What could I think of him? Nothing to think about."

That was true. Ivan Ivanovich was so smooth and correct, there was nothing for thoughts to hang on to. There was only one thing about him which I found of interest: he disliked the stoker and was always shouting at him, yet he always invited him to tea.

One day he said to Yakov:

"If we still had serfs and I was your lord, I'd tan your hide seven days a week, you loafer!"

"Seven days a week's a bit too much," observed Yakov seriously.

In spite of his constant scolding, the cook kept feeding him for some reason. He would hand him something to eat and say:

"Here, you guzzler!"

"It's a lot of strength I store up thanks to you, Ivan Ivanovich," Yakov would say as he chewed the food unhurriedly.

"And what do you want with all that strength, lazybones?"

"What do you mean? I still have a lot of living ahead."

"What do you want to live for, you old devil?"

"Devils also want to live. Or maybe you find no fun in living? Life's an amusing thing, Ivan Ivanovich."

"There's an idiot for you!"

"A nidiot?"

"An i-di-ot!"

"Who ever heard of such a word?" asked Yakov in amazement.

"Just look at that," said Teddybear to me. "You and me sweating and stewing over these damned stoves, and him just sitting here chewing away like a pig."

"To everyone his own fate," said the stoker, chewing his food unperturbed.

I knew it was hotter and more difficult to stoke the furnaces than stand over the stoves— once or twice I had tried working beside Yakov, and I could not understand why he did not insist that his job was the harder one. His attitude only convinced me the more that he was possessed of special knowledge.

Everybody complained of him—the captain, the mechanic, the boatswain—everybody who had anything to do with him. I wondered why they did not get rid of him. The other stokers were more kindly disposed toward him, though even they ridiculed his loquaciousness and his card playing.

Once I asked them:

"Is Yakov a good fellow?"

"Yakov? He's all right. Never takes offence. You can do anything you like to him, even to putting live coals down his neck."

In spite of his strenuous labour at the furnaces and his enormous appetite, the stoker slept very little. As soon as his shift was over he would appear on deck, dirty and sweaty, often without changing his clothes, and sit up all night, talking or playing cards with the passengers.

He was to me a locked chest, in which I felt that something indispensable was hidden away, and I stubbornly sought the key that would open it.

"I can't make out what the devil you're after, brother," he said, studying me with eyes deep-hidden under his brows. "You want to hear about the world? It's true I've travelled all over it. But what of it? You're a queer bird all right! Here, listen to what happened to me one day."

And he told me the following story. Once upon a time, in a provincial town, lived a young, consumptive judge and his German wife, a healthy, childless woman. She fell in love with a merchant whose handsome wife had born him three children. Noticing that the German woman was in love with him, the merchant decided to play a joke on her: he invited her to meet him in the garden at night, and hid two of his friends in the bushes.

"That was something now! The German woman comes, all hot and flustered, letting him know she's his for the asking. But he says to her: 'I can't take you, ma'am, being's I'm married, but I've brought two of my friends for you—one's a bachelor, the other's a widower.' The woman lets out a cry and gives him such a blow that he somersaults over the bench, and then she starts kicking his mug for him. I was the one brought her to the garden, being the judge's handy man, so now I peeks through a crack in the fence and sees the rumpus: the friends jumped out of the bushes and rushed at her, dragging her off by the hair. So I leaps the fence and hauls them off. 'That's no way to do,' says I. 'The lady comes to him in good faith and he disgraces her like this!' I led her away and they hit me over the head with a brick. She felt pretty bad—kept walking up and down the yard not knowing what to do with herself, and says to me: 'I'll go away—back to my own German folk, Yakov. Soon's my husband dies I'll go away!' 'That's right,' says I. 'Of course you must go away.' Well, the judge died and she went. She was a gentle thing, and sensible. And the judge was also a gentle man, may his soul rest in peace."

Failing to grasp the significance of the story, I said nothing. I sensed something familiarly cruel and senseless in it, but what was there to say?

"Like the story?" asked Yakov.

I muttered something under my breath, but he explained calmly:

"People of their sort, well-fed and comfortable, feel like having a little fun sometimes, but it don't always come off—they don't know how. And that's only natural, being's they're the weighty, trade sort. Takes brains to trade, and you get bored living by your brains all the time; want to have a little fun."

The river kept churning away from the prow of the boat in a cloud of foam; we could hear the rush of the water and see the black riverbanks slowly receding. From the deck came the snores of the passengers. A tall, thin woman, all in black, her grey head uncovered, threaded her way among the benches and the sleeping bodies. The stoker nudged me and said softly:

"See—she's moping."

It seemed to me he found amusement in other people's heartache.

He was always telling me stories to which I listened eagerly. I remember all of his stories, but I cannot remember his ever telling a cheerful one. He spoke more dispassionately than the books. In the books I was often aware of the author's feelings—his joy and anger, his grief and ridicule. The stoker never ridiculed or passed judgment. Nothing noticeably pleased or offended him. He spoke like a detached witness in court, like a person to whom the prisoner and the prosecutor and the judge were all the same. This indifference annoyed and oppressed me and roused my hostility.

Life seemed to dance in front of him like the flames in the furnaces under the boilers, while he stood with a wooden mallet in his bearlike paw, quietly tapping the lever which increased or decreased the flow of fuel.

"Has anyone ever hurt you?"

"Who could hurt me? I'm strong enough to knock anyone down. . . ."

"I didn't mean that. I meant hurt you inside—your soul."

"You can't hurt a person's soul. The soul don't take offence," he said. "You can't even touch it—not with anything at all."

The deck passengers, the boat-hands, and everyone else, spoke just as often and just as much about the soul as they did about the land, or their work, or about bread or women. The soul is a common word in the vocabulary of simple folk, as widely circulated as a five-kopek piece. I regretted the fact that sticky tongues had taken such fast hold of this word, and every time a muzhik would begin using foul language in which, either in jest or in earnest, he cursed the soul, it was a direct blow at my heart.

I well remembered with what reverence Granny had always spoken of the soul, this mysterious repository of love, joy, and beauty, and I firmly believed that whenever a good man died, white angels bore his soul away to the blue heaven, to Granny's kind God, who received it with loving tenderness:

"Ah, my lovely one, my pure one,— was it a bad time you had down there, was it a hurtful time?"

And He would bestow on the soul the six white wings of the seraphims.

Yakov Shumov spoke of the soul just as reverently, as little, and as reluctantly as Granny. He never cursed the soul when he swore, and on hearing others do so, he would become silent and lower his head on his red, bull-like neck.

When I would ask him what the soul was, he would say:

"A spirit, the breath of God."

This did not satisfy me, and when I would press him with other questions, he would drop his eyes and say:

"Even the priests don't know much about the soul, brother. That's something hidden—"

I was constantly thinking about him, concentrating all my efforts on understanding him, but in vain. I could see nothing but Yakov; the huge bulk of his body hid everything else.

The steward's wife was suspiciously attentive to me. Every morning I had to pour the water for her to wash, though this was rightfully the task of Lusha, the neat, cheerful little maid in second-class. As I stood in the narrow cabin next to this woman, who was stripped to the waist, I was repulsed by her sallow body, as flabby as sour dough, and could not help comparing it with the firm, bronze body of Queen Margot. The steward's wife kept babbling something or other, now in muttered complaint, now in mocking anger.

The ideas she expressed never reached me, though I could well guess their meaning. It was a base, shameful, meaning. But it left me unmoved. I lived mentally remote from the steward's wife, and from everything taking place on the steamer. A huge, moss-grown rock cut me off from the world about me, which kept floating on and on, day after day.

"The steward's wife is head over heels in love with you!" came Lusha's mocking words, as though in a dream. "Take your happiness while you have the chance."

She was not the only one who mocked me. All the servants in the dining room knew about this woman's attachment, and the cook observed with a grimace:

"The lady's had her taste of everything else, so now she'd like to try some French pastry! Phooh! Keep your eyes open, Peshkov, or you'll be getting into trouble!"

Yakov also offered me paternal advice:

"To be sure, if you was two or three years older—well, then I'd talk different. But at your age—better not give in. Still, you can do as you please."

"Forget it," I said. "Such rot."

"To be sure."

But a minute later he ran his fingers through his tangled hair and went on sowing his round little words:

"Have to see her side of it too—and hers is a dull side, a wintry side. Even a dog likes a little petting—all the more a human being. A woman lives on caresses like a mushroom on rain. Like as not she's ashamed, but what can she do? The body's a whore, and nothing more."

I gazed intently into his enigmatic eyes as I asked:

"Do you feel sorry for her?"

"Me? She isn't my mother, is she? And some people don't even feel sorry for their mothers. You sure are a queer bird!"

He gave his soft laugh, like the clatter of cracked bells.

Sometimes as I looked at him I seemed to plunge into silent emptiness, into a dark and bottomless pit.

"Everybody else gets married, Yakov. Why don't you?"

"What for? I can always get a woman—thank the Lord that's easy enough. A married man has to sit home and work the land. My land's no good, and not much of it, and what there is my uncle took away. My brother came back from soldiering and started wrangling with the uncle—threatened him with the law and clubbed him over the head. Spilled blood. For that they sent him to prison for a year and a half, and after that—there's only one road for an ex-convict, and that road leads back to prison. His wife was a taking little thing. But what's there to say? Once a fellow gets married, there's nothing to do but settle down and rule the roost. But a soldier can never rule even his own life."

"Do you pray to God?"

"What a queer bird! Of course I do."

"How?"

"Different ways."

"What prayers do you know?"

"I don't know any prayers. I just say: Lord Jesus, have mercy on the living, bring

peace to the dead, save us from sickness, and—
well, a few other things."

"What others?"

"Oh, I don't know. Whatever you say
reaches the Lord."

He treated me gently and with a sort of
curiosity, as though I were a clever puppy
that could do amusing tricks. Sometimes
I would be sitting beside him of an evening,
him smelling of oil and fire, and onions—
he loved onions, and would eat them raw,
like apples—and all of a sudden he would
say:

"Come now, Alyosha, let's have some
rhymes."

I knew many poems by heart, besides which
I had a thick notebook in which I had copied
out my favourite ones. I would recite *Ruslan
and Ludmilla*, and he would listen motionless—unseeing, unspeaking, restraining his
hoarse breathing. Then he would say softly:

"A taking tale, that. Did you think it
all up yourself? Pushkin, you say? There's a
nobleman named Mukhin-Pushkin. I saw him
once."

"Not him. They killed this Pushkin a long time ago."

"What for?"

I told him the story in the brief form in which I had heard it from Queen Margot. When I had finished, he said calmly:

"Lots of people come to their ruin through women."

Often I would tell him stories from books; they were all tangled up and interwoven to form one long story that was tumultuous and beautiful, filled with purple passion, mad adventure, noble heroes, incredibly good fortune, duels and death, fine words and villainous deeds. I conferred upon Rocambole the chivalrous aspects of la Môle, Hannibal, and Colonna; upon Louis XI, the qualities of Grandet's father; Cornet Otletayev became indistinguishable from Henry IV. At the dictates of inspiration I changed people's characters and rearranged events, creating a world in which I ruled as arbitrarily as grandfather's God, who also played at random with human beings. Without preventing me from seeing the reality of life, and without lessening my desire to understand living people, the chaos of this book world formed a transparent but impenetrable veil protecting me from the poisonous filth and innumerable contagions lurking in the life about me.

The books made me invulnerable to many things; a knowledge of how people loved and suffered made it impossible for me to enter a brothel. The cheapness of such debauchery roused my repugnance for it and contempt for those who found it sweet. Rocambole taught me to stoically resist the force of circumstances. Dumas' heroes filled me with the desire to dedicate my life to some great and significant cause. My favourite character was the jolly King Henry IV. It seemed to me that it was he whom Béranger had in mind when he wrote:

> *He treated all the simple folk*
> *And drank himself, we know.*
> *But why should not a king be gay*
> *If all his realm is so?*

The novels painted Henry IV as a kind man, dear to the heart of his people. The sunny brightness of his nature filled me with the unshakeable conviction that France was the finest land in the world, a land of chivalry, where people in peasant garb were as noble as those in royal robes. Ange Pitou was just as chivalrous as D'Artagnan. When Henry was killed, I wept mournfully and ground my teeth in hatred for Ravaillac. Henry was almost always the hero of the stories I told the stoker, and it seemed to me that Yakov too came to love him and France.

"A fine fellow, that King Henry. You could go fishing with him or anything you like," he remarked.

He never went into ecstasies or interrupted my stories by asking questions. He would listen in silence, with drawn brows, and an unchanging expression on his face— an ancient rock overgrown with moss. But if for some reason I would pause, he would immediately say:

"Is that all?"

"Not yet."

"Then don't stop."

Once when we were speaking about the French, he said with a sigh:

"They lived nice and cool."

"What do you mean?"

"You and me live in the heat, always working, but they lived nice and cool. Nothing to do—just drink and stroll about. An amusing way to live."

"They worked too."

"That's not seen from the stories you tell," observed the stoker justly. And suddenly it dawned on me that the overwhelming majority of the books I had read said almost nothing about how people worked, or by whose labour the highborn heroes were supported.

"Well, think I'll take a little nap," said Yakov, rolling over on his back. The next minute he was snoring peacefully.

In the autumn, when the banks of the Kama had turned red-brown, the trees golden, and the slanting sunrays had paled, Yakov suddenly left the steamer. On the eve he said to me:

"Day after tomorrow you and me'll get to Perm, Alyosha, and we'll go to the bathhouse to steam ourselves to our heart's content;

from there we'll head straight for a pub with music. That's a pleasing thing. Don't I like to see them grind that hand organ though!"

But at Sarapul a flabby-fat man with a beardless, womanish face boarded the steamer. The long coat and the cap with fox ear flaps he was wearing increased his resemblance to a woman. He immediately chose a table in a warm corner near the kitchen, asked for tea, and began to sip the boiling brew without taking off his coat or cap, sweating profusely.

A fine rain was exuded by the autumn clouds, and it seemed that whenever the man wiped his face with his checked handkerchief, there would be a lull in the drizzle, and the more he perspired, the harder it rained.

Soon Yakov sat down beside the man and they began to study a map in an almanac. The passenger traced something with his finger, and the stoker said calmly:

"What of it? That's easy for a fellow like me. Spit on it!"

"Good," said the passenger in a high voice as he thrust the almanac back into an open leather bag at his feet. They went on talking quietly and drinking tea.

Just before Yakov's shift began, I asked him who the man was. He answered with a short laugh:

"Looks like a pansy, don't he? That means he's a castrate. Comes from far-away Siberia. Queer bird—seems to live by plan."

He walked away from me, pounding over the deck with his naked heels, black and hard as hoofs. But he stopped to turn back and say, as he scratched his ribs:

"I've hired myself out to him. Soon's we reach Perm I'll get off the boat and it's farewell, Alyosha. We'll go by train, and then up a river, and then on horseback— it'll take us five weeks to get there. Just see the far corners people have crawled to!"

"Do you know him?" I asked, amazed at Yakov's unexpected decision.

"How could I? Never seen him before, and never been where he lives."

The next morning Yakov appeared in a short, greasy sheepskin, a battered, brimless straw hat that had once belonged to Teddy-bear, and ragged bast sandals. He gripped my hand with iron fingers and said:

"Come along with me, eh? He'll take you on too, the pansy will, if I just say so. Want me to? He'll cut off what you can do without, and give you some money. It's a regular holiday for them to butcher a fellow. They even pay him for it."

The castrate stood at the rail with a white bundle under his arm, gazing at Yakov with dull eyes, his figure as heavy and bloated as a drowned man's. I cursed him under my breath, and the stoker once more gripped my hand.

"Spit on him! Everybody prays to God in his own way—what's it to you? Well, goodbye. Hope you'll be happy!"

And Yakov Shumov went away, lunging along like a great bear, and leaving my heart torn by conflicting emotions: I was sorry for the stoker, and annoyed with him, and I remember wondering with a touch of envy and alarm why he should have gone off to such a distant, unknown place—and just what sort of a man he was anyway, this Jakov Shumov.

XII

Late in the autumn, when the steamer stopped running, I became an apprentice in an icon-painting workshop, but on the second day of study my mistress, a soft little old woman, given to drink, announced:

"The days are short now and the evenings long, so you'll be going to the shop every morning to help with sales and study in the evenings."

And she handed me over to a quick young shop assistant who was good-looking in a saccharine way. In the cold darkness of dawn, he and I would cross the city along the somnolent Ilyinka Street until we reached the Lower Market, where the shop was located on the second floor of the trade arcade. The shop, which had once been a storeroom, was small and dark, with an iron door and one little window giving out on to an iron-roofed balcony running the length of the façade. Our shop was chock-full of large and small icons and iconframes, some of them plain, some of them ornamented with arabesques. It also carried a stock of religious books in yellow leather bindings and printed in old Slavonic script. Next door to us was another icon and book shop run by a black-bearded merchant, kin to an Old-Faith fanatic well known along the Kerzhenetz River, beyond the Volga. The merchant had a puny son my age, with the wizened face of an old man and roving, rodent eyes.

After opening up the shop, it was my duty to run to the nearest tavern for hot water. We had our tea, and then I straightened up the shop and dusted the stock. When everything was in order I was expected to stand out on the porch and see that customers came to us, rather than to our neighbour.

"Customers are fools," the shop assistant told me. "It's all the same to them where they buy, long as it's cheap; they can't tell what's good from what's bad."

He would clap the icon-boards together briskly as he gave me my lessons, showing off his knowledge of the trade:

"Here's a fine piece of work—very cheap, three by four—well worth its price; another: six by seven—well worth it. . . . Know the saints? Try to remember: Vonifati—for drunkards; Varvara the Martyr—for toothache and untimely death; Vasili the Blessed—for fever and delirium tremens. Know the Virgins? Look: The Grieving One; The Three-Armed Virgin; The Weeping Virgin; The Assuage-My-Grief Virgin; The Kazan, The Pokrov, The Semistrelnaya. . . ."

I quickly memorized the prices of the icons according to their size and workmanship, and I learned to distinguish the different images of the Virgin, but I had difficulty in remembering the benefits bestowed by various saints.

The shop assistant used to test my knowledge whenever he found me daydreaming at the door of the shop.

"Who's the one to relieve birth pains?"

If my answer was wrong, he would say contemptuously:

"What's your head for, anyway?"

It was even harder to make the customers buy. I disliked the ugly faces on the icons and did not know how to sell them. Granny's tales had given me the impression that the Virgin was young and good and beautiful. It was thus I found her in magazine pictures, but on the icons she looked old and malign, with a long, curved nose and wooden hands.

We did a good business on market days— Wednesdays and Fridays. Our steps were constantly being climbed by muzhiks and old women and sometimes whole families —all of them adherents of the Old Faith, sullen, distrustful forest folk from over the Volga. I would see some cumbersome fellow swathed in sheepskins and thick homespun slowly making his way along the balcony as though afraid of collapsing, and I was ashamed and embarrassed to approach him. It cost me great effort to plant myself in his path and dance about his massive boots, whining like a mosquito:

"What will you have, good sir? Manuals, prayer books, Psalters with references and annotations, the books of Yefrem Sirin and Kirill. Be so good as to take a look. Any icon you wish—different prices, finest workmanship, dark colours. We take orders to paint whatever saint or Virgin you want. Perhaps you'd like to order somebody's patron saint, or the family saint? Ours is the best workshop in Russia! The best shop in town!"

The impenetrable customer would gaze at me in silence for some time, as though I were a dog, then all of a sudden he would push me aside with a hard hand and enter the neighbour's shop, while our assistant would rub his big ears and mutter angrily:

"So you let him go! Humph, a fine salesman you are!"

While from the next shop came a soft voice pouring out honeyed words:

"My dear man, it's not sheepskins we trade in, and not leather boots, but the blessings of God, dearer by far than silver or gold, beyond worldly price. . . ."

"Damn it all!" our shop assistant would whisper in envy and admiration. "Just listen how he

swabs the ears of that muzhik! Take lessons
from him!"

I conscientiously tried to learn, believ-
ing that once I had undertaken the job, I
ought to do it well. But I showed little talent
for enticing customers and making them buy.
I was always feeling sorry for those silent,
sullen muzhiks and those ratlike old women
with their frightened, hangdog expressions;
I kept wanting to whisper in their ears the
true worth of the icons, so that they should
not be done out of an extra twenty kopeks.
All of them seemed to me so poor and hungry
that I wondered how they could pay three and
a half rubles for a Psalter, the book most
commonly purchased.

I was amazed by their knowledge of books
and their appreciation of the ornamentation on
the icons. One day a grey-haired old man
whom I tried to tempt into the shop said
to me:

"It's not the truth you're telling, my boy,
when you say yours is the best icon workshop
in Russia. The best is the Rogozhin workshop in Moscow."

In my humiliation I stepped aside, while he slowly went on his way without entering the neighbour's shop.

"Caught you up?" said the shop assistant spitefully.

"Well, you never told me about the Rogozhin workshop."

The assistant began to curse:

"It's always the quiet, slinky little creatures like him goes slithering around, knowing everything and talking too much, the snake!"

This smug, conceited man, with his effete good looks, had an aversion for muzhiks, and he once said to me:

"I'm clever, and I love clean things and good smells—incense and toilet water, and such things, and just fancy a person of my taste having to go bowing and scraping to muzhiks so's the owner'll make her five kopeks! How do you think I stomach that? What's a muzhik anyway? A stinking pelt! A louse crawling over the earth! And me...."

He stopped in vexation.

I liked the muzhiks. In each of them I sensed something enigmatic, as I had in Yakov.

Into the shop would come a lumbering figure with a robe pulled on over his sheepskin; he would take off his shaggy fur cap, cross himself with two fingers, his eyes fixed on the icon corner where the lamp gleamed, then turn away, avoiding the sight of the unsanctified icons; at last he would say, with a silent glance about him:

"Let's have one of those Psalters with a commentary."

Turning back the sleeves of his robe, he would labour long over the letters of the title page, noiselessly moving his cracked, earth-coloured lips.

"Maybe you've got something goes back earlier than this?"

"The earlier scriptures cost a thousand rubles, you know."

"I know."

Wetting his finger, the muzhik would turn the page, leaving a dark smudge on the margin. The shop assistant would stare furiously at the top of the muzhik's head and say:

"The Holy Scriptures are all the same age; the Lord doesn't change his word."

"We've heard all that. The Lord don't change it, but Nikon did."

Closing the book, the customer would silently leave the shop.

Sometimes these backwoods folk would argue with the shop assistant, and I could see that they knew the holy writings better than he did.

"Swamp pagans," muttered the assistant.

I could also see that while modern books were not to a muzhik's liking, he would look upon them with reverence and handle them gingerly, as though afraid they would fly out of his hand like a bird. This pleased me greatly, for to me a book was a marvellous thing, in which the soul of the author was confined; whenever I read a book, I released this soul, which mysteriously communed with me.

Often these old men and women offered to sell us old books dating back before the time of Nikon, the reformer; or perhaps they brought lists of such books, beautifully inscribed by hermits from Irgiz or Kerzhenetz; they also brought copies of the *Lives* unrevised by Dmitri Rostovsky, ancient icons, crosses and enamelled brass triptyches, metal-work from the maritime country, silver ladles presented by Moscow princes to tavern keepers who had won their favour. All of these things were offered clandestinely, with furtive glances about.

Both our shop assistant and the neighbour kept their eyes open for such offers, trying to outdo each other in making shrewd buys, paying no more than ten rubles for ancient treasures which they then sold for hundreds of rubles to wealthy adherents of the Old Faith.

"You keep a sharp eye on those old witches and goblins," the shop assistant would admonish me. "They carry fortunes in those packs of theirs."

Whenever he received a good offer, he would send me for the dogmatist Pyotr Vasilyevich, who had a thorough knowledge of old books, icons, and such things.

He was a tall old man with intelligent eyes, a pleasant face, and the long beard of Vasili the Blessed. Having lost the toes of one foot, he always carried a staff. Summer and winter he wore a light coat resembling a priest's robe, and a potshaped velvet cap.

Though his walk was ordinarily erect and energetic, he would allow his shoulders to droop the minute he entered the shop, would sigh softly and cross himself with two fingers in the Old Faith way, mumbling prayers and psalms. This show of old age and piety inspired the sellers of rare objects with awe and trust.

"What is your worldly business with me?" asked the old man.

"This man's brought us an icon—claims it's a Stroganov."

"A what?"

"A Stroganov icon."

"I'm a little hard of hearing; the Lord's shielded my ear against the evil spread by the followers of Nikon."

Taking off his cap, he would hold the icon horizontally, studying the surface of the painting, then examine the sides and the wooden dowels, narrowing his eyes and murmuring:

"The godless Nikonites, seeing our admiration for ancient workmanship, and taught by the devil to falsify, copy the holy images these days with rare skill—with a most amazing skill. At first sight, a painting seems a true Stroganov or Ustyug, or maybe even a Suzdal, but the light of the inner eye immediately proclaims it a falsification!"

Once he called it a falsification, the icon was sure to be rare and expensive. A series of accepted terms indicated to the shop assistant how much he might offer. I knew that the words "grief and dejection" meant ten rubles, while "Nikon-tiger" meant twenty-five; it was shameful to see how they deceived the seller, but I was intrigued by the game the old man played.

"The Nikonites, black spawn of the Nikon-tiger, are taught by the devil to do all sorts of things—here now, you'd think this foundation was genuine, and the clothes painted by one and the same hand, but just look at the face—the face was done by a different brush. The old masters, like Simon Ushakov, even if he was a heretic, painted the whole image himself—the clothes, and the face, and whittled down the surface, and laid on the foundation; but the miserable creatures of our day aren't up to it. Icon painting used to be the labour of God; today it's just a craft, true believers."

At last he would place the icon on the counter and put on his cap, saying:

"Sin on their souls!"

That meant: go ahead and buy it.

Carried away by the dogmatist's eloquence and intimidated by his knowledge, the seller would ask reverently:

"So what about the icon, worthy father?"

"The icon's the work of the Nikonites."

"But how could that be? Our grand-fathers and great-grandfathers prayed to this icon."

"Nikon lived before your great-grand-fathers."

The old man would hold up the icon before the seller's face and say impressively:

"See the gaiety of her; do you call that an icon? That's a mere picture, blind art, a caprice of the Nikonites. There's no soul in such a work! Would I be telling an untruth? I'm an old man, persecuted for the sake of the faith; soon I'll be going to meet my God. What would I gain by selling my soul?"

He would emerge from the shop onto the balcony, faint with the weakness of age, wounded by the distrust shown his judgment. The shop assistant would pay a few rubles for the icon and the seller would leave, bowing low to Pyotr Vasilyevich, while I would be sent off to the tavern for hot water. On returning I would find the old man once more bright and energetic, lovingly gazing at the purchase and saying to the assistant:

"Just look how fine and simple it's painted, with the fear of God in the lines—everything human rejected. . . ."

"Whose hand is it?" the shop assistant would ask, jumping about excitedly, with shining eyes.

"It's too early for you to know that."

"What'll a knowing man give for it?"

"I don't know. I'll show it to somebody."

"Ah, Pyotr Vasilyevich. . . ."

"And if I sell it, fifty rubles goes to you, anything over to me."

"Ah. . . ."

"None of your 'ahing'. . . ."

They would drink tea, bargaining shamelessly and studying each other with thievish eyes. It was clear that the shop assistant was completely at the mercy of the old man, and when the latter left, he would say to me:

"See you don't let the owner know anything about that deal!"

When arrangements were made to sell the icon, the shop assistant would say:

"What's new in the city, Pyotr Vasilyevich?"

The old man would pat his whiskers with a yellow hand, exposing his oily lips, and embark on an account of the lives of rich merchants, of successful business deals, of illnesses, and marriages, and orgies, and the deceiving of husbands and wives. He flipped these rich stories off the griddle with the deftness of an experienced cook, and then poured over them the syrup of his sibilant laughter. The round face of the shop assistant flushed with envious delight and his eyes filmed dreamily as he said with a sigh:

"What a life some people live, while I. . . ."

"To everyone his own fate," boomed the old man. "One has it forged by the angels with little silver hammers, another by the devil with the blunt end of an axe."

That strong, sinewy old man knew everything—the life of the entire city, all the secrets of the merchants, clerks, priests and artisans. He was as sharp-eyed as an eagle and had something in him of the wolf and the fox. I always wanted to taunt him, but was disarmed by his manner of gazing at me as if from a hazy distance. It seemed to me that he was surrounded by an abyss which would swallow up anyone who dared approach him. And I felt that he and Yakov Shumov, the stoker, had something in common.

The shop assistant was enraptured by the old man's cleverness, admitting it to his face and behind his back, but he had his moments when he too wanted to anger and offend him.

"How you pull the wool over people's eyes!" he once said to the old man, glancing up at him challengingly.

"It's only God never fools people," replied the old man with a lazy chuckle. "The rest of us live off the fools. If you can't fool a fool, what's the good of him?"

The shop assistant became angry.

"Not all muzhiks are fools; it's from the muzhiks the merchants come."

"We're not talking about the ones who become merchants. Fools never grow into swindlers. Fools are saints without any brains."

The old man kept drawling his words in a most exasperating manner. He was like a man standing on a clump of earth in the middle of a bog. It was impossible to ruffle him; either he was inaccessible to anger, or knew how to hide it.

But often he himself would start teasing me. Thrusting his face close to mine, he would chuckle into his beard and say:

"What do you call that French writer again—Pontos?"

His manner of distorting names made me furious, but I would take myself in hand and answer:

"Ponson du Terrail."

"Whose eye?"

"Don't be foolish—you're no child."

"Right you are. I'm no child. What's that you're reading?"

"Yefrem Sirin."

"Who writes better—story writers or him?"

I made no reply.

"What do the story ones write about mostly?" he persisted.

"About everything that happens."

"About dogs and horses? They also happen."

The shop assistant guffawed and I fumed. I could scarcely keep from running away, but if I attempted to leave, the assistant would shout:

"Where are you going?"

The old man kept testing my endurance:

"Now then, try to solve this riddle, long head: in front of you stand a thousand naked people—five hundred men, five hundred women, and among them Adam and Eve. How can you tell which are Adam and Eve?"

After pressing me for some time, he announced triumphantly:

"You dunce! They were created by the Lord without ever being born—which means they had no belly-buttons!"

The old man knew an infinite number of such "riddles" and kept torturing me with them.

During my first days in the shop, I had recounted to the shop assistant the stories of some of the books I had read; now I was made to rue it. The assistant retold them to Pyotr Vasilyevich, purposely distorting them and giving them a lewd interpretation. The old man helped him along by asking smutty questions; my beloved Eugénie Grandet, Ludmilla, and Henry IV were spattered with filth from their foul tongues.

I knew that they did this out of boredom rather than malice, but the knowledge made it no easier to bear. They wallowed like pigs in mud of their own creating and grunted with the pleasure of soiling beautiful things which they found strange and incomprehensible, and therefore funny.

The entire arcade, with its merchants and shop assistants lived a peculiar sort of life, finding amusement in the playing of tricks that were as stupid and puerile as they were vicious. If a muzhik who happened to be in our town for the first time should ask how to find a certain address, they would invariably send him in the opposite direction. This had become so common a practice that it ceased to be diverting. The merchants would take two rats and tie their tails together, then stand and watch them bite and claw and strain in opposite directions; sometimes they would even pour kerosene over the poor creatures and set fire to them. Or they would tie a tin can to a dog's tail; the terrified animal would rush away yelping, the can banging behind it, while the audience roared with laughter.

They played many such pranks; it was as if everyone—especially the peasants coming in from the village—existed solely for the entertainment of the market place. The merchants and their shop assistants were always seeking an opportunity to laugh at somebody, or to cause pain or discomfort, and it strange that the books I read said nothing of this perversion.

One such incident in the arcade particularly repulsed me.

There was a shop assistant in the wool and
felt shop underneath ours, whose reputation as
a glutton had spread throughout the Lower
Market. The merchant who owned the shop
boasted of his assistant's ability to consume food
as people boast of the fierceness of their dogs
or the strength of their horses. Often he would
make bets with his neighbours.

"Who'll put up ten rubles? I'll bet anyone
that Misha can gobble up ten pounds of ham
in two hours."

But no one doubted Misha's ability to
do this, so they said:

"We're making no bets, but we'll buy
the ham; let him go ahead and we'll watch the
fun."

"Only it must be ten pounds of *meat*, no
bones."

They argued a bit, lackadaisically, until
out of the dark storeroom climbed a lean,
beardless, high cheekboned fellow in a long
cloth coat all covered with tufts of wool
and tied at the waist with a red sash. Respect-

fully baring his tiny head, he turned a filmy gaze to his master's round, beefy face, overgrown with coarse stubble.

"Can you manage to put away this ham?" asked the latter.

"In how much time?" replied Misha in a thin, matter-of-fact voice.

"Two hours."

"That'll be hard."

"Not for you!"

"Add a couple of mugs of beer?" asked Misha.

"Set to!" said his master, and turned to his neighbours boastingly:

"Don't think he's starting on an empty stomach! Oh no, he made away with two pounds of bread this morning and had a good meal at noon."

They brought the ham, and a crowd of onlookers gathered, merchants all, tightly girdled in heavy winter coats which made them look like enormous weights; potbellied people, with tiny eyes buried in fat and glazed with boredom.

Thrusting their hands up their sleeves

they pressed in a tight circle about the glutton, now armed with a knife and a large loaf of rye bread. After first crossing himself quickly and repeatedly, he took his seat on a heap of wool, placed the ham on a packing case, and appraised it with blank eyes.

Then he cut off a thin slice of bread and a thick slice of ham, neatly placed the one on the other, and raised them with both hands to his mouth. He licked his trembling lips with a long tongue, like a dog's, revealing sharp little teeth; then, doglike, he clamped his jaws on the meat.

"He's begun!"

"Mark the time!"

All eyes were fixed on the glutton's face, on his champing jaws, on the shifting lumps in front of his ears, on the rhythmic rise and fall of his sharp chin, and from time to time they exchanged opinions:

"Chews like a bear."

"Ever see a bear chew?"

"Do I live in the woods? That's just a saying: chews like a bear."

"The saying is: chews like a pig."

"Pigs don't eat pig."

They laughed mirthlessly, and then some wiseacre added:

"A pig'll eat anything—even its offspring, or its own sister . . . ."

Gradually the face of the glutton turned red, his ears blue; his sunken eyes started out of their orbits and his breathing grew strident. But his chin went on moving with the same regularity.

"Hurry up, Misha—your time's running out!" they egged him on. He appraised the remaining ham uneasily, took a drink of beer, and continued chewing. The audience became more animated, glancing frequently at the watch in the hands of Misha's master. They began warning each other:

"See he don't turn back the hands! Better take the watch away from him."

"Keep your eye on Misha; he may try to slip something up his sleeve!"

"He'll never finish it on time!"

"I'll stake twenty-five rubles on it!" shouted Misha's master recklessly. "Don't let me down, Misha!"

The audience shouted encouragement, but nobody took him up on the bet.

Misha kept on chewing and chewing; his face had come to resemble the ham, and his sharp, gristly nose was whistling plaintively. It was dreadful to look at him; at any moment I expected him to burst out crying and say:

"Have mercy!"

Or perhaps, when his throat was filled with ham to the very top, he would collapse at the feet of the onlookers and die.

At last he finished the ham. Rolling his eyes at the crowd, he gasped wearily:

"Give me a drink."

His master glanced at his watch and grumbled:

"Four minutes late, the bastard!"

"Too bad we didn't take you up on your bet," teased the crowd. "You'd have lost."

"But there's no denying the fellow's a horse!"

"His place is in the circus."

"What freaks the Lord makes out of some people!"

"Well, let's have a drink of tea, eh?"

And they sailed off to the tavern like a string of barges.

I wondered what caused these solemn, lumpy people to crowd about this miserable fellow; what amusement could they find in such unwholesome gluttony?

Dark and gloomy stretched the narrow gallery of the arcade, cluttered with bales of wool, sheepskins, hemp, rope, felt boots, and harness. It was separated from the pavement by brick columns, thick and clumsy, crumbling with age and blackened by the dirt of the street. Thousands of times I seem to have counted the number of bricks and the cracks between them, so that the network of their ugly patterns sank deep into my memory.

Down the walk, unhurriedly, came the passers-by; down the street, just as unhurriedly, drove the *izvozchiki* and sleighs loaded with merchandise. A square formed by two-storeyed red brick shops lay at the far end of the street. Here the ground was strewn with packing cases, straw, and wrapping paper, all trampled into the dirty snow.

In spite of the constant movement, it seemed that all of this, including the people and horses, was static, revolving in one spot to which it was held by invisible chains. I found that this life suffered from a poverty of sound making it well-nigh inarticulate. Sleigh runners squeaked over the snow, shop doors banged, pie-vendors shouted their wares, but human voices were so dull and lifeless and identical that the ear soon ceased to hear them.

Church bells tolled funereally. Never shall I forget their dreary sound. From morning to night it floated above the market place, penetrating all of one's thoughts and feelings, covering all of one's impressions with a brassy sediment.

A cold, withering boredom emanated from everything—from the earth under its blanket of dirty snow, from the grey snow piled on the roofs, and from the meat-red bricks of the buildings. Boredom wreathed in tendrils of grey smoke from the chimneys and crawled across the low, grey, empty sky. Boredom billowed from the flanks of the horses and the nostrils of the people. It had its own peculiar odour—the dull, heavy odour of sweat, fat, smoke, hempseed oil, and greasy pies. It clamped the head like a warm, tight cap and penetrated the pores, causing a sort of intoxication that made a person want to close his eyes, roar with all his might, and rush away to bang his head against the first stone wall.

I would often study the faces of the merchants—sated, charged with thick, rich blood, stung with frost, and as immobile as though they were asleep. They often yawned, opening wide their mouths like fish cast up on the shore.

In the winter, trade was slack, and the eyes of the tradesmen lacked that cautious, calculating glint that animated and almost embellished them in the summer. Their heavy coats hindered their movements and pinned them down to the earth. The merchants spoke lazily, and argued at length when angered. It seemed to me they did this on purpose—anything to prove to each other that they were alive!

I could clearly see that they were languishing under this all-consuming boredom, and I could explain their cruel and senseless amusements only as a desperate effort to combat it.

Sometimes I would speak of this to Pyotr Vasilyevich. Although in general his attitude toward me was sarcastic and teasing, he was pleased by my love for books, and occasionally he allowed himself to speak with me seriously and instructively.

"I don't like the way the merchants live," I said.

Winding a bit of his beard about his finger, he asked:

"How can you know how they live? Or perhaps you often go to visit them? This is the street, my lad, and people don't live in the street. They trade in the street, or else go walking past in a hurry, on their way home. In the street, people are all bundled up in their clothes, and there's no knowing what they're like underneath. It's only when a person is home, within his own four walls, that he lives wide open; but how that is, you've no means of knowing."

"But their thoughts are all the same, home or here."

"Who can tell what his neighbour is thinking about?" said the old man in a weighty tone, glaring at me severely. "Thoughts are like lice—not to be counted, as the old folks say. Maybe, on coming home, a person falls on his knees and even begins weeping and praying: 'Forgive me, Oh Lord, for sinning on your holy day!' Or maybe his home is his monastery, where he lives alone with God. Every spider to its own corner—spin your web, but know your weight, so's it'll hold you."

When he spoke seriously his voice became even deeper, as though he were confiding some important secret.

"Here you are reasoning things out, and it's too early for you to do that. At your age it's not with your brains you should live, but with your eyes. In other words, see, and remember, and hold your tongue. Brains are for business; faith for the soul. It's a commendable thing to read books, but there's a limit to everything. Some people read so much that they lose their minds, and lose their God."

It seemed to me that he must be deathless. I could not imagine his changing or growing older. He loved to tell stories about merchants or robbers or counterfeiters who became famous. I had heard many such stories from grandfather, but grandfather told them better than he. But the idea of the stories was one and the same: riches were always obtained by sinning against God and man. Pyotr Vasilyev had no compassion for people, but he spoke fondly of God, sighing and dropping his eyes.

"Just see how people go fooling their God, but the Lord Jesus sees everything and weeps for them: 'Ah, my people, my people, my miserable people, it's hell that's awaiting you!'"

Once I found the courage to say to him:

"But you also fool the muzhiks."

He took no offence.

"Humph, it's little harm I do!" said he. "I just nick off four or five rubles for myself—just that and nothing more."

When he found me reading, he would take the book out of my hands, question me as to its contents, and turn to the shop assistant with a kind of suspicious amazement:

"Just look at that—he understands the books, the little monkey!"

Then he would instruct me in a precise, unforgettable manner:

"Hear my words—they'll serve you in good stead. There were two Kirills, both bishops, one of Alexandria, the other of Jerusalem. The former combatted the accursed heretic Nestor with his obscene teachings that the Virgin was a mere mortal, and therefore could not give birth to God, but gave birth to a man named Christ, saviour of the world; so it turns out we mustn't call her Mother of God, but Mother of Christ, understand? That's what you call a heresy. Now Kirill of Jerusalem fought the heretic Aria. . . ."

I was deeply impressed by his knowledge of church history. He would stroke his beard with a soft, popish hand, and say boastfully:

"I'm a general when it comes to such

things; I went to Moscow on Whitsunday to do battle with the poisonous tongues of learned Nikonites, priests and laymen. I argued with the most learned of the learned. One theologian even got a nosebleed from the tongue lashing I gave him. Just think of that!"

His cheeks flushed and his eyes shone.

Apparently he counted his opponent's nosebleed his greatest achievement, a glowing ruby in the golden crown of his glory. He spoke of it triumphantly:

"A handsome fellow he was, a very giant. There he stood in the pulpit with his nose dripping—drippity, drip—and he unaware of his shame. He was fierce as a lion, with a voice like a booming bell. And all the while I kept thrusting my words like daggers into his soul, quietlike, right between the ribs. And he warmed up to his evil heresy till he grew hot as a stove-top. Ah, those were the days!"

Our shop was frequented by other dogmatists as well. There was Pakhomi, a cushiony man with a large belly and only one eye; he had a snorting manner of speech and always wore a greasy old coat. Then there was old Lukian, little and sleek as a mouse, gentle in manner, and sprightly. He was always accompanied by a large, sullen fellow resembling a coachman—black-bearded, with immobile eyes and a blank expression on his handsome, but unpleasant face.

Almost always they tried to sell us old books, icons, censers, and church vessels; occasionally they brought someone else along—an old man or an old woman from over the Volga, who also offered objects for sale. When the deal was over, they would sit down on the counter like crows on a fence, drink tea with buns and fruit-flavoured sugar, and recount the persecutions inflicted by the Nikonite church; here a search had been made and holy books confiscated; there the police had shut down one of their chapels and taken its attendants to court, charging them with a violation of Article 103.

Article 103 was their favourite subject of conversation, but they referred to it dispassionately, as though it were inevitable, like frost in winter.

Words like police, search, prison, court, Siberia—words which they used over and over again as they spoke of their sufferings for the faith—fell like hot coals upon my heart, kindling sympathy and good will toward these old people. The books I had read taught me to admire moral courage and respect those who were unswerving in achieving their end.

I forgot the individual shortcomings of these apostles of an ancient creed, conscious only of their calm persistence, beneath which— or so it seemed to me—lay an unshakeable faith in the rightness of their cause, and a willingness to endure all hardships and sufferings for its sake.

Later, after I had met many such people among the intelligentsia, as well as among simple folk, I realized that their persistence was nothing more than the passivity of people who had nowhere to go beyond the point already reached, and who, indeed, had no desire to go further, caught as they were in a tangle of obsolete words and outworn conceptions. Their will had become enervated and incapable of developing toward the future, and had they been suddenly emancipated, they would have rolled mechanically downhill, like a stone on a mountainside. They were kept imprisoned in a graveyard of dead ideas by the lifeless force of backward-looking, and by a morbid love of suffering and persecution. Once deprived of the opportunity to suffer, they would be drained of all substance, and vanish like clouds on a fresh, windy day.

The faith for which they sacrificed themselves so eagerly and with such false pride, was unquestionably a firm faith, but it resembled old garments, so caked with dust and dirt as to be inaccessible to the ravages of time. Their thoughts and feelings had grown used to being tightly encased in prejudices and dogmas, and the fact that they became deformed and earth-bound did not disturb them in the least.

This faith-by-habit is one of the most vicious and regrettable phenomena of our life. Within the bounds of such faith, as in the shadow of a stone wall, anything that is new grows slowly—twisted and anaemic. Too few rays of love penetrate that dark faith, and too many of vengeance, malice, and envy— bloodbrothers to hate. The fire of such faith is merely the phosphorescent glow of decay.

But it took many years of hard living, the tearing down of many idols and the up-rooting of many ideas to convince me of this. Indeed, when I first met these apostles amid the dull and unscrupulous life about me, it seemed to me that they were possessed of tremendous moral strength, that they were, in fact, the salt of the earth. Almost every one of them had at some time been taken to court, thrown into prison, driven out of towns, forced to march the weary road of deportation along with other convicts. All of them lived under tension, in hiding.

However, I noticed that while they com-plained of the "hounding of the spirit" prac-tised by the Nikonites, these old men willingly, and with apparent pleasure, hounded each other.

When in his cups, the one-eyed Pakhomi loved to show off his truly remarkable memory.

He knew some of the holy books "by finger," as Hebrew scribes know the Talmud; he would point his finger arbitrarily at some word in the book and proceed from that point to recite from memory in a soft, nasal voice. He always bent his gaze on the floor, and his single eye would dart about eagerly, as though searching for something of great value. Most often he used Prince Myshetsky's book *Grapes of Russia* to demonstrate his talent. Best of all he knew "the most patient and most courageous suffering of valorous and fearless martyrs." Pyotr Vasilyev was always trying to catch him in a mistake.

"Wrong! That happened to Denis the Chaste, and not to Kiprian the Holy."

"Denis? Who ever heard of Denis? Dionysius is the name."

"Don't go quibbling over a name."

"Nor you go teaching me."

A minute later both of them, red with rage and staring each other down, were saying:

"You guzzler, you shameless snout, look at the belly on you!"

Pakhomi would reply with the detached air of one figuring sums:

"And you're a goat and a reprobate and a skirt-trailer."

The shop assistant, his hands up his sleeves, would smile maliciously and encourage these guardians of an ancient faith as though they were schoolboys.

"Go at him! That's it!"

One day the old men had a real fight. Pyotr Vasilyev delivered Pakhomi a slap in the face and forced him to take to his heels, shouting in his wake as he wearily wiped the sweat off his brow:

"Just wait and see—it's to your soul this sin will be charged! It's you that drove my hand to sin. Fie upon you!"

He took special pleasure in accusing his companions of insufficient faith, and of falling into "negativeness."

"It's all that Alexander stirs you up, that crowing cock!"

"Negativeness" irritated, and apparently frightened him, but when asked just what this teaching represented, he was not very lucid in explaining:

"'Negativeness' is the bitterest of all heresy, with God barred, and nothing but the mind. Take the Cossacks—it's only the Bible they accept, and the Bible's taken from the Germans in Saratov—from their Luther, of whom it has been said: 'Well has he been named Luther; Luther from Lucifer; Luther-the-lecher; Lecherous-Luther.' The tribe of Germans have been dubbed scapegraces, or again, shtundeezers, and all of this comes from the West, from the heretics out there."

Stamping the ground with his lame foot, he would say with cold weightiness:

"They're the ones should be ferreted out; they're the ones to be persecuted and burnt at the stake, and not us! We're Russians from time immemorial, and our faith is the true eastern faith, Russian to the very core. That other's all from the West—twisted free-thinking. From the Germans, from the French. What good could come of them? Just look back in 1812—"

In his ardour, he would forget that he was addressing a mere boy. He would grab my girdle in a strong hand, now yanking me toward him, now thrusting me away as he went on speaking with fine, youthful fervour:

"The wisdom of man wanders blindly through the forest of its own fabrications; like a ferocious wolf it wanders, inspired by the devil to the damnation of the human soul, God's highest gift. What have they thought up, these servants of the devil? Here are the teachings of the priests of negativeness: that Satan too is the son of God, elder brother to Christ Jesus—think of it! And they teach people to defy authority, to drop their work, to abandon their wives and children; nothing is demanded of man—no order—let him live as he likes, or as the devil dictates. Ah, here's that Alexander again, miserable worm. . . ."

Sometimes the shop assistant would call me away to do some task. Left alone on the porch, the old man would continue to address the emptiness about him:

"Oh, wingless souls, oh, blind puppies, to whom shall I flee for refuge?"

Then, throwing back his head and resting

his palms on his knees, he would sit gazing intently into the grey, wintry sky.

Gradually he became more kind and attentive toward me. Whenever he found me reading a book, he would pat me on the shoulder and say:

"Go ahead and read, my lad, it'll all come in handy. You seem to have a good head on your shoulders; too bad you don't listen to your elders, pitting yourself against everybody so. How far do you think such mischief will get you? No further than a convict squad, my lad. Go ahead and read your books, but don't forget—a book's a book, but you must stir your own brains. Once there was a preceptor among the *khlisti* named Daniel, who claimed no books were any good—old or new—and he took them all and dumped them in the river. No sense in that either. Then there's that evil-minded Alexander who goes muddling people up. . . ."

More and more often he kept mentioning this Alexander, and one day he entered the shop with a worried look on his face and said to the shop assistant sharply:

"Alexander is here in town—arrived yesterday. I've been looking everywhere, but haven't found him yet. Hiding away! I'll sit here for awhile. Maybe he'll drop in."

"I don't know anybody or anything!" said the shop assistant inimically.

The old man nodded his head.

"That's right—the only people you recognize are buyers and sellers—nobody else exists. You might treat me to a glass of tea."

When I returned with the large brass teakettle full of hot water, I found some other guests in the shop. One of them was the old man Lukian, grinning happily, while in a dark corner behind the door sat a stranger wearing high felt boots and a warm coat with a green girdle and a hat pulled low over his eyes. I found his face unpleasant, though he seemed a quiet, modest soul and resembled a shop assistant who had just been dismissed and was greatly cast down by the fact.

Without glancing in his direction, Pyotr Vasilyev was saying something with stern weightiness, while the stranger kept shifting his cap with a convulsive movement of his right hand: raising his arm as though about to cross himself, he would give his cap a little shove, then another, and another, until it hung precariously on the back of his head, when he would once again pull it down tight over his eyes. These convulsive movements brought back memories of the idiot Igosha, "Death-in-the-pocket."

"Many the carps that go swimming about in our muddy waters, stirring them up the more," said Pyotr Vasilyev.

The man who looked like a shop assistant asked quietly and calmly:

"Is it me you mean?"

"What if it is?"

Then the man asked once again, quietly, but soulfully:

"And what would you say about yourself, my man?"

"I speak about myself only to God— that's my business."

"Oh no, my man, it's my business as well," said the stranger forcefully and triumphantly. "Turn not your face away from the truth, nor blind your eyes with self-sufficiency, for great is the sin before God and man."

I liked the fact that he called Pyotr Vasilyev "my man," and I was moved by his quiet, exalted voice. He spoke as a good priest reads "Lord God, creator of this flesh . . .," and kept edging forward on his chair, waving his hand before his face.

"Why do you pass judgment on me? I am no more of a sinner than you."

"How the samovar's spitting and sputtering!" said Lukian scathingly, but the stranger went on, unheeding:

"Only God can know who most muddies the wellsprings of the Holy Spirit. Perhaps that is your sin, the sin of bookish, learned people. I know not books nor learning. I am but a live, simple man."

"I know that simplicity of yours—heard plenty of it!"

"It is you who muddle people's heads, you readers-of-books and pharisees, distorters of simple thoughts. As for me—can you tell me what I teach?"

"Heresy!" said Pyotr Vasilyev, but the stranger only held his palm before his face as though he were reading something written thereon and continued ardently:

"Think you that you improve the lot of the people by moving them from one sty into another? I say unto you—this is not so! I say unto you—free thyself, Oh Man! For what are home, and wife, and all of thy chattels in the face of God? Free thyself, Oh Man, from all that leads to violence and killing— from gold and silver and all riches, for they are but dust and decay! Not on the fields of this earth shall man find salvation, but in the valleys of Paradise! Deny thyself everything, I say, break all ties, all bonds, all that holds thee to this world, for it has been wrought by the Anti-Christ. I walk the straight and narrow path, unwavering in spirit, denying this dark world. . . ."

"And do you deny bread, and water, and a covering for your body? They're all of this world," put in the old man spitefully.

These words left Alexander unmoved; he continued to speak ever more soulfully, and while his voice was low, he seemed to be sounding a brass trumpet:

"Wherein lie thy riches, Oh Man? In God alone are riches to be found. Stand before Him untainted; tear from thy soul the fetters of this world and behold thy God: Thou, alone; He, alone. Thus shalt thou approach thy God, for only one path leads to Him. It has been said: seek salvation by abandoning father and mother, by abandoning everything, and by ripping out the eye that offers temptation. For the sake of the Lord, destroy thyself in substance and save thyself in spirit, that thy soul may glow with divine love for ever and ever. . . ."

"Phooh, to the dogs with you!" said Pyotr Vasilyev, getting up. "I thought you might have grown some sense since last year, but it seems you're worse than ever."

The old man hobbled out of the shop on to the porch; this alarmed Alexander, who asked hurriedly, and in some surprise:

"Are you leaving? But—how is that?"

The gentle Lukian winked consolingly and said:

"That's all right, that's all right."

But Alexander flew at him:

"You too, blabberer of this world, sowing your worthless seed. What's the sense of it? Twice-sung hallelujahs—thrice-sung. . . ."

With a smile at him, Lukian also went out on to the porch, while the stranger turned to the shop assistant to say with conviction:

"The strength of my spirit is too much for them—too much! They flee like smoke from fire!"

The shop assistant glanced up from under his brows and remarked dryly:

"I don't go in for such things."

The stranger was taken aback by these words; he pulled down his cap and muttered:

"How can you not go in for them? Such things—they demand that they be gone in for."

For a moment or so he continued to sit there in silence, with hanging head; then the old men called him, and all three of them went away without saying goodbye.

The stranger had sprung up before me like a bonfire in the night, flaring and subsiding, and impressing me with a certain rightness in his denial of this world.

At a convenient moment that evening I enthusiastically described him to Ivan Larionich, a quiet, gentle man who was head master at our workshop. When he had heard me out, he said:

"Must be a runner—that's a sect that doesn't accept anything."

"How do they live?"

"By running—wandering all over the earth. That's how they got to be called runners. They say the earth and everything on it is to be denied, and the police find them harmful and hunt them down."

My life was bitter enough, yet I could not understand how anyone could deny everything on the earth. There was much that I found dear and interesting in the life about me at that time, and soon the image of Alexander faded in my memory.

But from time to time, in bad moments, he would reappear, walking down a grey path through the fields, headed for the woods; he would push back his cap with a convulsive movement of his white hand, unsoiled by work, and mutter:

"I am walking the straight and narrow path, and I deny everything! Break all ties!..."

Alongside of him I would see my father, as he had appeared to Granny in her dreams, beech staff in hand and a spotted dog running at his heels, its tongue lolling....

XIII

The icon workshop was located in two rooms of a half-stone building. One of the rooms had three windows overlooking the yard, and two overlooking the garden; the other had one window facing the garden, another the street. The windows were small and square, and the glass, rainbow-hued with age, barely admitted the faint, dispersed light of winter.

Both rooms were filled with tables, each of which had one, or even two icon-painters bending over it. Glass balls filled with water were suspended on cords from the ceiling in order to reflect the light of the lamps in cold, white rays on the square boards of the icons.

It was hot and stuffy in the workshop. Some twenty "God-painters" from Palekh, Kholui, and Mstera were gathered here; all of them wore gingham shirts open at the collar and trousers made of ticking, and they were either barefoot, or disreputably shod. The heads of the painters were enveloped in grey clouds of makhorka smoke, and the air was heavy with the smell of drying oil, lacquer, and bad eggs. Heavily, like hot tar, flowed a Vladimir folk song:

> *Oh, shameless people that you are,*
> *To let a boy seduce a maid.*

They sang other songs, just as cheerless, but this was their favourite. The long-drawn melody did not impede one's thoughts or the movement of one's fine ermin-hair brush, tracing the lines of the drawing, colouring the folds in the saint's raiment, or adding lines of suffering to the bony faces. Through the window came the hammering of chaser Gogolev, a drunken old man with a huge purple nose. The sharp tapping of the hammer punctuated the lazy flow of the song and made one think of a worm gnawing into a tree.

No one was interested in painting these icons. Some evil genius had divided up the task into a series of set processes utterly lacking in beauty, so that it was impossible to develop any love for, or even interest in the work. The cross-eyed carpenter Panfil, a mean and spiteful man, would bring in cypress and linden boards of various size, which he had planed and glued; the consumptive lad Davidov would lay on the foundation; his friend Sorokin would prepare the board for gilding; Milyashin would make a pencil drawing of the icon, copied from some original; old man Gogolev would do the gilding and chase designs into the gold; the "plain" artists would put in the scenery and the robes of the saints, and then the icon would be stood against the wall, headless and handless, waiting for the "face" artists to make their contribution.

It was extremely unpleasant to see large icons for the iconostasis or for altar doors standing there without faces or hands or feet—

just empty robes, or armour, or the short tunics of the archangels. These brightly painted boards emanated a sense of death; the life which should have animated them was lacking, but it seemed that it had once been there, and had miraculously escaped, leaving behind only its burdensome apparel.

When the "face" artists were through with the icon, it was turned over to a workman who added enamel to the gold border design. The inscription was also done by a special master, while the finished icon was lacquered by Ivan Larionich himself, a quiet person, manager of the workshop.

He had a grey face and a grey beard, fine and silky, and grey eyes which seemed particularly deep and sad. He had a gentle smile, but somehow it seemed wrong to smile back at him. He resembled the icon of Simeon-of-the-Pillar—just as thin and wasted, and his fixed eyes had the same preoccupied expression as he gazed into the distance, beyond walls and people.

A few days after I joined the workshop, the gonfalon painter, a handsome, powerful

Don Cossack named Kapendyukhin, came to work drunk. Clenching his teeth and narrowing his beautiful, feminine eyes, he silently began pummelling everybody with iron fists. His lithe body, not very large, whirled about the workshop like a cat in a rat-infested cellar. The distraught men ran to hide in corners, from where they shouted to each other:

"Punch him!"

The "face" artist Yevgeni Sitanov managed to stun the raging bully by striking him over the head with a stool. The Cossack slumped down on to the floor; in a trice they stretched him out and bound him with towels which he gnawed and ripped with tigerish teeth. This set Yevgeni wild. He jumped up on a table and pressed his elbows against his sides ready to leap down upon the Cossack; his great weight would surely have crushed Kapendyukhin's chest, but at that moment Larionich appeared beside him in hat and coat. Shaking his finger at Sitanov, he said to the others in a quiet, matter-of-fact tone:

"Take him out into the entranceway; let him sober up."

They dragged the Cossack out of the workshop, put back the tables and chairs, and resumed their work, exchanging remarks about the strength of Kapendyukhin and prophesying that he would yet meet his death in a fight.

"It would be hard to kill him," observed Sitanov very calmly, as one speaks about work of which he has a thorough knowledge.

I glanced at Larionich and tried to guess why these strong, unruly people should obey him so readily.

He showed everyone how to work; even the most experienced masters willingly took his advice. He spent more time and words on teaching Kapendyukhin than anyone else.

"An artist—that's what you're called, Kapendyukhin. An artist must make his work lifelike, in the Italian manner. Oil painting demands a unity of warm tones, but look at all the white you've put here; that's why the Virgin's eyes are so cold and wintry. The cheeks are round and red, but the eyes don't match. And they're not placed properly—one is too close to the nose, the other shying off to the temple, so instead of the face having a pure and holy look, it's cunning and worldly. You don't put enough mind into your work, Kapendyukhin."

The Cossack screwed up his face as he listened, then smiled shamelessly with his feminine eyes and said in a pleasant voice, somewhat hoarse from drinking:

"Ekh, Ivan Larionich, this is no work for me! I was born to make music, and here I am—in a monastery."

"You can master anything if you try hard enough."

"Who am I to be doing this? It's a coachman I should be, with a troika of spirited steeds . . . ekh!. . ."

And opening wide his mouth, he let out a long, wild note:

Ekh-h-h, I'll harness up my troika swift,
Two chestnuts and a bay,
Ekh-h-h, I'll drive them through the
sparkling drift,
To my true love—away!

Ivan Larionich succumbed with a smile, adjusted the glasses on his blue, lugubrious nose, and walked away, while a dozen voices took up the song, merging in a powerful stream which seemed to lift the whole workshop into the air and rock it gently back and forth.

Full well the horses know the road
To where my lady dwells. . . .

Apprentice Pashka Odintsov stopped separating egg yolks, and with a shell in each hand, led the chorus in a fine tenor.

Intoxicated with sound, they forgot everything else, breathing in unison, filled with a single emotion. They kept one eye on the Cossack, who, when he sang, was lord and master of the workshop. At such times everyone would turn to him and follow the movements of his arms, which he waved as if about to fly away. I am certain that, had he suddenly interrupted his song to cry: "Come on—let's smash everything to bits!" all of them, including the most prim and respectable of the masters, would have turned the workshop into a heap of ruins in five minutes.

He rarely sang, but his wild songs always wielded a triumphant and irresistible power. He succeeded in rousing people, however low their spirits, so that they strained every nerve, and in the fusion of their forces became transformed into one mighty organ.

These songs made me keenly envious of the singer and of the fine power he exercised over people. My heart became filled with a quivering awe, swelling till it hurt, so that I wanted to weep and cry out to the singing people:

"How I love you all!"

The yellow, consumptive Davidov, all tufted with hair, also opened wide his mouth like a newly-hatched jackdaw.

But it was only the Cossack who started up such gay, wild songs; ordinarily the painters sang sad, long-drawn pieces like "Hard the hearts of the people," "Ah, through the woods, the little woods," or the song about the death of Alexander I: "How he came, our Alexander, to survey his gallant troops."

Occasionally, at the suggestion of Zhikharev, the best "face" painter in our workshop, they would undertake to sing church music, but the attempt was rarely successful. Zhikharev always craved for harmonies comprehensible to him alone, and kept criticizing the singing of the others.

He was a lean man of about forty-five, with a half-moon of Gypsy hair curling about his bald pate, and heavy black brows, like moustaches. A thick, pointed beard was a definite ornament to his swarthy, fine-featured, un-Russian face, but beneath his aquiline nose flared whiskers which were superfluous in view of his brows. His blue eyes differed—the left one was noticeably larger than the right.

"Pashka!" he called in his high tenor to my fellow apprentice. "Start up 'Praise ye the name.' Listen, folks."

Wiping his hands on his apron, Pashka began:

"Pr-a-a-ise ye. . . ."

"The n-a-a-a-m-e of the Lo-o-o-rd," chimed in several voices, while Zhikharev shouted excitedly:

"Lower there, Sitanov! Drop your voice to the very depths of your soul!"

Sitanov rumbled in a voice that sounded as though he were beating a barrel bottom:

"Slaves of the Lo-o-o-rd. . . ."

"Phooh, not like that! You want to let go so's the very earth will tremble and the doors and windows will open of themselves!"

Zhikharev twitched all over in some incomprehensible agitation, his amazing brows rising and falling, his voice breaking, his fingers plucking invisible strings.

"Slaves of the Lord—don't you see?" he asked significantly. "You have to feel through to the very kernel of it, right past the shell. Praise ye the Lord, ye slaves! Can't you feel that, good folk?"

"We never get that place right, as you know," commented Sitanov tactfully.

"All right then, drop it."

Somewhat offended, Zhikharev turned back to his work. He was our best master—he could paint a face in the Byzantine manner, or in the Fryazhsky or Italian tradition. Whenever Larionich accepted an order for an iconostasis he would consult

Zhikharev, who was a connoisseur of originals. All expensive copies of miracle-working icons such as the Feodorov, Smolensk, and Kazan Virgins, passed through his hands. But as he studied originals he would complain vociferously:

"They've tied us down to these originals—that's just what they've done—tied us down!"

In spite of the importance of his position in the workshop, he was more modest than others and very kind to the apprentices—Pavel and me. He was the only one who showed any desire to teach us his art.

He was difficult to understand. On the whole he was not a very cheerful person, sometimes working for a week at a time without saying a word, like a deaf-mute. He would glance at everyone with a surprised and distant look, as though seeing us for the first time. And while he was very fond of singing, he would remain silent at such times, and even seemed not to hear the others. Everybody kept looking at him and passing winks behind his back. There he sat, bending over the slanting icon board, one end on his knees, the other against the edge of the table, while his fine brush painstakingly traced the features of a face as dark and alien as his own.

Suddenly he would say, very precisely and in an injured tone:

" 'Predtecha'—what does that mean? 'Tech' in old Slavonic meant 'to go,' and 'pred' means 'before,' so 'predtecha' means a 'foregoer,' that is, a forerunner, and nothing more."

Everybody would grin silently and cast furtive glances in his direction, while his strange words kept sounding in the silence:

"He shouldn't be painted in a sheepskin, but with wings. . . ."

"Er—who might you be speaking to?" someone would venture to ask.

But he would give no answer, either not having heard the question or not deigning to reply. Then once more his words would come falling through the expectant silence:

"We ought to know their Lives, and who knows them, those sacred books? What do we know? Living along—wingless. . . . Where's the soul—the soul? That's what I'm asking you! We have the originals—that's true. But no heart."

These thoughts spoken aloud brought smiles to the lips of everyone but Sitanov. Almost always someone would remark derisively:

"Saturday he'll go on a bout."

The tall, sinewy Sitanov, a lad of twenty-two with a round face innocent of beard or even eyebrows, would gaze sadly and seriously into the corner.

I remember how Zhikharev once proclaimed in a loud, excited voice as he placed a finished copy of the Feodorov Virgin on the table:

"Finished, Blessed Mother, bottomless chalice into which shall flow tears wrung from the hearts of the people. . . ."

Then, throwing someone's coat over his shoulders, he went out—to the tavern. The young people laughed and whistled; those who were older sighed enviously; but Sitanov went up to the icon, studied it attentively, and said:

"Of course he'll get drunk. He'll get drunk from the hurt of parting with his picture. Not everyone can understand that."

Zhikharev's bouts always began on Saturday. They were not the ordinary excesses of a workman addicted to alcohol. They would begin in the following way: in the morning he would write a note and dispatch it with Pavel, then, just before the dinner hour he would say to Larionich:

"Today I'll be going to the bathhouse."

"For long?"

"Well, now—"

"Please don't make it longer than Tuesday!"

Zhikharev nodded his bald head, his eyebrows aquiver.

On returning from the bathhouse he would dress himself up like a dandy, donning a shirt front and a cravat and attaching a long silver chain to his silk vest. Then he would leave, admonishing Pavel and me:

"Take special pains in cleaning up the workshop this evening; wash the long table and scrape it down."

Suddenly everyone was in holiday mood. The painters put their tables in order, ran off to the bathhouse, and had a hurried supper; after supper Zhikharev appeared with

beer and wine and food. Behind him came
a woman of such huge proportions as to be
almost a freak. In height she was six feet
five, so that all our chairs and stools looked
like toys, and even the tall Sitanov seemed
a mere child in comparison. She was well-
built, but her bosom was bunched up high
under her chin. All her movements were slow
and clumsy. Though she was over forty, her
round, expressionless face with its enormous
horsy eyes was still fresh and smooth, and
her tiny mouth seemed painted on, like that
of a cheap doll. The woman smiled and held
out a broad, warm palm to everybody, and
made unnecessary remarks:

"How do you do. It's cold today. How
smelly your room is!—that'll be the paints.
How do you do."

It was pleasant to look at her, so strong
and serene she was, like a broad-flowing river,
but she became tedious when she spoke, always saying things that were dull and superfluous. Before enunciating a word, she would
blow out her purplish cheeks, making them
even rounder.

The young people giggled and whispered to each other:

"There's a woman for you!"

"A regular church steeple!"

With her lips pursed and her hands folded beneath her bosom, she sat down at the table behind the samovar, and looked at everyone in turn with her good-natured, horsy eyes.

Everyone treated her respectfully, the young people even standing in awe of her. A lad would stare greedily at her enormous body, but if his eyes chanced to meet her all-encompassing gaze, he would blush and hang his head. Zhikharev too treated her with esteem, using the formal mode of address, calling her "neighbour," and bowing low whenever he offered her anything from the table.

"Oh don't trouble about me," she would drawl sweetly. "How you do trouble yourself, really!"

She herself seemed never to hurry. Her arms moved only from the elbow down since she kept her elbows pressed tightly to her sides, and from her great body emanated the heady odour of fresh-baked bread.

Old man Gogolev, stuttering in ecstasy, paid her endless compliments, to which she listened with her head tilted reverently, as though he were the deacon reading the service. Whenever he became entangled in words, she would make her own contribution:

"I wasn't pretty when I was young; that all came of a matron's experience. By the time I was thirty I had grown so very attractive that even the gentles took notice, and one nobleman even offered me a coach and pair. . . ."

Kapendyukhin, who by this time was tipsy and dishevelled, flashed her a hostile glance and said roughly:

"In exchange for what?"

"For my love, naturally," explained the guest.

"Love," grunted Kapendyukhin, somewhat embarrassed. "What do you mean, love?"

"A handsome fellow like you ought to know all about love," she answered simply.

The workshop rocked with laughter and Sitanov mumbled to Kapendyukhin:

"She's a fool—or worse. It'd take an awful ache to make you fall in love with a woman like that, that's clear."

The wine had blanched his face, beaded his temples with perspiration, and lighted warning fires in his clever eyes. Old man Gogolev swung his ugly nose and wiped his bleary eyes with his fingers as he asked:

"How many babies have you had?"

"Only one."

A lamp hung above the table, another in the corner beyond the stove. Their meagre light left the corners of the workshop filled with dense shadows, out of which peered faceless figures. The blank grey patches in place of hands and faces gave rise to weird fancies; more than ever it seemed that the bodies of the saints had mysteriously taken flight, leaving their painted robes in these dim rooms. The glass balls were raised and hooked to the ceiling, where they gleamed bluely, amid clouds of smoke.

Zhikharev walked restlessly about the table, playing the host to everybody, his bald skull inclined now toward one, now toward another, his skinny fingers moving incessantly. He had grown thinner and his hawklike nose had grown sharper, throwing a long black shadow across his cheek when he stood against the light.

"Eat and drink your fill, friends," said he in his ringing tenor.

And the woman chanted, as though she were mistress of the board:

"Dear me, neighbour, why should you trouble yourself? Everybody has his own arms and his own appetite; nobody can eat more than he has a wish to."

"Enjoy yourselves, folks," cried Zhikharev excitedly. "We're all the slaves of God, friends; let's sing 'Praise ye the Name.'"

The singing was a failure; by this time everyone had grown mellow with food and vodka. Kapendyukhin had taken up an accordion, while young Victor Salautin, as grave and dark as a raven, was thrumming on a tambourine, which gave off a deep rumble accompanied by the merry jingle of the discs around the edge.

"A Russian step!" ordered Zhikharev. "Neighbour, be so kind!"

"Ah me!" sighed the woman, getting up. "How you do trouble yourself!"

She walked into the centre of the floor and stood there as solid as a watchtower. She was wearing a wide brown skirt and a yellow batiste waist and had a red kerchief on her head.

The accordion struck up a lively tune, its tiny bells chimed, the tambourine gave out heavy, dull gasps that were unpleasant to hear, as though some lunatic were sobbing and sighing and beating his head against a wall.

Zhikharev did not know how to dance. He simply shifted his feet, tapping with the heels of his shiny boots or taking little goat-leaps, out of time with the music. His feet seemed not to belong to him, and he twisted his body in a horrid way, like a wasp in a web, or a fish in a net. It was a sad spectacle. But everyone, even those who were drunk, followed his convulsions attentively, their eyes glued to his face and hands. Zhikharev's expression changed amazingly, now becoming gentle and shy, now proud, now sternly frowning. Suddenly something would astound him, causing him to cry out and close his eyes. When he reopened them he seemed overwhelmed by sadness. Clenching his fists, he would creep toward the woman and suddenly, with a stamp of his foot, fall on his knees before her, throwing wide his arms and lifting his brows as he flung her a fervent smile. She would look down at him, smile her indulgence, and warn him in her calm way:

"You'll wear yourself out, neighbour!"

She tried to close her eyes graciously, but these eyes, the size of three-kopek pieces, refused to be closed, and the resulting wrinkles only made her unsightly.

She too was a poor dancer. She could only swing her huge body slowly and shift it noiselessly from place to place. In her left hand she held a handkerchief which she waved languidly; she kept her right hand on her hip, giving her the look of an enormous jug.

Conflicting emotions flitted across Zhikharev's face as he kept circling about this statue. It seemed that it was not he alone who was dancing there, but ten men, all of them different: one was shy and modest; another crabbed and intimidating; a third was himself intimidated, and gave little cries as he tried to slip away from that colossal, repellent woman. Suddenly another appeared, baring his teeth and twisting his body like a wounded dog. This ugly dance oppressed me and roused bad memories of soldiers and cooks and laundresses and dog-mating.

I remembered Sidorov's quiet words:

"Everybody lies about such things. They're ashamed, because nobody is really in love— they just do it for fun."

I was unwilling to believe that "everybody lies about such things." What about Queen Margot? And certainly Zhikharev did not lie. I knew that Sitanov loved a streetwalker who had infected him with a shameful disease, but he had not beaten her for this, as his comrades advised; instead, he had rented a room for her and was having her doctored, and he always spoke of her with particular tenderness and diffidence.

The big woman kept swaying there, the set smile on her face, the handkerchief waving in her hand. Zhikharev still jumped convulsively about her, and as I watched them I thought: Could Eve, who deceived God Himself, have possibly resembled this horse? I began to hate her.

The faceless icons stared down from the dark walls, the dark night pressed against the windowpanes, the lamps burned low in the stuffy workshop. Above the stamping of feet and the hum of voices, I could catch the sound of water dripping quickly from the copper washbasin into the slop bucket.

How unlike the life in the books this was! How dreadfully unlike! Soon everyone became bored. Kapendyukhin pushed the accordion into the hands of Salautin and shouted:

"Come on, let's make the boards smoke!"

He danced like Vanka Tsiganok, as though he were flying through the air. Then Pavel Odintsov and Sorokin did some quick, nimble steps. Even consumptive Davidov shuffled across the floor, coughing from the dust and the smoke and the acrid smell of vodka and smoked sausage, the latter always suggesting tanned leather.

On they went, dancing, singing, and shouting, but they seemed to be making a point of having a good time, and to be putting each other through a test of sprightliness and endurance.

Sitanov, who was now tipsy, went from one to another asking in a maudlin tone:

"How could he possibly love a woman like that, eh?"

Larionich shrugged his bony shoulders and replied:

"She's no worse than many another; what's it to you?"

But soon the couple they were speaking about disappeared.

"Have they gone?" asked Sitanov as he swept the room with his sad, grey-blue eyes.

They had indeed, and Zhikharev, I knew, would return to the workshop only in two or three days' time. After a visit to the bathhouse he would go on working in his corner for some two weeks, silent, important, aloof.

Sitanov had an oldish face, not at all handsome, but with clear, kindly eyes.

He was friendly toward me, and for this I could thank my notebook full of verse. He did not believe in God, but it was difficult to determine who here, except Larionich, did believe in Him and loved Him. Everyone spoke of God with a tinge of sarcasm, as workmen refer to their employer. Yet whenever they sat down to dinner or supper they would cross themselves, and on going to bed they said their prayers. And all of them attended church on Sundays.

Sitanov, on the other hand, did none of these things, and he was considered an atheist.

"There is no God," he asserted.

"Then where does everything come from?"

"I don't know."

Once I said to him:

"How could there be no God?"

"Don't you see—God is the Heights," he replied, stretching his long arm above his head, then pointing to the floor. "Man is the Depths. Isn't that so? But it has been said: 'And

473

God made Man in His own image.' In whose image was Gogolev made?"

That baffled me. In spite of his age, the filthy, drunken Gogolyev was guilty of the sin of Onan. I also recalled Granny's sister, and Yermokhin, the soldier from Vyatka. What traces of the godhead could be discovered in these people?

"People are pigs," said Sitanov, but he immediately tried to console me:

"Don't worry, Maximich, there are good ones among them too—there are indeed."

I felt at ease with him. Whenever he did not know a thing, he would admit it frankly:

"I don't know," he would say. "I haven't thought about it."

This too was unusual. All the other people I had met felt that they knew everything and did not hesitate to hold forth on any subject.

I found it strange that, in addition to fine, soul-stirring verse, his notebook contained many rhymes that made your cheeks burn. When I spoke to him about Pushkin, he pointed to the "Gavriliada," which he had copied out.

"Pushkin? Can't take him serious. But Benediktov—there's someone you want to pay attention to, Maximich!"

Closing his eyes, he would recite softly:

> *Behold the wondrous bosom,*
> *Of this lovely lady. . . .*

For some reason he particularly emphasized three lines, reciting them with joyful pride:

> *Nor can the eagle's lancelike eye*
> *These searing portals pierce,*
> *To glimpse her inmost heart.*

"Understand?"

I was ashamed to admit that I could not understand what delighted him so.

XIV

My duties in the workshop were not very involved. In the morning, before anyone else was up, I had to heat the samovar for the painters. While they took tea in the kitchen, Pavel and I cleaned up the rooms, separated the yolks from the whites of the eggs used for mixing colours, and then I set out for the trade arcade. In the evening I had to mix paints and "observe" the masters at work. At first I "observed" with the greatest interest, but soon I realized that most of these men disliked their piecemeal jobs and were tortured by insufferable boredom.

Having little to do, I spent the evenings telling the painters about life on the steamer or stories from books, and without my noticing it I came to occupy a special place in the workshop—that of reader and storyteller.

I soon realized that none of these people knew or had seen as much as I had. In earliest childhood most of them had been clapped inside the tiny cage of their craft, where they had been confined ever since. Zhikharev alone, of all those in the workshop, had been to Moscow, and he always spoke about it with an impressive frown:

"Moscow's not to be taken in by tears. You have to keep your eyes open there!"

None of the others had been further than Shuya or Vladimir. If Kazan were mentioned, they would ask me:

"Are there many Russians there? And are there churches too?"

For them, Perm meant Siberia; they could not believe that Siberia was beyond the Urals.

"Don't they bring Urals perch and sturgeon from over there, from the Caspian Sea? That means the Urals must be on that sea!"

Sometimes I thought they were just trying to make fun of me when they said that England was beyond the ocean, and that Bonaparte came from a family of Kaluga nobles. When I told them about things I had seen with my own eyes, they rarely believed me, but they loved to listen to hair-raising tales and stories with intricate plots. Even the elders preferred fiction to truth. I could see very well that the more farfetched the tale and the more incredible the situations, the more attentively they listened. In general, they were not interested in reality; all of them cast wistful glances into the future, eager to blot out the ugliness and poverty of the present.

477

This amazed me the more in that I already had a sharp sense of the contradictions between truth and fiction. Here were these real people before me, but I found none like them in the books—no Smuries, no stoker-Yakovs, no Alexanders, no Zhikharevs, no washwomen like Natalya.

In Davidov's trunk lay a worn collection of stories by Golitsinsky, Bulgarin's *Ivan Vyzhigin*, and a volume of Baron Brambeus. I read all these books to the painters, who enjoyed them immensely.

"Reading sweeps out the noise and the quarrelling, and that's a good thing," observed Larionich.

I began to search for books; whatever I found I would read to the men. Those were memorable evenings; the workshop became filled with a midnight quiet; the glass balls hung overhead like cold white stars, their rays lighting the bald or tousled heads bending over the tables. I saw calm, thoughtful faces; sometimes someone would say a word in praise of the author or hero. These timid, attentive people little resembled their day-time selves. I loved them dearly at such moments, and they felt drawn to me. I seemed to have found my place.

"With these books it's like in the spring, when you open the windows and let in the fresh air for the first time," said Sitanov one day.

Without joining a library, a thing which none of us thought of, I had difficulty in getting books. I managed only by asking everyone for them, like a beggar. One day the fire-chief gave me a volume of Lermontov. The reading of this book was for me a vivid demonstration of the power of poetry, and the tremendous influence it wields over human beings.

I remember that Sitanov, when I had just begun to read *The Demon*, glanced first into the book and then into my face, then laid down his brush, thrust his long arms between his knees, and began to rock back and forth with a smile on his face, his chair squeaking.

"Hush, brothers," said Larionich, also putting aside his work and coming over to

Sitanov's table where I was reading. The poem filled me with poignant rapture; my voice broke and I could scarcely see the lines for the tears in my eyes. But I was even more enraptured by the hushed, cautious movement in the room; everything about me seemed to heave and swell as some powerful magnet drew these people toward me. When I had finished Part One, almost all the painters were pressing closely about the table, smiling and frowning, their arms about each other's shoulders.

"Read on, read on," said Zhikharev, pushing my head into the book.

When I had finished, he took the volume, read the title, and thrust it under his arm, saying:

"You'll have to read this again. Tomorrow. I'll take care of the book."

He walked away, locked Lermontov in a drawer of his table, and went back to work. A stillness settled down over the workshop; people quietly resumed their places; Sitanov walked over to the window and stood there motionless, his head pressed against the pane, while Zhikharev, once more laying down his brush, said sternly:

"That's what I call living, slaves of God— it is indeed!"

He shrugged his shoulders, lowered his head, and continued:

"I could even paint the Demon: a dark, shaggy body, flame-coloured wings—red lead— with face and feet and hands a palish blue, like snow on a moonlit night."

Until suppertime he kept twisting about on his stool with an unwonted restiveness, drumming with his fingers and muttering unintelligibly about the Demon, about Eve, and women, and Paradise, and about how the saints had sinned.

"That's all true!" he asserted. "If the saints sin with sinful women, a Demon would surely take pride in luring a pure soul!"

No one made reply; perhaps all of them, like me, were loath to speak. They worked reluctantly, with one eye on the clock, and when the hour of nine struck, everyone stopped at once.

Sitanov and Zhikharev went out into the yard, where I joined them. There, glancing up at the stars, Sitanov said:

> *Caravans wandering*
> *Through nebulous spaces.*

"To think of finding words like that!"

"I don't remember any words," commented Zhikharev, shivering in the sharp cold. "I don't remember anything, but I see it all. A strange thing, that a man should make you pity the devil! For you *do* pity him, don't you?"

"Yes, you do," agreed Sitanov.

"Just see what it means to be a man!" exclaimed Zhikharev unforgettably.

When he returned to the entranceway, he warned me:

"Don't speak to anyone in the shop about that book, Maximich. It's sure to be a forbidden one."

I was overjoyed: so this was the kind of book the priest had asked me about at confession!

Supper proceeded listlessly, without the usual noise and conversation, as though something stupendous had occurred which everyone wished to ponder. After supper, when all had retired, Zhikharev took out the book and said to me:

"Here, read it again. Slowly, without any hurry."

Several of the men silently rose from their beds and came over to the table, squatting about it, undressed, their legs drawn up under them.

And once again, when I had finished reading, Zhikharev said, tapping the table with his fingers:

"That's living for you! Ekh, Demon, Demon . . . how did such a thing ever happen to you, brother?"

Sitanov leaned over my shoulder to read some lines that caused him to laugh with delight and remark:

"I'll copy them out in my notebook."

Zhikharev rose and took the book to his table, but suddenly he halted and said in a hurt, agitated voice:

"We live along like blind puppies, what for?—nobody knows; unwanted by God or Demon. Do you call us slaves of God? Job was a slave, but God Himself spoke with him. And with Moses. But who do we belong to?"

He locked up the book and began to put on his clothes, calling to Sitanov:

"Coming to the tavern?"

"I'm going to see my girl," answered Sitanov quietly.

When they had gone, I lay down on the floor near the door next to Pavel Odintsov. For some time he kept sniffling and tossing about, and suddenly he began to cry softly.

"What's the matter?"

"I feel so sorry for them," he said. "I've been living with them almost four years now; I know them all."

I too pitied these people. We lay awake for a long time, discussing them in whispers, recalling the goodness and kindness lodged in each of them, and discovering qualities that deepened our childish pity.

Pavel Odintsov and I became fast friends; later he developed into a first-class master, but did not work at his craft for long. By the time he was thirty he had become a confirmed drunkard. Some time later I saw him, a tramp, at the Khitrov Market in Moscow, and not long ago I heard that he died of typhus. It is dreadful to remember how many fine people have perished to no good purpose during my lifetime. People everywhere become worn out and die; that is only natural. But nowhere do they become worn out so swiftly and so senselessly as in Russia. . . .

At that time Pavel was a round-headed lad, some two years older than myself. Besides being quick, clever, and honest, he possessed artistic talent. He had a knack for drawing cats, dogs, and birds, and made witty cartoons of our painters, always representing them as feathered folk: Sitanov was a mournful woodcock perched on one leg; Zhikharev was a rooster with a ragged comb and bald brow; the ailing Davidov was a sad little pewit. His best cartoon was that of Gogolev, the elder chaser, whom he represented as a bat with large ears, a monstrous nose, and tiny feet with six claws on each. From out of his round, dark face glanced the white circles of his eyes, with pupils like lentils standing on end, giving him an alert, scoundrelly look.

The painters took no offence when shown the cartoons, but everyone found the cartoon of Gogolev repulsive, and they said to the artist, very earnestly:

"You better tear it up, or the old man may see it and make things hard for you."

The old man, dirty and foul and forever drunk, was importunately pious, indefatigably vicious, a talebearer in the service of the shop assistant who, in view of the fact that the mistress intended marrying him to her niece, already considered himself head of the establishment and all the people in it. Everyone feared and hated him, and for that reason they feared Gogolev as well.

Pavel harried the chaser unceasingly, as though his sole aim was to keep Gogolev from enjoying a moment's rest. He found in me a worthy accomplice, and everyone was diverted by our efforts, which were almost always harsh and crude. But the painters said:

"Watch out, fellows! Kuzma-the-beetle will get you yet!"

"Kuzma-the-beetle" was the shop assistant's nickname at the workshop.

But we paid no heed to these warnings. Often we put paint on the chaser's face while he slept, and once when he lay in a drunken stupor, we gilded his spongelike nose. For three days he was unable to get the gold out of the pores. But whenever we threw the old man into a rage I recalled the steamer, and the little soldier from Vyatka, and my conscience gave me no peace. In spite of his age, Gogolev was no match for us; he often caught us off our guard and thrashed us soundly. After each thrashing he would complain to the mistress.

She too was habitually tipsy, and for that reason always jolly and good-natured. She would try to frighten us by banging the table with her puffy hands and shouting:

"Up to your mischief again, you devils! He's an old man; you ought to show him respect! Who poured that ink into his wine-glass?"

"We did."

The mistress blinked.

"Heavens above, they even admit it, the little wretches! Don't you know that old folks must be respected?"

She shooed us away, and that evening complained to the shop assistant.

"How's that?" he said to me sternly. "You read books, even the Bible, and yet you're always up to something. Watch out, brother!"

The mistress was a lonely soul and very pathetic. Sometimes, having taken too much liquor, she would sit at the window and sing:

No one cares about my sorrow,
No one knows about my grief,
No one loves me, no one pities,
No one offers me relief.

She would sniffle and wail in a voice wobbly with age: "Oo-o-o-o-o!"

One day I saw her start downstairs with a jug of milk. Suddenly her knees gave way and she collapsed, continuing her descent in bumps from step to step, the jug firmly clutched in her outstretched hands, the milk spilling over her dress, while she berated the jug.

"Look how you're spilling, you devil, you!"

She was not fat, but soft and flabby, like an old cat whose mice-catching is a thing of the past, and who, heavily sated, can only lie and purr at fond remembrances of feasts and conquests.

"Hm-m," Sitanov would muse with a frown. "This was once a big business and a fine workshop, with a clever man at the head. But now it's all gone to the dogs, and the rewards are all pouring into the lap of that Kuzma-the-beetle. How we worked! And all for him, it turns out. The very thought's enough to make something snap inside you, so that all you want to do is drop work and climb up on the roof, to lie gazing up at the sky all summer long."

Pavel Odintsov became infected by Sitanov's ideas. Puffing at a cigarette in the manner of the grownups, he would philosophize on God, drunkenness, women, and the futility of labour: some people spent all their time making things which others only destroyed, unappreciative of their value.

At such moments his sharp, attractive little face would look old and wrinkled. Most often these thoughts would come to him as he sat on his bed on the floor, his arms clasped about his knees, his eyes staring through the blue squares of windows at the stars in the wintry sky, and at the shed roof, now sagging under a weight of snow.

The painters snored and muttered in their sleep; someone garbled words in a nightmare; Davidov coughed away the remnants of his life up on the top bunk. Over in a corner the "slaves of God" Kapendyukhin, Sorokin, and Pershin sprawled side by side, shackled by sleep and drunkenness. Down from the walls stared the icons, faceless, handless, footless. The stench of oil, rotten eggs, and the filth festering in the cracks of the floor, made breathing almost impossible.

"How I pity them all!" whispered Pavel. "Oh Lord!"

I too was becoming ever more oppressed by this pity. Both of us, as I have already said, found these men good, but the life they lived was bad, unworthy of them, and unbearably dull. When the Lenten bells chimed drearily, and the blizzards blew, making houses and trees and everything on earth shudder and wail and weep, then gloom, like a leaden curtain, settled down over the workshop, suffocating the painters, smothering the life out of them, driving them into taverns, or the arms of women, who, like vodka, helped them to forget.

On such evenings reading did not help, and Pavel and I resorted to other means of diversion. Making up our faces with paint and soot, and adding wigs and whiskers of hemp, we acted out various comedies of our own improvisation, heroically fighting the gloom, and forcing people to laugh. I remembered the *Legend of How Peter the Great Was Rescued by a Soldier,* and reduced the story to dialogue form. We climbed up on Davidov's bunk and acted it out, gaily lopping off the heads of imaginary Swedes. Our audience roared.

The painters especially enjoyed the legend of the Chinese devil Tsingi Yu-tong. Pashka played the part of the unfortunate devil who had conceived the idea of doing good, while I played everything else: people of both sexes, stage properties, a Good Spirit, and even the stone on which the Chinese devil rested disconsolate after each unsuccessful attempt to do good.

The audience laughed, and I was painfully surprised to discover how easily people could be amused.

"Ekh, you clowns! You caperers!" they would shout at us.

But the more we played, the more insistent became the thought that grief was more accessible to these people than joy.

Merriment is never long-lived among us, and is not valued for its own sake, but is evoked with great effort as an antidote for the brooding Russian heartache. There is nothing reliable about a merriment which has no life of its own, nor any will to live, but comes only to lighten dreary days.

And only too often does Russian merriment turn unexpectedly and imperceptibly into cruel drama. In the midst of a dance, wherein the dancer seems weaving himself free of his bonds, the beast in him suddenly breaks loose, and in bestial anguish throws itself at everyone and everything, roaring, raging, shattering. . . .

This forced merriment, roused by outside impulses, irritated me to such an extent, that in a frenzy of self-forgetfulness I would begin to recount and act out whatever my fancy conjured up on the spur of the moment. How desperate was my desire to excite in these people a free and spontaneous joy! And my efforts were not wholly without success; the painters praised and marvelled, but the gloom which I seemed to have dispersed, would only gather again, thickening and pressing down as heavily as before.

The mousy Larionich would say gently:

"What a little rogue you are, Lord bless you!"

"A real comfort!" confirmed Zhikharev. "Why don't you go join a circus, or perhaps a theatre? You ought to make a fine clown."

Of all the people in the workshop, only Kapendyukhin and Sitanov went to the theatre, and they only at Yuletide and Shrovetide. The elder masters advised them to atone for this sin by dipping themselves in the Jordan through the baptismal hole in the ice. Sitanov kept saying to me:

"Drop all this and become an actor."

And he would give me a moving account of the sad *Life of Yakovlev, the Actor.*

"You could live like that too!"

He loved to tell about Marie Stuart, calling her "the vixen," and he was particularly enthusiastic about *The Spanish Noble.*

"Don Cesare de Bazan was the noblest of the noble, Maximich. Really exceptional!"

He himself had something of *The Spanish Noble* in him. One day three firemen beat up a muzhik out on the square in front of the watchtower. A crowd of some forty people watched the sight, goading on the firemen. Sitanov rushed into the fray, beat off the assailants with his long arms, lifted up the muzhik and thrust him into the crowd, shouting:

"Take him away!"

He himself remained to fight it out, one against three.

The firehouse was only a dozen steps away, so that the firemen could easily have called for help and given Sitanov a thorough trouncing. But fortunately for him they took to their heels.

"Sons of dogs!" he cried after them.

On Sundays the young people went out to the timberyards beyond the Peter and Paul Cemetery to engage in fisticuffs with the members of the Sanitary Brigade and muzhiks from the surrounding villages. The brigade put up a famous fighter—a Mordovian giant with a pinhead and sore eyes. He would take up his stand in front of his supporters, his feet planted wide apart, and cry out good-naturedly to the town fellows as he wiped his running eyes on his dirty sleeve:

"Come on if you're coming, before I catch a chill!"

Kapendyukhin always fought him for our side, but the Mordovian invariably got the better of him.

"What am I worth if I can't lick that fellow?" Kapendyukhin would cry, panting and bloody.

That finally became the sole aim of his life. He went into strict training: he gave up drinking, ate mostly meat, rubbed himself down with snow every evening before going to bed, and crossed himself with two-pood weights to develop muscle. But none of these things helped. Finally he sewed pieces of lead into his gloves and boasted to Sitanov:

"This'll be the end of the Mordovian!"

"Take them out, or I'll give you away before the fight," Sitanov warned him sternly.

Kapendyukhin did not believe he would do it, but just before the fight Sitanov suddenly called out to the Mordovian:

"Wait a bit, Vasili Ivanovich! First I'll fight Kapendyukhin!"

The Cossack reddened and shouted:

"I'm not fighting with you! Get out of here!"

"Yes you are," said Sitanov, fixing him with a compelling glance as he advanced. Kapendyukhin hesitated for a minute, then tore off his gloves, thrust them into the breast of his coat, and quickly walked away.

This was an unpleasant surprise for both sides, and a respectable-looking man said to Sitanov angrily:

"That's against the rules, fellow, settling private scores in a public fight."

People shouted at Sitanov from all sides; for a long time he remained silent, then said to the respectable-looking man:

"And what if I've stopped a murder?"

The respectable-looking man immediately understood; he even doffed his cap, saying:

"In that case, here's a thank-you from our side."

"Only don't go talking about it, if you please."

"Why should I? Kapendyukhin's a rare fighter and it gets a man's dander up to be always licked—we can understand that. But from now on we'll take a look at his gloves before a fight."

"That's your business."

When the respectable-looking man had gone away, our side began expostulating with Sitanov.

"What did you do that for, you fool? The Cossack would have licked him, and now we're the ones who are licked."

We chided him long and persistently, taking pleasure in it.

Sitanov only sighed and said:

"Ah, the scum. . . ."

Then, to everyone's surprise, he challenged the Mordovian. The latter took up his position, flourished his fists, and called out jokingly:

"A little tussle—just to warm up!"

Several of the bystanders grabbed hands and pushed against those standing behind to form a wide circle.

Round and round sparred the fighters, eyes glued to each other's faces, right fists extended, left fists clenched against their chests. Experienced onlookers immediately noted that Sitanov's arms were longer than the Mordovian's. Everything grew still except for the crunching of the snow under the feet of the fighters. Someone, unable to stand the strain, muttered in greedy complaint:

"High time they lit into each other."

Sitanov swung his right, the Mordovian raised his left in defence, and received a direct blow from Sitanov's left in the pit of his stomach. He retreated with a grunt, remarking with approval:

"You're no fool, young as you are."

Then they went at it, swinging hard at each others' chests. In a few minutes both sides were shouting excitedly:

"At him, God-painter! Decorate his mug for him!"

The Mordovian was much stronger than Sitanov, but less agile; unable to swing as quickly, he took two or three blows to every one he delivered. But the pummelling seemed to have little effect on him, for he kept roaring and mocking his opponent, and then all of a sudden, with a powerful upward shot, he knocked Sitanov's right arm out of the socket.

"Pull them apart. A draw!" shouted several voices at once. The onlookers rushed forward and separated the fighters.

"He's not very strong, the God-painter, but he's quick," said the Mordovian good-naturedly. "He'll make a fine fighter yet, and I'm not ashamed to say it."

The youngsters who had been watching began a general free-for-all, while I led Sitanov off to a bonesetter. What he had done raised him even higher in my estimation and increased my fondness and respect for him.

He was very just and honest, seeming to feel that this was merely his duty; but the belligerent Kapendyukhin made fun of him.

"Ekh, always puffing yourself up, Sitanov!" he would say. "You've polished up your soul like a samovar, and go vaunting it about— just see what a shining light I am! But it' a brass soul you've got, and you're a bore in the bargain!"

Sitanov would go right on working, or copying Lermontov's verse into his notebook. He spent all his free time copying, and once I said to him:

"But you've got money. Why don't you go buy yourself the book?"

"No, it's better when you copy it out in your own hand," he replied.

While waiting for the ink to dry, having
nished a page of his elaborate caligraphy,
e would read softly:

> *Unregretting and unfeeling,*
> *From this earth you turn away,*
> *Where all happiness is fleeting,*
> *And all beauty for a day.*

"That's the truth," he would say, screw-
ng up his eyes. "Ekh, how well that poet
ould see the truth!"

I was amazed by the way Sitanov treated
apendyukhin. Whenever the latter was tipsy,
e would start a fight with Sitanov, who would
atiently try to dissuade him:

"Keep away! Don't touch me."

In the end Sitanov would begin to beat the
runk mercilessly, so mercilessly, in fact, that
ne other painters, who usually were only too
illing to watch a fight, would step in and
ull the friends apart.

"If we don't stop Sitanov in time, he'll
eat him to death, without a thought for
imself," they would say.

Even when he was sober, Kapendyukhin was forever plaguing Sitanov, mocking his passion for poetry and his unfortunate love affair, and making smutty, but futile effort to rouse his jealousy. Sitanov would listen to the Cossack's teasing without replying or taking offence, sometimes even laughing along with Kapendyukhin.

They slept next to each other, and would lie awake whispering until late at night.

These nocturnal conversations intrigued me. I wondered what two people, so utterly different, could find to talk about in such an amiable way. But whenever I approached them, the Cossack would say:

"What are you doing here?"

And Sitanov would ignore me.

But once they called me over.

"Maximich," said the Cossack, "if you had a lot of money, what would you do with it?"

"Buy books."

"And what else?"

"I don't know."

"Ekh!" sighed Kapendyukhin in disappointment, turning away.

"See?" said Sitanov calmly. "Nobody can tell—neither the old nor the young. I'm telling you that riches alone don't mean a thing. It's what goes with them."

"What were you talking about?" I asked.

"Nothing much. Just killing time—couldn't sleep," answered the Cossack. But later they allowed me to listen to their talk, and I discovered that they spent their nights discussing the same things people discuss in the daytime: God and justice and happiness, the cunning and stupidity of women, the greediness of the rich, and the fact that life in general is an incomprehensible muddle.

I was always an eager listener; their conversations stirred me deeply, and I was glad they agreed that life was bad and should be made better. But at the same time I saw that the mere desire to make it better placed no obligation on anybody, nor did it change the life in the workshop or the relation of the painters to each other. All this talk, while giving me some insight into life, revealed it as a kind of dreary emptiness in which people, like dry leaves on the surface of a wind-swept pond, drift about without aim or purpose, they themselves resenting and denouncing the aimlessness of their drifting.

The painters were always boasting, or repenting, or blaming someone, starting fierce quarrels over mere trifles and hurting each other deeply. They spent their time guessing what would happen to them in the next world, while here, near the slop bucket by the door, one of the floor boards had rotted away, leaving a hole through which damp, cold air reeking of mouldy earth rose to freeze our feet. Pavel and I stopped up the hole with straw and rags. Often the men talked about putting in a new floor board, but the hole kept getting larger and larger. On stormy days the wind blew through it like a trumpet, causing coughs and colds. The metal disc on the ventilation window had a horrid squeak which made the men curse it in the foulest language; but when I oiled it, Zhikharev cocked his ear, and said:

"It's all the drearier without that squeak."

On returning from the bathhouse they would throw themselves down on their filthy beds. Dirt and stench went unnoticed here. There were innumerable trifles making life miserable that might easily have been removed, but nobody made the effort.

Often they would say:

"Who has any pity for people? Nobody, not even God."

But when Pavel and I washed the dying Davidov, who was being tortured by filth and insects, they made a laughingstock of us, calling us bath-attendants, offering us their own shirts to de-lice, and in general mocking us as if we were doing something shameful and very funny.

From Christmas until Lent Davidov lay up on his bunk coughing continuously, spitting down great blobs of blood and mucus that missed the slop bucket and fell on the floor. At night he woke us up with his delirious shrieks.

Almost every day they said:

"We'll have to take him to the hospital."

But first it turned out that Davidov's passport needed renewing and therefore he would not be accepted in the hospital; then he seemed to be feeling better; finally they said:

"What difference does it make? He'll be dying soon anyway."

"Yes, it'll be soon," promised the sick man himself.

He was a quiet humourist who also did his best to disperse the gloom of the workshop. Hanging his dark, cadaverous face over the edge of his bunk, he would announce in a wheezy voice:

"Listen to the voice of him who hath ascended to the upper bunk, good people!"

And then he would solemnly recite some gruesome nonsense like:

> *Perched up here upon my bunk,*
> *No disturbance do I make,*
> *Though the roaches chew my flesh*
> *When I sleep and when I wake.*

"He doesn't lose heart!" said his hearers admiringly.

Sometimes Pavel and I would climb up to him and he would greet us with forced merriment:

"What can I be treating you to, good friends? How would you like a nice, fresh spider?"

Death came very slowly, and this wore on his nerves.

"I just can't seem to die!" he would say with undisguised vexation.

His fearlessness in the face of death frightened Pavel, who would wake me up at night to whisper:

"Maximich! Perhaps he's died.... He'll go and die some night like this, with us lying down here. Oh Lord, how I fear the dead!"

Or else he would say:

"Why did he ever have to live? Dying before he's twenty!"

One moonlit night he woke me up to say, his eyes bulging with terror:

"Listen!"

Up on his bunk Davidov could be heard breathing hoarsely and muttering quickly, but distinctly:

"Here, let's have it, here. . . ."

Then he began to hiccough.

"He's dying, honest to God, you'll see!" whispered Pavel feverishly.

All day long I had carted snow from our yard out to the fields; I was dead tired and wanted nothing so much as to sleep.

"For the love of Christ, don't sleep," implored Pavel. "Please don't."

Suddenly jumping to his knees he shouted wildly:

"Get up! Davidov's died!"

Some of the men woke up, and a few of them even got out of bed, asking irritably what had happened.

Kapendyukhin climbed up to the bunk and said in amazement:

"Sure enough, looks like he's dead—though there's still a little warmth in him."

Everyone grew quiet. Zhikharev crossed himself, pulled his blanket tighter, and said:

"Well, may his soul rest in peace!"

"Better carry him out into the entrance-way," suggested someone.

Climbing down, Kapendyukhin glanced through the window and said:

"Let him lay there till morning—he was never in the way even when he was alive."

Pavel buried his head in the pillow and sobbed.

Sitanov never even woke up.

XV

The snow melted on the fields and the wintry clouds melted in the sky, falling to earth in wet snow and rain; the sun took more time to make its daily round, the air grew warmer, and it seemed that spring had already arrived, but was hiding playfully somewhere in the fields outside of town before it came rushing in. The streets were covered with red-brown mud, little streams went gurgling alongside of the pavements, and sparrows hopped merrily about the thawed patches on Arestanskaya Square. People grew restive, like the sparrows. Above and beyond the murmur of spring sounded the Lenten bells, ringing almost uninterruptedly from morning to night, rocking the heart with soft little jolts. In their chiming, as in the speech of old men, some hurt was hidden; it was as though the bells kept saying, with cold melancholy:

"Lo-o-o-ng, long ago; lo-o-o-n-g. . . ."

On my name day the workshop presented me with a little icon, beautifully painted, of Alexei, Man-of-God. Zhikharev made a long and solemn speech which I shall never forget:

"And who might you be?" he said, raising his brows and tapping on the table with his fingers. "Only a little boy, an orphan of thirteen years, yet I, almost four times your age, commend you and praise you for not turning away from life, but facing it squarely. That's the way; always face things squarely."

He spoke about the slaves of God and of His servants, but I never came to understand the difference between the slaves and the servants, nor do I think he himself saw this difference. His speech was dull, and the men made fun of him, while I stood with the icon in my hands, deeply moved and embarrassed and not knowing what to do. At last Kapendyukhin shouted to the orator in exasperation:

"Sounds like a service for the dead. Better stop it—his ears are turning blue."

But then he himself slapped me on the shoulder and praised me.

"The best thing about you is that you're kin to everybody. I like that in you, but it makes it hard to beat you or scold you, even when you deserve it."

Everybody turned glowing eyes on me, making kindly fun of my embarrassment; if the ceremony had lasted much longer I would probably have burst into tears from the sheer joy of feeling that I meant something to these people. Yet that very morning the assistant in the shop had said to Pyotr Vasilyev, nodding toward me:

"A nasty fellow—can't do a thing."

I had gone to the arcade that morning as usual, but in the early afternoon the assistant had said to me:

"Go home and shovel the snow off the roof of the barn and pack it in the cold-storage cellar."

He had not known that it was my name day; I thought nobody knew.

When congratulations were over in the workshop I changed my clothes, ran out into the yard, and climbed up on the roof of the barn to shovel off the snow that had fallen in such quantities that winter. But in my excitement I forgot to open up the cellar door, which became buried under the snow I shovelled down. When I saw my mistake I immediately began to dig out the door, but the snow was wet and hard-packed, and the wooden shovel I used, there being no metal one, broke under its weight. Just at that moment the shop assistant appeared in the gateway, confirming the Russian saying: "Joy is always trailed by sorrow."

"Hm," said the assistant angrily, coming over to me. "A fine workman you are, devil take you! I'll give you a crack on that crazy dome of yours. . . ."

He picked up the broken handle of the shovel and swung it at me, but I ducked and said angrily:

"I never hired out as your yard cleaner!"

He hurled the stick at my feet; I grabbed up a lump of snow and struck him full in the face. Sputtering, he ran away, while I aban-

doned my task and returned to the workshop.
A few minutes later the shop assistant's betrothed, a fidgety young woman with a vapid,
pimply face, came running downstairs.

"Maximich! You're wanted upstairs!"

"I'm not going," I said.

"What's that—you're not going?" asked
Larionich in quiet wonder.

I told him what had happened; with a
worried frown he himself went upstairs, saying to me in an undertone:

"That's being a bit bold, my lad."

The workshop buzzed with imprecations
directed at the assistant.

"They'll surely get rid of you now," said
Kapendyukhin.

That did not frighten me. My relations
with the assistant had long been strained to
breaking point. He hated me with a stubborn,
growing hate that I reciprocated. But I was
baffled by the strange way he treated me.

He would intentionally scatter coins on
the floor of the shop so that I would find them
when I swept up. I always dropped them
into the cup kept on the counter for beggars.

When at last I guessed why he dropped them, I said to him:

"Nothing will come of throwing me those coins."

Taken off his guard, he reddened and shouted at me:

"How dare you try to teach me! I know what I'm doing!" But presently he added: "What makes you think I do it on purpose? They just happen to fall on the floor."

He forbade my reading books in the shop, saying:

"That's not for the likes of you. Or maybe you think of becoming a theologian, eh? You sponger!"

He continued his efforts to catch me in the theft of a coin, and I realized that if a twenty-kopek piece should roll into some crack while I was sweeping the floor, he would accuse me of having stolen it. Once more I suggested that he drop the game he was playing with me, but that very day, on returning from the tavern with a teakettle full of boiling water, I overheard him saying to our neighbour's shop assistant:

"Get him to steal a Psalter—soon we'll be getting in some new ones—three boxes full."

I realized that they were talking about me, for when I entered, they both showed signs of embarrassment.

The neighbour's assistant, a weak, emaciated creature with cunning eyes, was employed only from time to time, for while he was considered a good assistant, he was a drunkard. Whenever he went off on a bout, his master would dismiss him, only to take him on again. Outwardly humble, obeying his master's slightest wish, he always kept a supercilious smile tucked away in the corner of his mouth and loved to make pointed remarks. His breath was tainted, like that of people with bad teeth, though his teeth were white and sound.

An experience I had had with him some time earlier gave me additional reason to suspect him of conspiring with our assistant against me. One day he had approached me with an affectionate smile, then suddenly had knocked off my cap and seized me by the hair. We began to fight. He forced me from the gallery into the shop, where he tried to push me against some large icons standing on the floor. Had he succeeded, I would unquestionably have smashed the glass, broken the carvings, and damaged the expensive paintings. Since he had little strength, I easily overcame him, and to my great surprise, this bearded man then began to cry bitterly, sitting on the floor and nursing his injured nose.

On the following morning, when we were alone, both our masters having gone away, he had said to me amicably, as he rubbed the swelling on the bridge of his nose and under one eye:

"Do you think I went after you of my own accord? I'm no fool; I knew you would get the better of me. I'm a weakling, and a drunk. The master ordered me to do it. 'Give him a thrashing,' says he, 'and see that he does as much damage as possible in their shop. That will be a good loss for them.' As for me—never would have done it of my own accord. Just see what a mug you've given me!"

I believed him, and began to feel sorry for him. I knew that he was half starved and lived with a woman who beat him. But still I asked him:

"If they should tell you to poison a person, would you do it?"

"He'd make me," replied the man softly, with a piteous smile. "He's—capable."

Another time he had said to me:

"I haven't a kopek to my name; there's nothing in the house to eat, and my old woman keeps nagging me. If you'd steal an icon out of your storeroom, I'd go and sell it. Would you do that for me? Or maybe a Psalter?"

Recalling the bootshop and the church watchman, I thought to myself: this fellow would be sure to tell on me. But I had not the heart to refuse him. I gave him an icon; for some reason it seemed too great a crime to steal a Psalter costing several rubles. Yes, strange as it may seem, all of our morals are tinged by commercial calculation. Our Criminal Code, with all its naive sanctity, exposes this little secret, behind which lurks the enormous wrong of private property.

I remembered this theft of the icon when I heard our shop assistant urging this pitiable fellow to get me to steal a Psalter, and was frightened. It was clear that our assistant knew of the generosity I had displayed at his expense; in other words, the neighbour's man had told on me.

The cheapness of showing magnanimity at another's expense and the pettiness of their plot roused my indignation and a sense of disgust with myself and everyone else. I suffered tortures until the arrival of the new books. At last they came. While I was unpacking them in the storeroom, the neighbour's man joined me and asked me for a Psalter.

"Did you tell my master about the icon?" I asked him.

"Yes," he admitted abjectly. "I can't keep secrets, brother."

I was stunned. I sat down on the floor and stared at him while he muttered hastily, looking distraught and desperately pathetic:

"Your master guessed, or rather, mine guessed and told yours. . . ."

I felt that I was done for; these people had trapped me, and now I would surely be sent off to a colony for juvenile delinquents.

If that were the case, nothing else mattered. If I had to drown, let it be in deep water! I thrust a Psalter into the shop assistant's hand; he hid it in his coat and went away, but presently he returned and the Psalter fell at my feet.

"I can't take it! You'll be the ruin of me," he said as he walked away.

I did not grasp the meaning of his words. Why should I be the ruin of him? But I was greatly pleased that he had not taken the book. After that, our little shop assistant began to regard me with even greater hostility and suspicion.

All this came back to me as Larionich climbed the stairs. Presently he returned, more glum and quiet than ever, and just before supper, when he and I were alone, he said to me:

"I tried to get them to release you from working in the arcade and let you remain in the workshop. But I failed. Kuzma wouldn't hear of it. He's dead set against you. . . ."

I had another enemy living in this house— the shop assistant's betrothed, a playful damsel.

All the young men in the workshop played with her; they would wait for her in the entrance-way and maul her. She took no offence, merely squealing softly, like a puppy. From morning to night she chewed the cookies and lozenges with which her pockets were always stuffed. Her vapid face with its roving grey eyes was an unpleasant sight. She was always asking Pavel and me riddles with suggestive answers, or telling us tongue-twisters that ran together to form obscene words.

One of the elder painters once said to her: "It's a shameless lass you are!"

To which she blithely answered, quoting a ribald song:

> *If a maiden is too shy,*
> *All the boys will pass her by.*

Never before had I seen such a girl; I found her loathsome, and her crude approaches frightened me. Seeing that I repulsed them, she became all the more insistent.

One day when Pavel and I were helping her steam pickle kegs down in the cellar, she said to us:

"Would you like me to teach you how to kiss, boys?"

"I know how better than you," answered Pavel with a short laugh, while I advised her, not very politely, to go kiss her own young man. This made her angry.

"You boor! That's what a girl gets for trying to be nice to you! You turn up your nose at her!" And she added, with a shake of her finger: "Just you wait! I won't forget this!"

Pavel added, in support of me:

"That young man of yours will give it to you if he hears the tricks you're up to!"

She wrinkled up her pimply face superciliously.

"I'm not afraid of him! With a dowry like mine I can get dozens of husbands, lots better than him! It's only till her wedding day a girl has a chance to have a good time."

And she began flirting with Pavel, while from that day on she kept telling tales on me.

It became ever more irksome to work in the arcade. I had read all the religious books and had grown tired of the arguments of the dogmatists, ever repeating one and the same thing. The only attraction that remained was Pyotr Vasilyev, with his knowledge of the dark flow of human life and his ability to express himself in such an interesting, ardent manner. Sometimes I imagined that the prophet Yelisei must have wandered thus about the earth, lonely and vindictive.

But whenever I told the old man my thoughts or my observations about people, he would listen readily, then repeat everything to the shop assistant, who would either scold me or make fun of me.

One day I informed the old man that sometimes I wrote down what he said in the notebook into which I copied out poetry or quotations from books. This frightened him and he quickly leaned toward me and began to question in alarm:

"Why should you do such a thing? That's not right, my lad. In order to remember it? Oh, no, you mustn't do that! What a little rogue you are! But you'll give me those notes, won't you, eh?"

Long and persistently he urged me to give him the notebook, or at least to burn it. Then he began to whisper excitedly to the shop assistant.

On our way home, the latter said to me:

"It seems you're keeping some sort of notes. See that you put an end to it, do you hear? It's only detectives do things like that."

"And what about Sitanov?" I said unguardedly. "He keeps notes too."

"Him too? The lanky fool!"

After a long pause, he suggested with unwonted gentleness:

"Come, now, show me your notebook, and Sitanov's too. I'll pay you half a ruble. Only do it quietlike, without letting Sitanov know."

Apparently he was sure that I would fulfil his request, for without another word he trotted off on his short legs.

On reaching home I told Sitanov what the shop assistant had suggested. He frowned.

"Why did you tell him? Now he'll get somebody to steal our notebooks, yours and mine. Here, give me yours and I'll hide it away. He'll be getting rid of you soon, you'll see!"

I did not doubt this, and made up my mind to leave as soon as Granny returned to town. All winter she had lived in Balakhna, invited there to teach lacemaking to somebody's daughters. Grandfather was living in Kunavino again. I never went to see him, and he did not visit me on the rare occasions when he came to town. One day I met him in the street; he was walking along in his enormous racoon coat, as staid and important as a priest. When I greeted him, he raised one hand to shield his eyes and said absent-mindedly:

"Ah, so it's you. Yes, yes, you've become a God-painter it seems. Well, get along, get along."

Pushing me aside, he continued on his way as staidly and importantly as ever.

I rarely saw Granny these days; she worked ceaselessly, supporting grandfather, whose mind was softening with age, and helping her son's children. Mikhail's Sasha, a handsome youth, a dreamer and book-lover, caused her particular anxiety. He worked in dyeing establishments, frequently shifting from one to another, a burden to Granny in the intervals, when he calmly waited for her to find him new employment. No less of a burden was Sasha's sister, who had made an unfortunate marriage with a drunken workman who beat her and drove her out of the house.

Whenever I met Granny I became more appreciative of the beauty of her spirit, but I already sensed that this wonderful spirit lived in a world of fairy tales which made her blind to the bitter reality about her. She was inaccessible to the fears and alarms which beset me.

"We must endure, Alyosha."

That was the only thing she could say in response to my accounts of the ugliness and dreariness of life, of the sufferings of the people—of everything against which I protested so vehemently.

I was not made for endurance, and if occasionally I exhibited this virtue of cattle, wood, and stone, I did so only to test myself, to try my strength and the firmness with which I stood rooted in the earth. Sometimes young people, in the foolishness of immaturity, or in envy of the strength of their elders, strive, even successfully, to lift weights that overtax their bones and muscles; in their vanity they attempt to cross themselves with two-pood weights, like mature athletes.

I too did this, in the literal and figurative sense, physically and spiritually, and only good fortune kept me from injuring myself fatally, or crippling myself for life. For nothing cripples a person so dreadfully as endurance, as a humble submission to the forces of circumstance.

And if in the end I return to Mother Earth a cripple, at least I shall be able to say, not without pride, that for some forty years I stood adamant against the stubborn efforts of good people to warp my soul.

More and more often was I seized with an irresistible desire to make merry, to entertain people and excite their laughter. And I succeeded in this, too. I had a knack for describing and imitating the merchants of the Lower Market; I would show how the muzhiks and their women bought and sold icons, how cleverly the shop assistant cheated them, and how the dogmatists carried on their endless arguments.

The people in the workshop would roar with laughter, often laying down their brushes to watch my performances; but when they were over, Larionich would say:

"You'd better do your tricks after supper, so's not to interfere with the work."

I always felt relieved after such "performances," as though I had cast off a great weight. For an hour or so my head would be blessedly empty, but then again it became filled with sharp little nails, pricking unpleasantly.

All about me seethed a polluted porridge, in which I could feel myself slowly stewing.

"Is it possible that my whole life will be like this?" thought I. "And will I live on like these people, without ever knowing, without ever seeing, anything better?"

"You're growing snarly, Maximich," said Zhikharev, studying me intently.

"What's wrong?" Sitanov would often ask.

I never knew what to answer.

With rude persistence life erased from my soul the best of its own inscriptions, spitefully substituting worthless scrawls. Angrily and stubbornly I resisted its violence. I was floating down the same river as everyone else, but for me the water was colder and less buoyant, and at times I felt myself sinking to the depths.

Yet people began treating me better. They did not shout at me as they did at Pavel, nor did they order me about, and they called me by my patronymic to emphasize the respect in which they held me. All of this was very agreeable, but it pained me to see how many people drank vodka, how repellent they became when drunk, and how unwholesome their relations with women were, though I realized that wine and women were the only diversions this life offered them.

Sadly I recollected that Natalya Kozlovskaya, herself a wise, courageous woman, had also thought women to be merely a diversion.

Then what about Granny? And Queen Margot?

I recalled Queen Margot with a feeling of awe. She was so much apart from everything else that it was as though I had seen her in a dream.

I began to think too much about women, already considering the possibility of spending my next day off where the others took their pleasure. This was not prompted by physical desire. I was healthy and fastidious. But at times I had a desperate longing to embrace someone tender and understanding, someone to whom I could pour out my anguish, as to a mother.

I envied Pavel. One night, as we lay side by side, he confided to me the love affair he was having with the chambermaid across the way.

"Just think, brother: a month ago I pelted her with snowballs and had no use for her. But now when I feel her sitting close beside me out there on the bench—well, there's just nobody like her."

"What do you talk to her about?"

"Everything. She tells me about herself and I tell her about myself. And then we kiss. . . . Only she's—upright. . . . You can't imagine how good she is!. . . Say, you smoke like a trooper!"

I smoked excessively; the tobacco went to my head, dulling my anxious thoughts. Fortunately for me, I was repelled by the taste and the smell of vodka, but Pavel drank a lot. When he was drunk he would wail plaintively:

"I want to go home! Let me go home!"

He was an orphan; his mother and father

had died long since, and he had no sisters or brothers. From the age of eight he had lived with strangers.

In this fretful, restive mood, heightened by the lure of spring, I decided once more to find work on a steamer, so that, on reaching Astrakhan, I could run away to Persia.

I do not remember why my choice fell on Persia—perhaps because I was greatly attracted by the Persian merchants at the Nizhni-Novgorod Fair: There they would sit basking in the sun and calmly smoking hookah—stone idols with dyed beards and large, dark, all-knowing eyes.

Probably I would indeed have run away, had it not been for the fact that during Easter Week, when some of the painters had left for their native villages and the rest were on a drunken spree, I met my former master, Granny's nephew, taking a stroll in a sunny field above the Oka. He was walking along in a light grey coat, his hands in his trouser pockets, a cigarette between his teeth, his hat pushed jauntily to the back of his head. As I approached, he gave me a friendly smile. He had the winning air of a gay, liberty-loving person, and he and I were alone in the field.

"Ah, Peshkov! Christ is risen!"

After exchanging the Easter kiss, he asked how I was getting along, to which I answered frankly that I was sick of the workshop and the city and everything in general, and had decided to go to Persia.

"Drop the idea," said he seriously. "Persia be damned! I know, brother; at your age I also wanted to run away, the devil only knows where!"

I liked the dashing way in which he tossed the devil about; there was something good and springlike in his manner; everything about him seemed very cocky.

"Smoke?" he asked, extending a silver case filled with fat cigarettes.

This won me over completely.

"Listen, Peshkov, how about coming back to work for me? This year I've made contracts at the Fair for something like forty thousand. I'll keep you out at the fairgrounds; you'll be a sort of overseer, receiving building materials, seeing that everything gets delivered to the right place on time, and that the workmen don't steal. Suit you? Salary—five a month and five kopeks for dinners. You'll have nothing to do with my women—leave in the morning, return in the evening—the women out of the picture. Only don't tell them we've met. Simply drop in on St. Thomas' Sunday and—there you are!"

We parted the best of friends. He shook my hand when he left, and even waved his hat to me from a distance.

When I announced to the painters that I was leaving, most of them expressed a regret which I found very flattering. Pavel was particularly upset.

"To think of your leaving us to go live with those muzhiks!" said he reproachfully. "Carpenters, paper-hangers. . . . Phooh! That's what's called climbing from bishop to sexton."

Zhikharev muttered:

"Youth seeks trouble like fish seek the depths."

The farewell given me by the painters was dull and dreary.

"To be sure, you have to try this and that," said Zhikharev, green with drink. "But it would be better to grab hold of one thing right from the start and hang on to it."

"For good and all," added Larionich quietly.

But I felt they were forcing themselves to say this, as a duty. The thread binding us had somehow rotted and snapped all at once.

The drunken Gogolev tossed about on the upper bunk and muttered hoarsely:

"If I like, I'll have you all put in prison! I know a secret: you don't believe in God! Aha-a-a!"

The faceless, unfinished icons still stood against the wall and the glass balls clung to the ceiling. For some time now we had been working without artificial light, so that the balls were not needed and had become coated with a grey layer of dust and soot. Everything impressed itself so deeply on my memory that even now I have only to shut my eyes to see that dark room with its tables, the cans of paint on the window sills, the clusters of paint-brushes, the icons, the slop bucket in the corner under the copper washbasin resembling a fireman's helmet, and Gogolev's bare leg, blue as a corpse's, hanging over the edge of his bunk.

I was eager to get away, but Russians love to drag out sad moments; a farewell gathering becomes a regular funeral service.

Zhikharev, frowning, said to me:

"I can't give you back that book, *The Demon*. If you want, you can have twenty kopeks for it."

It was hard to part with Lermontov, especially since the book had been a present from the old fire-chief. But when, somewhat petulantly, I refused the money, Zhikharev calmly returned it to his purse and announced unperturbed:

"Just as you like, but I won't give up the book. That book's not for you; you can get yourself in trouble in a twinkling with a book like that."

"But they sell it in the stores. I saw it myself."

"What of it? They sell pistols in the stores too," he answered convincingly.

And he never returned it.

When I went upstairs to say goodbye to the owner's widow, I met her niece in the entranceway.

"They say you're leaving us," she said.

"Yes, I am."

"It's a good thing, else they'd have given you the sack," she announced, not very politely, but sincerely enough.

My drunken mistress said:

"Farewell, and God be with you! It's a bad boy you are—very impudent. You've never shown me your bad side, but everyone says you're no good."

Suddenly she began to cry, murmuring through her tears:

"If only my poor husband was alive, the blessed soul; he'd have tweaked your ears for you and he'd have thumped you over the head, but he'd have kept you here and not driven you away. Everything's different these days; soon as something goes wrong, it's out you go. Ah me! whatever will become of you, my lad?"

XVI

My master and I were making our way in a boat along the streets of the fairgrounds, between stone structures flooded up to the second storey with the swollen waters of the river in spring. I was rowing; my master, seated in the stern, was steering clumsily, with an oar as rudder. The boat poked its nose up one street and down another, over the quiet, turbid, brooding water.

"How high the water is this spring, devil take it! It'll hold up our work!" grumbled my master, lighting a cigar whose smoke smelled like burning rags.

"Careful!" he shouted in fright. "We're headed for a lamppost!"

After righting the boat, he said:

"A fine boat they gave us, the bastards!"

He pointed out the place where, once the water had subsided, we should begin repairing the stalls. He did not resemble a contractor, smooth-shaven as he was, with clipped moustaches and a cigar between his teeth. He was wearing a leather jacket and knee-boots and had a gamebag thrown over his shoulder, while at his feet lay an expensive, double-barrelled Lebel shotgun. He kept jerking uneasily at his leather cap, now pulling it low over his eyes, pursing his lips and gazing about him anxiously; now thrusting it to the back of his head, growing suddenly younger, and smiling into his moustaches at some pleasant fancy. Carried away thus on a wave of thought divorced from business, he gave no sign of being pressed with work and worried by the slow receding of the water.

I, on my part, was depressed by a feeling of quiet wonder: how strange it was to see that dead, flooded city with its rows of blank-windowed buildings floating quietly past our boat!

The sky was grey. The sun was caught in a network of clouds, through which it occasionally glanced, a large, silver, wintry disc.

The water too was grey and cold, and the flow of the current was scarcely discernible; it seemed to have congealed and fallen asleep along with the empty buildings and the rows of dirty-yellow stalls. When the whitish sun peeped through the clouds, everything brightened faintly, the water reflected the grey fabric of the sky and our boat seemed suspended in mid-air, between two skies. The stone buildings also rose up and floated imperceptibly toward the Volga and the Oka. Broken barrels, boxes, and baskets, bits of sticks and straw rocked on the surface, while logs and poles floated past like dead serpents.

Here and there a window was open, clothes were drying on the roof of the gallery running the length of the trade row, some felt boots were poking through a railing; a woman sat at one of the windows gazing out on to the grey water; to the top of an iron gallery-support a boat was tied, its red flanks casting an oily, meaty reflection on the water.

Nodding at these signs of life, my master explained:

"That's where the fairground watchman lives. He climbs out of his window on to the roof, gets into his boat, and paddles about looking for thieves. If he finds none, he himself does the thieving."

He spoke with a lazy detachment, his mind on something else. Everything was quiet and empty and as incredible as a dream. The Volga and the Oka had merged to form one enormous lake; on a shaggy hill in the distance rose the spotted city covered with orchards still darkly barren, but with swelling buds, so that the trees wrapped houses and churches in a mantle of green. Over the water came the rich chimes of Eastertide, and we could catch the hum of the city, but here everything was as silent as an abandoned churchyard.

Our boat veered between two rows of dark trees as we made our way along the main thoroughfare to the Old Cathedral. The smoke from my master's cigar kept getting in his eyes and the boat kept bumping into the trunks of trees until he cried out in exasperation.

"Damn this boat!"

"Stop steering."

"How can I?" he grumbled. "When there's two in a boat, one rows and the other steers. There—look: Chinese Row."

I knew the fairgrounds inside out, and was only too well acquainted with that ludicrous Row with its fantastic roofs, on the corners of which squatted plaster figures of Chinamen; my playmates and I had once thrown stones at them, and I myself had deprived some of these Chinamen of heads and hands. But I no longer was proud of the fact.

"Shanties," said my master, indicating the buildings. "Now if they had let *me* build them—"

He gave a whistle and pushed his cap to the back of his head.

But for some reason I felt that he would have built them just as uninterestingly, and on that very site, low as it was, flooded each spring by the waters of two rivers. And he would have thought up something as hideous as the Chinese Row.

Tossing his cigar over the stern, he spat after it in disgust and said:

"What a bore life is, Peshkov, what a bore! No educated people; no one to talk to. Sometimes you'd like to do a little boasting, but who's there to boast to? Nobody. Only carpenters, stonemasons, muzhiks, thieves. . . ."

Glancing off to the right, where a white mosque emerged daintily from a flooded hillside, he went on talking as though recalling something forgotten:

"I've begun to drink beer and smoke cigars, like a German. The Germans are good businessmen—such roaring chickens, brother! Beer-drinking—that's a pleasant pastime, but I can't seem to get used to cigars. Whenever you smoke, your wife starts complaining. 'What makes you smell like a saddler?' she says. Ah yes, the things we do to make life interesting! . . . Here, do your own steering."

Resting his oar against the side of the boat, he took up his gun and shot at one of the figures on a roof. The Chinaman suffered no injury; the shot merely scattered over the roof and the wall, raising a cloud of dust.

"Missed," he admitted indifferently as he reloaded his gun.

"How do you stand with the girls? Have you broken fast yet? No? I began falling in love at thirteen."

As if recounting a dream, he told me about his first sweetheart, a chambermaid employed by the architect to whom he was apprenticed. His tale was accompanied by the soft plashing of the water at the corners of the buildings; beyond the Cathedral glistened a vast watery expanse with black willow-wands rising out of it here and there.

In the icon workshop the painters often sang the student song:

> *The blue, blue sea,*
> *The stormy sea. . . .*

How dull that blue, blue sea must have been!

"I couldn't sleep nights," said my master. "I'd get out of bed and stand at her door shivering like a puppy, for the house was full of draughts. Her master often visited her at night and might easily have caught me there, but I wasn't afraid—not the least."

He spoke contemplatively, as though examining some old clothes to see if they could be worn again.

"She noticed me and took pity on me; she even opened the door and called to me: 'Come along, you silly boy!'"

I had heard so many such tales that I was sick of them, although they all had one good point in common: people spoke about their first experience of love without boasting, without obscenity, and often with such fond regret that I realized it was the finest moment in their lives. Indeed, for many it seems to have been the only good thing they ever knew.

Laughing and shaking his head, my master exclaimed in surprise:

"But I wouldn't dare tell my wife this story! Oh no! Not that there is anything wrong in it. But still I wouldn't dare tell her. Well...."

It was not to me he was relating the story, but to himself. Had he remained silent, I would have spoken. In that silence and emptiness it was essential to talk, to sing, to play the accordion, lest one should fall asleep forever in that dead city, submerged in cold, grey water.

"First of all—don't marry young!" he exhorted me. "Marriage, brother, is tremendously important! Wherever and however you live—as a Mohammedan in Persia, or a policeman in Moscow, weaving or thieving, you can always change things if they are not to your taste. But you can't change your wife! Your wife's like the weather, brother—can't be helped! A wife's no boot, to be taken off and cast aside at will!"

A shadow flitted over his face; he sat gazing at the grey water with knitted brows, rubbing his humped nose with one finger as he muttered:

"Yes, brother. . . . Have to look sharp! Maybe you're one who can bend to the wind and still stay rooted. But even so, everybody has his own trap waiting for him. . . ."

We rode into the thickets of Meshcherskoe Lake, now merged with the Volga.

"Row slower," whispered my master, aiming his gun into the bushes.

After shooting a few emaciated woodcocks, he said:

"Head for Kunavino! I'll stay there until evening and you tell them at home I had business with a contractor."

I left him on one of the streets of the settlement, which was also flooded, and returned through the fairgrounds to the Strelka. There I tied up the boat and sat gazing at the junction of the two rivers, at the city, the steamers, and the sky. The sky was now feathered with white clouds, like the wing of an enormous bird. Through blue crevices glimpsed the golden sun, one beam of which was sufficient to transform the whole world. Everything about me was now in brisk movement; an endless chain of rafts was being borne swiftly down the current; on the rafts stood sturdy muzhiks manipulating long oars and shouting to each other and to a passing steamer. The little steamer was pulling an empty barge against the current, and as the river tossed it about, it edged its nose from side to side like a pike, panting and puffing as it stubbornly pushed its wheels through the water ruthlessly bearing down upon it. Four muzhiks sat shoulder to shoulder on the barge, their legs hanging over the edge; one of them was wearing a red shirt, and all were singing; the words were indistinguishable, but I knew the song.

It seemed to me that here, on the river, everything was known to me; everything was familiar, and everything comprehensible. But the flooded city behind me was an evil dream, an invention of my master, as incomprehensible as he himself.

When I had drunk my fill of the river scene, I returned home, feeling that I was a full grown man, equal to any task. On my way I stopped on the Kremlin hill to have a last look at the Volga. From this height the earth seemed limitless, and full of promise.

I would read on returning home. Queen Margot's flat was now occupied by a large family boasting five young girls, each one prettier than the other, and two students at the Gymnasium. These young people supplied me with books. Greedily I devoured Turgenev, marvelling at the simplicity and lucidity of his style, as crystal as autumn air, and at the purity of his characters, and at the beauty of everything he so modestly championed.

I read *The Seminary* by Pomyalovsky, and again was surprised to discover how strangely it resembled life in the icon workshop; only too well did I know that desperate boredom which sought relief in cruel pranks.

It was good to read Russian books; in them I always sensed something sad and familiar, as though the Lenten chimes were imprisoned within their pages, and one had only to open the covers to release the faint music.

Reluctantly I read *Dead Souls*; the same was true of *Notes from a Dead House*. *Dead Souls*, *Dead House*, *Death*, *Three Deaths*, *The Live Mummy*—one could not help noting the similarity of these titles, which only stirred up a vague antipathy for the books. Nor did I like *Signs of the Times*, *Step by Step*, *What is to be Done?*, *Chronicle of the Hamlet of Smurin*, and other books of this type.

But I was very fond of Dickens and Walter Scott. I read their books two and three times over with the greatest delight. The books of Walter Scott reminded me of a holiday mass held in a splendid cathedral—a bit long and tiresome, but always festive. Dickens has remained to this day a writer whom I deeply admire—an author who attained supreme mastery in that most difficult of arts—the art of loving people.

In the evenings a large group of us would gather on the porch: the brothers and sisters from Queen Margot's flat, a snub-nosed student named Vyacheslav Semashko, and a few others. Sometimes we would be joined by the daughter of an important official named Pti-

tsin. We spoke about books and poetry, things which were very dear and comprehensible to me—I had read more than any of these young people. But more often my companions talked about school, complaining about their teachers. As I listened, I felt that I enjoyed more liberty than they did and wondered at their endurance. But still I envied them: they were studying.

My friends were older than I was, but it seemed to me that I was more mature and experienced. This somewhat upset me; I wanted to feel closer to them. I would return home late at night, covered with dirt and dust and steeped in impressions of a different order than theirs; in essence, their experiences were all very much the same. They spoke a lot about the girls, falling in love first with one, then with another, and they attempted to write poetry. Often my help was solicited. I gladly tried my hand at versifying; rhymes came easily to me, but for some reason my poems always turned out to be humourous. I invariably compared the Ptitsin girl, to whom the poetry was most often dedicated, to some vegetable, usually an onion.

Semashko said to me:

"Do you call those lines poetry? They're shoemaker's nails!"

Eager to keep up with the others, I too fell in love with the Ptitsin girl. I no longer remember how I expressed my feelings, but the affair had a sad ending. One day I offered to take her for a ride on a board floating on the stagnant waters of Zvezdin Pond. She accepted my offer; I brought the board to the bank and stood on it; it was strong enough to support my weight, but when the girl, all decked out in lace and ribbons, gracefully mounted the other end, the accursed board gave under her feet and she found herself in the pond. With true chivalry I threw myself in after her and quickly pulled her up on the bank. But fright and green muck had wrought unspeakable havoc with the damsel's beauty.

Shaking a wet fist at me, she cried:

"You drowned me on purpose!"

She refused to accept my apologies and became my mortal enemy.

Life in town was not very interesting. The old mistress still disliked me and the young one looked upon me with suspicion. Victor, more freckled than ever, snorted at everyone, harbouring some deep-rooted grudge.

My master had more draughting than he and his brother could manage, so he called in my stepfather to assist.

One day, on returning from the fairgrounds at an unusually early hour, I entered the dining-room to find this man, long forgotten, sitting beside my master at the tea-table. He held out his hand to me.

"How do you do?" he said.

I was stunned by the unexpectedness of the meeting. Immediately the past flared up like a flame, searing my heart.

"You've given him a fright," observed my master.

My stepfather gazed at me with a smile on his wasted face. His dark eyes had grown larger than ever and he looked terribly worn and crushed. I thrust my hand into his thin, burning fingers.

"Well, so we've met again," he said with a cough.

I went out, as weak as though I had taken a beating.

Our relations became guarded and constrained. He called me by my first name and patronymic and addressed me as an equal.

"When you go to the store, be so kind as to buy me a quarter of a pound of Laferm tobacco, a hundred Victorson cigarette-wrappers, and a pound of boiled sausage."

The coins he handed me were always unpleasantly warm. It was clear that he was consumptive and had not long to live. He knew this and would remark in a calm, deep voice, as he twisted the tip of his black goatee:

"There is practically no cure for my illness. Although if one eats a lot of meat, one may recover. Who knows—perhaps even I shall."

He consumed incredible quantities of food. He ate and smoked, removing a cigarette from his mouth only to put food into it. Every day I bought him sausage, ham, and sardines, but Granny's sister declared with unaccountable satisfaction and finality:

"There's no treating Death to titbits. No fooling Death! No indeed!"

The women paid an annoying amount of attention to my stepfather, forever insisting that he try some new kind of medicine, while behind his back they made fun of him.

"A nobleman, no less!" said the young mistress. "'You should brush the crumbs off the table more often,' says he; 'crumbs,' says he, 'bring flies!'"

"A nobleman indeed!" scoffed the elder one. "Just see how threadbare and shiny his coat's become, but he keeps right on brushing it. A squeamish creature — not a speck of dust!"

"Bide your time, you roaring chickens, he'll be dying soon," said my master consolingly.

The senseless hostility which ignorant townsfolk felt for intellectuals led me to take my stepfather's side. Toadstools may be poisonous, but at least they are beautiful.

In the stifling presence of these people, my stepfather felt like a fish in a chicken-coop—a comparison as incongruous as the life we lived.

I began to discover in him qualities similar to those of "That's Fine," a man whom I shall never forget. I embellished my memories of "That's Fine" and Queen Margot with all the beauty culled from books; I bestowed upon them the finest of what was within me—all the lovely fantasies born of my reading. My stepfather was just as aloof and unloved as "That's Fine" had been. He treated everyone in our house alike, never spoke the first word, and answered all questions briefly and with marked politeness. I especially enjoyed hearing him teach my master: he would stand at the table bent nearly double, tapping the heavy paper with a long fingernail as he calmly explained:

"At this point it is necessary to fasten the rafter with a joint in order to disperse the pressure; otherwise the rafter will break through the wall."

"True enough, damn it all!" my master would mutter, while his wife would say, when my stepfather had left:

"How can you let him teach you like that!"

For some reason she was especially irritated by the fact that after supper my stepfather would always clean his teeth and rinse his mouth, throwing back his head in a way that made his Adam's apple stick out.

"To my mind, it must be harmful for you to lean back like that, Yevgeni Vasilyevich," she once said in a sour tone.

He only smiled and asked politely:

"Why should you think such a thing?"

"Well—just because."

Taking out a small bone pick, he began to clean his bluish fingernails.

"Just to think! He even cleans his nails!" exclaimed the mistress when he had left. "One foot in the grave, and still. . . ."

"Ekh-h-h!" sighed my master. "How foolish you are, you roaring chickens."

"Why in the world should you say such a thing?" objected his wife.

At night the old woman would bitterly complain to God:

"They've forced that festering creature on me, and now Victor's pushed into the background again."

Victor began to imitate my stepfather's manners—his slow gait, the sure movements of his aristocratic hands, his knack of knotting his tie, and his ability to eat without smacking his lips. He was always asking him rudely:

"Maximov, how do you say 'knee' in French?"

"My name is Yevgeni Vasilyevich," corrected my stepfather.

"Oh, all right. And 'breast'?"

At the supper table Victor would give orders to his mother:

"Ma mère, donnez-moi encore du corn-beef."

"Oh you Frenchman, you!" exclaimed the old lady, greatly tickled.

My stepfather would go on chewing his meat unperturbed, as though he were deaf and dumb, without a glance at anyone.

One day the elder brother said to the younger:

"Now that you've learned how to speak French, Victor, you better be getting yourself a mistress."

That was the only time I remember seeing my stepfather give a quiet smile.

But my master's wife threw down her spoon indignantly and shouted at her husband:

"How dare you say such shameful things in my presence!"

Sometimes my stepfather would join me in the back entrance where I slept under the attic stairs; it was here, at the window on the stairway, that I read my books.

"Reading?" he once asked me, inhaling so much smoke that something inside his chest sizzled like burning logs. "What's the book?"

I showed it to him.

"Ah," he said, glancing at the title. "I seem to have read it. Have a smoke?"

We smoked, gazing out of the window into the dirty yard.

"Too bad you can't study," he said. "You seem to have ability."

"But I am studying—reading a lot—"

"That's not enough. You need schooling, system."

I wanted to say to him: "You've had schooling and system, my fine gentleman, and what good has it done you?"

As though reading my thoughts, he added:

"If one has strength of purpose, a school gives good training. It's only the educated who are capable of budging this life."

More than once he said to me:

"You would do well to get away from here; I can't see any sense or advantage in your staying."

"But I like the workmen."

"What do you find likeable about them?"

"They aren't dull."

"Perhaps. . . ."

And once he said:

"When you come down to it, what beasts our employers are—what beasts!"

Recalling when, and under what circumstances, my mother had used that very word, I involuntarily recoiled.

"Don't you agree?" he asked with a smile.

"Yes, I do."

"Of course. I can see that."

"But still I like my master."

"To be sure, he seems to be a good-natured muzhik. But he is ridiculous."

I wanted to discuss books with him, but apparently he had little use for books.

"Don't spend too much time with them," he would often say. "Everything is exaggerated in books—distorted in one direction or another. Most authors are like our master here—petty people."

I found such opinions very bold and admired him for them.

"Have you read Goncharov?" he asked me one day.

"*The Frigate Pallada*," I replied.

"*The Pallada* is dull. But in general Goncharov is the most intelligent writer in Russia. I advise you to read his *Oblomov*—the most daring and truthful of his books. And in general it is the best work of Russian literature."

Of Dickens, he said:

"Trash—take my word for it. But there's a very interesting thing now being printed in the supplement to the *New Times*: *The Temptation of St. Anthony*. You should read it. It seems you are fond of the church and things ecclesiastical. It will do you good to read *The Temptation*."

He himself brought me a pile of supplements, and I read this sagacious work of

Flaubert; it reminded me of the innumerable lives of the saints I had read, and of some of the stories told by the dogmatists. But it did not make a very deep impression on me. I received much greater pleasure from reading *The Memories of Upilio Faimali, Animal-Trainer,* which was printed in the same supplement.

When I admitted this to my stepfather, he calmly remarked:

"That means you are still too young to read such things. But don't forget about that book."

Sometimes he sat with me for a long time without saying a word, merely coughing and breathing out clouds of smoke. His handsome eyes had a dreadful glitter. As I sat there looking at him quietly, I forgot that this man, dying simply, without complaint, was once intimate with my mother and had been cruel to her. I knew that he now lives with some seamstress, and I thought of her with wonder and pity. How could she bear to embrace those long bones, to kiss that mouth, breathing corruption?

Like "That's Fine," my stepfather would unexpectedly make remarks that were highly original.

"I love hunting dogs; they are stupid, but I love them anyway. They are very beautiful. Beautiful women are often very stupid."

I thought to myself, not without some pride:

"You should have known Queen Margot!"

"People who live together for a long time gradually grow to look alike," he said one day. I wrote this down in my notebook.

I awaited his dictums like beatitudes— it was a joy to hear original phrases in a house where everyone spoke a colourless language, congealed in worn, monotonous forms.

My stepfather never spoke to me of my mother; I think he never even mentioned her name. This pleased me, and roused a certain respect for him.

One day I asked him about God—I do not remember on what occasion. He glanced at me and replied, very calmly:

"I don't know. I don't believe in God."

I remembered Sitanov, and told my stepfather about him, but when I was through, he remarked just as calmly:

"He reasons things out, and people who reason things out always believe in something or other. I have no faith at all."

"But that is impossible!"

"Why? You can see for yourself—I don't believe in anything."

I could see only one thing—that he was dying. It could scarcely be said that I pitied him, but this was the first time I had ever been deeply touched by the death of a fellowman, by the mystery of death itself.

Here sat a man, his knee touching mine, sensate, intelligent, seeing people according to their relationship to him, speaking about everything as one who had the right to judge and draw conclusions; possessing something essential to me, or at least setting off that which was nonessential; a creature inexpressibly complex, a very volcano of thought. Whatever my feeling for him, he represented part of myself, a being dwelling somewhere within me, for I thought of him, and the shadow of his soul lay across mine. Tomorrow he would vanish—vanish entirely, with all that brooded in his head and heart, with all that I seemed to read in his handsome eyes. When he vanished, one of the threads binding me to the world would be severed; there would remain only a memory, but this memory would exist wholly within me, changeless and complete, while the living, changing man would be gone. . . .

But these are mere thoughts, beyond which lies that indefinable something which conceives and nourishes thought, a something imperiously forcing us to ponder life phenomena and demand an answer to the question—Why?

"I'm afraid I shall soon be taking to my bed," said my stepfather one rainy day. "Such a foolish weakness! And no wish to do a thing!"

At tea the next afternoon he brushed the crumbs from the table and off his knees with particular fastidiousness and waved off something invisible. The old woman, glancing at him from under her brows, whispered to her daughter-in-law:

"Look—he's preening and pluming him-self, making himself ready."

Two days later he failed to come to work, and then the elder mistress handed me a large white envelope, saying:

"Here, a girl brought it yesterday about noon but I forgot to hand it to you. She was just a little thing—I'm sure I don't know why she should be bringing you notes."

Within the envelope, on a sheet of hospital paper, I found the following message written in large letters:

"If you happen to be free for an hour or so, come see me. I'm in the Martynovskaya Hospital. Y. M."

The next morning I was sitting at the foot of my stepfather's bed in a hospital ward. He was longer than the bed, and his feet, in sagging grey socks, stuck through the rods of the bedstead. His handsome eyes kept wandering over the yellow walls and coming to rest on my face and on the small hands of the girl sitting on a stool at the head of the bed. Whenever she placed her hands on his pillow, my stepfather would rub his cheek

against them, his mouth wide open. The girl
was plump and wore a simple dark dress.
Slow tears were rolling down her oval face
and she kept her blue eyes fixed upon my
stepfather's face, with its protruding cheek-
bones, pinched nose, and discoloured mouth.

"If only he'd have a priest," she whispered.
"But he won't — he doesn't understand. . . ."

Removing her hands from the pillow,
she pressed them to her breast as though in
prayer.

For a moment my stepfather's mind
cleared. He gazed at the ceiling with a frown, as
though trying to recall something, then stretched
a wasted hand toward me.

"You? Thank you. You see . . . I feel . . .
quite foolish. . . ."

This exhausted him, and he closed his
eyes; I patted his long, cold fingers with the
bluish nails, and the girl pleaded softly:

"Yevgeni Vasilyevich, do give your consent!"

"I want you to know her," he said, indicating the girl with his eyes. "A dear
girl. . . ."

He became silent, opening his mouth ever wider, and suddenly he gave a hoarse cry, like a crow; he tossed on the bed, upturning the blanket and clutching at the mattress. The girl also cried out and buried her head in the tortured pillow.

My stepfather died quickly, and instantly his features became serenely beautiful.

I left the hospital with the girl on my arm. She wept and staggered as if she were ill. In her hand she clutched a handkerchief screwed up into a ball, pressing it first to one eye, then to the other. She kept screwing it ever tighter and looking at it as though it were her last and dearest possession.

Suddenly she stopped and nestled close to me, saying with a note of reproach in her voice:

"And he didn't even live until winter. . . . Ah, dear Lord, dear Lord, why did it have to happen?"

Then she held out her hand, wet with tears.

"Goodbye. He always praised you. The funeral . . . tomorrow."

"Shall I see you home?"

She glanced about.

"Why? It's daytime."

I stood on the corner and watched her go down the street. She walked unhurriedly, like one who has lost all interest in life.

It was August, and the leaves were falling.

I had no time to attend my stepfather's funeral, and I never saw the girl again. . . .

XVII

Every morning at six o'clock I set out for work at the fairgrounds. There I was met by interesting people: the grey-haired, sharp-tongued carpenter Osip, a skilled workman who looked like St. Nikolai; the hunchbacked roofer Yefimushka; the pious stonemason Pyotr, of a meditative turn of mind, also resembling a saint; the handsome plasterer Grigori Shishlin, blond-bearded, blue-eyed, ever radiating quiet good will.

I had known these people during my second term of service in the draughtsman's family. Every Sunday they had put in their

appearance in the kitchen, staid and digni-
fied, with a pleasant manner of speech full
of luscious words that were new to me.
I had found these weighty muzhiks thoroughly
good; each was interesting in his own
way, and all of them compared favourably
with the mean, drunken, thievish tradesmen
of Kunavino.

Then I had chosen the plasterer Shishlin
as my favourite; I had even asked him to take
me on as an apprentice, but he had gently
refused, saying, as he scratched his golden
eyebrows with his white fingers:

"You're too young yet; our job is not
an easy one—wait a year or two." Then,
tossing back his handsome head, he had added:
"Maybe you're finding life hard? That's
all right, try to bear it; take a tighter grip
on yourself, and you'll manage."

I do not know that I derived any benefit
from his kind advice, but I remembered it
gratefully.

Now too they would visit my master
every Sunday morning, taking their places
on the benches about the kitchen table, hold-

ing interesting conversation while they waited for him. My master would greet them with noisy joviality, shaking their strong hands and sitting down in the icon corner. Out came money and receipts; the muzhiks placed their bills and worn account-books on the table: the week's business was being settled.

With much joking and bantering, my master tried to cheat them, and they him; sometimes serious tiffs ensued, but usually they laughed together amicably.

"Ah, friend, it's a rogue you were born," the muzhiks would say to my master.

He would reply, laughing sheepishly:

"Well, you're not so bad at thieving yourselves, you roaring chickens!"

"Naturally," admitted Yefimushka, while the serious-minded Pyotr put in:

"A person lives by what he steals; his honest earnings all go to God and the tsar."

"So that's why I have nothing against shaving you a bit," laughed my master.

They took him up good-naturedly:

"In other words, skinning us?"

"Bamboozling us?"

Grigori Shishlin, laying his hands on the bushy beard covering his chest, said in a singsong voice:

"What if we do our business without any cheating, brothers? If we just live honest. Can't you see how fine and easy it would be, eh? What do you say, good people?"

His blue eyes became moist and dark; he was wonderfully handsome at that moment; everyone seemed a bit embarrassed by his suggestion, and faces were turned away uneasily.

"A muzhik can't cheat a person out of very much," muttered the comely Osip with a sigh, as though pitying the muzhik.

The dark, round-shouldered stonemason bent lower over the table as he observed thickly:

"Sinning's like a bog—the further you go, the deeper you sink."

My master adopted their tone to reply:

"I fit my echoes to your hallooing."

They went on philosophizing like this for some time, then again tried to get the better of each other. When accounts were settled they rose, tired and sweating from strain, and set off for the tavern for tea, inviting my master to accompany them.

At the fairgrounds it was my duty to see that these people did not steal nails and bricks and timber; each of them, besides working for my master, did his own contracting, and tried to slip away materials for his own use.

They greeted me in a friendly manner, but Shishlin said:

"Remember how you asked me to take you on as apprentice? And now just see how you've been advanced—to being my overseer, eh?"

"Oh that's all right," joked Osip. "Spy and pry to your heart's content."

Pyotr said with some hostility:

"Why should they set a young cat to watch old mice?"

My duties were a cruel burden to me; I felt ashamed in the presence of these people, all of whom, it seemed to me, were in possession of some good knowledge known to them alone, while here was I, watching them as if they were thieves and swindlers. The first few days were very difficult, and Osip, noticing this, said to me, looking me straight in the eye:

"Listen, young fellow, don't you go sulking—no sense in that, understand?"

Of course I did not understand, but I sensed that the old man realized the incongruity of my position, and we immediately became very frank with each other.

He would take me off in a corner and give me instructions:

"The main thief among us, if you must know, is the stonemason Pyotr: he's a greedy fellow, with a large family. Keep a sharp eye on him; anything's good enough for him to take: a pound of nails, a dozen bricks, a sack of mortar—it all goes! He's a good man, pious and strict in his thoughts; he can read and write, but he's got a weakness for stealing. Yefimushka, now—he lives for the women. He's meek and harmless so far as you're concerned. It's a good head he's got on his shoulders; all hunchbacks are smart. As for Grigori Shishlin, he's a bit addlebrained; can't even hang on to what's his own, let alone take other people's. Anybody can fool him, but he can't fool a soul. There's no sense to what he does."

"Is he a good man?"

Osip studied me as if from a distance, and then said memorable words:

"Yes, he's good. There's nothing easier than for a lazy man to be good; goodness wants no brains, young fellow."

"Well, and what about you?" I asked Osip.

He replied with a short laugh:

"I'm like a girl. When I get to be a grandmother, I'll tell you what I'm like. But you'll have to wait till then. Or else use your brains to find me out; go ahead and try!"

He upset all my notions about him and his friends. I did not doubt the truth of what he said. I could see that Yefimushka, Pyotr, and Grigori considered this comely old man more clever and knowing in practical matters than they themselves. They sought his advice in everything, listened to him attentively, and paid him every mark of respect.

"Be so kind as to give us your advice," they would say to him, but after one such request, when Osip had left, I heard the stone-mason say to Grigori softly:

"Heretic!"

"Clown!" Grigori added with a snort.

The plasterer warned me, as a friend:

"Watch out for that old man, Maximich. You have to be careful with him; he'll wind you round his little finger in the twinkling of an eye! Those old men with their jaws always working—the Lord only knows what harm they do!"

I could not make head or tail out of it.

It seemed to me that the most honest and virtuous of them all was the stonemason Pyotr; all his remarks were brief and impressive, his thoughts turning most often to God and death and damnation.

"Ah, brothers, try as a man will and hope as he may, he'll only come to a grave and a coffin."

He suffered from some stomach ailment. There were days when he could eat nothing at all, when even the tiniest piece of bread would cause convulsions of pain and nausea.

The hunchback Yefimushka also appeared to be kind and honest, though he was a bit ridiculous and sometimes assumed a blissful air that made him seem half-witted. He was always falling in love, and he described each of his women in the same words:

"I'll tell you plain—she's no woman; she's a blossom in a pot of cream, that's what she is!"

When the flippant women of Kunavino came to wash the floors of the stalls, Yefimushka would climb down off the roof and take up his position in some corner, where he would stand purring with pleasure, his bright, grey eyes screwed up tight, his mouth stretched from ear to ear.

"Oh what a juicy morsel the Lord's brought my way today! Oh what a joy's come flitting into my hands! Just see what a blossom she is, and how am I to thank my fate for such a gift, eh? Won't I burn up fast from a beauty like that, though?"

At first the women would only laugh at him, calling to each other:

"Just look how the hunchback's melting! Lord a-mighty!"

The roofer remained untouched by their raillery; gradually his high-cheekboned face grew drowsy, and he spoke as though delirious, spilling sweet words in a drunken stream that evidently intoxicated the women. Finally an elder one among them said, in some amazement:

"The muzhik might be a lad, the way he's going on!"

"Singing like a bird."

"Or a beggar at the church door," insisted the elder one harshly.

But Yefimushka bore little resemblance to a beggar; he was planted firmly in the earth, like a rugged stump, and his voice became ever more alluring, his words ever more seducing, causing the women to stop their talk and listen. It was as though he were weaving a spell with his honeyed speech.

It ended up by his returning at suppertime or on Monday morning, shaking his large, square head and exclaiming to his comrades wonderingly:

"Ah, what a sweet woman, what a dear one—first time in my life I ever had one like that!"

In telling about his conquests, Yefimushka never bragged or poked fun at his women as others did; he only smiled wide-eyed, in happy, grateful astonishment.

Osip exclaimed, with a shake of his head:

"You incorrigible male! How old did you say you were?"

"Forty and four. But that means nothing. Today I'm younger by five years; I dipped into living waters and emerged whole, my heart at ease. Ah me, what women there are!"

The stonemason said to him sternly:

"Watch out—your loose living will leave a bitter taste in your mouth when you've crossed the threshold of fifty."

"You're a shameful creature, Yefimushka," sighed Grigori Shishlin.

But it seemed to me that the handsome young man envied the hunchback his conquests.

Osip glanced at everyone from under his twisted silver brows and boomed jovially:

"All your girls are lured by churls—some with sweets, some with pearls, but all your girls will soon be—grannies."

Shishlin was married, but his wife had remained in the village; he too cast longing eyes at the scrub women. All of them were accessible; each was eager to earn a little something "on the side," and such a source of income was considered as good as any other in this poverty-stricken community. But this handsome muzhik did not touch women; he merely gazed at them from a distance with a peculiar expression, as though sorry for them, or for himself. And when they themselves began to flirt with him and tempt him, he would laugh with embarrassment and walk away, saying:

"Come, come, now. . . ."

"Are you crazy?" Yefimushka would say, unbelieving. "How can you let a chance like that slip by?"

"I'm a married man," Grigori reminded him.

"Your wife will never find out."

"A wife will always find out if her husband lives dishonest. There's no fooling a wife, brother!"

"How will she find out?"

"That I don't know, but she can't help finding out if she herself is honest. And if I live honest and she lives in sin, I shall find out."

"How?" cried Yefimushka, but Grigori calmly repeated:

"That I don't know."

The roofer waved his hand in exasperation.

"Just look at that! 'Live honest,' 'don't know!' What a head you've got!"

Shishlin's workmen, seven in all, felt at ease with him, as if he were not their master. But behind his back they called him a calf. If he arrived at work and saw that they were idling, he himself would take up a trowel and set to work with a vengeance, calling out amicably:

"Come along, fellows, come along!"

One day, in compliance with the orders of my impatient master, I said to Grigori:

"Those workmen of yours are no good."

"Really?" he exclaimed, as though the idea had never occurred to him.

"This work should have been finished yesterday at noon, and it won't be finished even today."

"That's true. They won't manage," he agreed, but after a short pause he added hesitantly:

"I see what goes on, of course, but I'm ashamed to drive them—they're all our boys, from my own village. The Lord decreed that man was to earn his bread by the sweat of his brow. That was meant for all of us, wasn't it, including you and me? But you and me work less than they do. That's why I'm ashamed to drive them."

He was given to meditation; sometimes he would walk down one of the empty streets of the fairgrounds until he came to a bridge over the Obvodny Canal, where he would stand for hours leaning over the rail and gazing into the water, the sky, the spaces beyond the Oka. If anyone overtook him and said: "What are you doing?" He would start up with an embarrassed smile and say, "Oh, nothing special. Just stopped for a little rest and a look around."

"The Lord's built everything as it should be," he often remarked. "The sky, and the earth, with the rivers flowing on it, and the boats. You can take a boat and go wherever you like—to Ryazan, or to Rybinsk, to Perm or to Astrakhan. I was in Ryazan once—not a bad town, but dreary—drearier than Nizhni-Novgorod. Our Nizhni's a cheerful place. Astrakhan's drearier too. The main thing is that Astrakhan's full of Kalmyks, and I don't like them. I have no use for your Mordovians and Kalmyks and Persians and Germans and all the foreign-born."

He spoke slowly, his words cautiously searching for someone who would agree with him, and the stonemason Pyotr usually did.

"They're not foreign-born; they're out-born," asserted Pyotr acrimoniously. "Born out of the pale, out of Christ, and living without Him."

Grigori beamed.

"Say what you will, but as for me, brother, I'll take the pure-born, the Russian, the straight-eyed. I have no use for Jews either, and for the life of me I can't see why God had to make foreigners. It's a deep wisdom."

The stonemason added sullenly:

"It may be deep, but there's lots of things in this world we could do without."

Having listened to these remarks, Osip would put in his word, mocking and caustic:

"Yes, there's lots of things we could do without—those remarks of yours, for instance. Always clashing. What you need's a lashing!"

Osip held himself aloof, never indicating with whom he agreed, with whom he disagreed. Sometimes it seemed that he agreed with everyone and everything, but more often you could see that he was simply sick of everything and looked upon all people as fools.

"Ekh, you pig's puppies, you!" he would say to Pyotr and Grigori and Yefimushka.

They would give a little laugh, not very cheerful or enthusiastic, but still they would laugh.

My master gave me five kopeks a day for food. This was not enough, and I often went hungry. Seeing this, the workmen would invite me to have lunch and supper with them, and sometimes the contractors would take me along to the tavern for tea. I accepted their invitations gladly; I enjoyed sitting in their company, listening to their slow speech and strange stories. They were pleased by my knowledge of religious books.

"You've ate your fill of books; crammed your craw to bursting," said Osip, fixing me with blue eyes whose expression was hard to define — the irises seemed melting into the whites.

"Treasure your knowledge, store it up; some day it will come in handy. When you grow up you can become a monk, to console the people with kind words. Or else a millionary."

"Missionary," corrected the stonemason in a voice which for some reason sounded hurt.

"Eh?" asked Osip.

"Missionaries is what they're called, I say. You're not deaf."

"Very well—missionaries—to argue with heretics. Or maybe you can join the heretics themselves—that don't pay so bad either. If you use your head you can make a good living out of heresy."

Grigori gave an uneasy laugh and Pyotr muttered into his beard:

"Witches don't live bad either, and all sorts of godless creatures."

"Witches aren't learned—witches have no need of book-learning," objected Osip, then, turning to me: "Here, listen to this: once there was a lonely fellow lived in our volost— Tushnikov was his name—a poor sort of good-for-nothing. Lived like a feather—here and there, wherever the wind blew—neither workman, nor loafer. Then one day, having nothing better to do, he went off on a pilgrimage. For two years he was gone, and all of a sudden he turns up dressed different — hair to his shoulders, calotte on his head, a rusty sort of cassock made of denim on his body. He pierces people with a fierce eye and keeps crying: 'Repent, thrice-damned!' Who's to keep people from repenting—especially the women? He did a fine business. Tushnikov had food. Tushnikov had drink. Tushnikov had all the women he wanted. . . ."

"Food and drink don't count," interrupted the stonemason angrily.

"Then what *does*?"

"The word—that's what counts!"

"Well, I didn't look into his word. I have more words than I know what to do with myself."

"We know that Tushnikov. Dmitri Vasilyevich is his name and patronymic," said Pyotr in an injured tone, while Grigori silently dropped his eyes and stared at his glass.

"I'm not out for an argument," announced Osip by way of conciliation. "I just wanted to show Maximich the various ways to earn your daily bread."

"Some of those ways lead to jail."

"Many of them," agreed Osip. "Very few lead to the priesthood. You have to know where to turn off."

He was always slightly ironic in respect to pious people like the plasterer and stonemason. Perhaps he disliked them, but he carefully hid his feelings. In general it was difficult to discover his attitude toward people.

He was more kind and gentle with Yefimushka. The roofer did not participate in the discussions of God, justice, sects, and the griefs of human life—the favourite themes of his companions. Placing his chair sidewise, so that the back would not rub his hump, Yefimushka would calmly drink his tea, one glass after another. But suddenly he would become alert, glancing about the smoke-filled room, listening through the babble of voices, finally jumping up and disappearing. That meant that one of his creditors, of whom Yefimushka had a good dozen, had entered the tavern. Since some of them were inclined to take out their debts in beatings, the roofer was kept on the jump.

"Funny the way they fly off the handle," he would say wonderingly. "I'd be only too glad to pay if I had the money."

"Phooh, the lump!" Osip would fling in his wake.

Sometimes Yefimushka would sit lost in thought, seeing nothing, hearing nothing, his bony face relaxed, his kindly eyes even more kindly.

"What are you thinking of, friend?" they would ask him.

"I'm thinking that if only I was rich, I would marry a real, genuine lady, a noblewoman, true as I'm living—a colonel's daughter, for instance, and wouldn't I love her though? Lord, how quick I'd burn up alongside of her! It was like this, brothers: once I put a new roof on a country house belonging to a colonel. . . ."

"Who had a widowed daughter. We've heard all that!" interrupted Pyotr testily.

But Yefimushka went on unperturbed, rubbing his knees with his palms and cleaving the air with his hump as he swayed back and forth:

"She used to come out into the garden, all white and fluffy, and I'd look down at her from the roof and think to myself: what good's the sun, what good's the whole world without her? If only I could fly down like a dove to rest at her feet! A blossom she was, a sweet blue blossom in a pot of cream. Ah, lads, with a lady like her, life ought to be one long night!

"And what would you do for food?" demanded Pyotr sternly. But this did not disturb Yefimushka either.

"Lordy!" he exclaimed. "Would we want much food? And her so rich besides!"

Osip laughed.

"You wastrel, you, Yefimushka! You'll soon be wasted clean away at this business."

Yefimushka never spoke about anything but women, and he was not a steady workman. At times he would work quickly and well, at others he was inefficient, wielding his wooden mallet listlessly and carelessly, leaving gaps in the seams. He always smelled of blubber-oil, but he also had his own odour, a pleasant, wholesome odour, like that of fresh-hewn logs.

It was interesting to talk to the carpenter about everything; interesting, but not very pleasant. His words were always disconcerting, and it was difficult to tell when he was joking and when in earnest.

Grigori's favourite subject of conversation was God, whom he loved and firmly believed in.

"Grigori," I once said, "do you know that there are people who don't believe in God?"

He gave a short laugh:

"What's that?"

"They say there is no God."

"Ah, yes. I know."

Making a pass at an invisible fly, he went on:

"Remember how King David said, 'The fool saith in his heart there is no God'? Just see how long ago judgment was passed on such ignoramuses. You can't get along without God."

And Osip remarked, as though in agreement:

"Just try to deprive Pyotr of his faith in God—he'll show you!"

Shishlin's handsome face became solemn; touching his beard with fingers whose nails were caked with plaster, he observed mysteriously:

"God dwells in all flesh; the conscience and the inner essence are the gifts of God."

"And sin?"

"Sin is born of the flesh, of Satan. Sin is on the outside, like pockmarks; no more than that. He sins most who thinks most of sin; if your mind avoids thoughts of sin, you won't commit it. Thoughts of sin are sown by the devil, master of the flesh."

, "Somehow I don't think—it's not just exactly . . ." said the stonemason doubtingly.

"Just exactly. God is sinless, and man is the image and likeness of God. Sinning is done by the image, the flesh; the likeness is incapable of sinning. The likeness is the spirit."

He smiled triumphantly, but Pyotr muttered:

"It seems to me it's not just exactly. . . ."

"According to you," said Osip to the stonemason, "if there's no sin, there's no repentance, and if there's no repentance, there's no salvation."

"That's right. 'Devil out of sight, God out of mind,' as the old folks used to say."

Not being a drinker, Shishlin was made tipsy by two glasses of wine. His face would grow rosy, his eyes childlike, his voice lilting.

"Ah, brothers, what a wonderful life we live—working a bit, and not going hungry, praise the Lord! It's a wonderful life!"

He wept, the tears pouring down his cheeks and shining like beads on his silky beard.

I was repelled by these glassy tears, and

by the fact that he was forever eulogizing life. Granny's eulogies were much more convincing—more simple and less cloying.

These talks kept me in a state of constant tension and roused vague fears. I had read many stories about muzhiks and I was aware of the striking difference between book muzhiks and actual muzhiks. All the muzhiks in the books were unfortunate creatures; and all of them, good and bad alike, lacked the richness of thought and speech characteristic of living muzhiks. The book muzhik spoke less of God and sects and the church, more of his betters, of the land, of life's injustice and hardships. He also spoke less of women, and his attitude toward them was less crude and more well-disposed. For the real muzhik, a woman was a diversion, but a dangerous diversion; he had to be sly with her, lest she overpower him and ruin his life. The book muzhik was either good or bad, but all of him was right there, in the book, while the real muzhik was neither good nor bad and was vastly intriguing. However garrulous the real muzhik, you always felt there was something about him which remained unsaid, and that this something was kept for himself alone, and that perhaps it was just what remained unsaid which represented his very essence.

Of all the book muzhiks, I liked Pyotr from *The Carpenters' Artel* best. I wanted to read this story to my friends, and took the book with me to the fairgrounds. Often I spent the night at one or another of the workmen's artels, often because I was too tired after my day's work to make the trip home.

When I said that I had a book about carpenters, all of them were greatly interested, especially Osip. He took the book out of my hands and leafed through it, shaking his saintlike head sceptically.

"As if it was written about us! Think of that, now! Who wrote it, one of the gentles? Hm, I thought so! Gentles and officials don't stop at anything! What God leaves out, your official puts in; that's what they're here for."

"You don't speak very respectfully about God," observed Pyotr.

"That's all right. My words mean just about as much to the Lord as a snowflake on my bald pate. Don't you worry, you and me're not reaching up as far as God."

Suddenly he flared up and began tossing off sharp words like sparks from a flint, directing them against the things he hated. Several times in the course of the day he asked:

"Will you read us something, Maximich? Good, very good. That was a fine thing to have thought up."

When work was over, we returned to his artel for supper, and after supper Pyotr dropped in with his workman Ardalion, and Shishlin with a young chap named Foma. A lamp was lighted in the shed where the workmen slept, and I began to read. They listened without stirring or saying a word until Ardalion exclaimed irritably:

"I've had enough."

He went out. Grigori was the first to fall asleep, his mouth hanging open in an expression of wonder. The carpenters soon did the same, but Pyotr, Osip, and Foma, grouped close about me, listening with strained attention.

When I had finished, Osip immediately put

out the lamp. The stars showed that it was almost midnight.

Pyotr asked in the darkness:

"What's the point of a book like that? Who's it against?"

"Time to go to sleep," said Osip, pulling off his boots.

Foma silently withdrew to one side.

"I'm asking—who's it written against?" repeated Pyotr insistently.

"They know," answered Osip, making a bed for himself on some scaffolding.

"If it's written against stepmothers, then there's no point in it: a book like that's not going to reform stepmothers," insisted the stonemason. "And if it's against Pyotr, there's no sense in it either. He had to take what was coming to him. Once he committed a murder, he got Siberia, and fair enough. A book can't help in a case like that . . . it can't, can it?"

Osip made no reply, so the stonemason concluded:

"These writers have nothing else to keep them busy, so they go poking their fingers into other people's business. Like when a

593

bunch of women get together. Well, good night, time to sleep."

For a moment he stood in the moon-blue square of the doorway and asked:

"What do you think, Osip?"

"Eh?" replied Osip sleepily.

"Oh, all right, go to sleep."

Shishlin stretched out on the floor where he had been sitting; Foma lay down on the crushed straw beside me. The whole settlement was asleep. From the distance came the whistle of trains, the heavy rumble of iron wheels, the clanking of buffers. The shed was filled with the sounds of snoring in various keys. I was disappointed; I had expected some discussion, but there was none.

Suddenly Osip said quietly and distinctly:

"Don't take any of that to heart, fellows. You're young yet and have a long life ahead of you. Store up your own ideas. One thought of your own is worth two that are borrowed. Asleep, Foma?"

"No," responded Foma eagerly.

"You both know how to read, so go ahead, but don't put too much store in it.

They print whatever they like—theirs is the power."

He slipped his legs over the edge of the scaffolding, grabbed the edge with his hands, and leaned toward us as he continued:

"A book—what's a book, after all? An informer, that's what a book is. Like as if it said: look, here's what an ordinary man's like—a carpenter, or some other such person; and then look, here's what the gentles are like, as though they were different from other folk. A book's not written without a purpose; it's written to protect somebody or other."

"Pyotr did right to kill that contractor," said Foma thickly.

"Why should you say such a thing? It's never right to kill a man. I know you don't like Grigori, but get that thought out of your head. None of us are rich. Today I'm the master, tomorrow I'm a simple workman again."

"I'm not talking about you, Uncle Osip."

"It's all the same."

"You're a just man."

"Wait, I'll tell you what the book's about," said Osip, interrupting Foma's resentful words.

"It's a sly book. Here's a nobleman without a muzhik, and here's a muzhik without a nobleman. So look you—the nobleman's bad off, and the muzhik not much better. The nobleman grows dull and weak, the muzhik turns into a drunk and a braggart with a grudge in his heart. That's what the story says. It tries to show it was better being serfs to the landlord: the nobleman hid behind the muzhik, the muzhik behind the nobleman, and the two of them went round and round, full-bellied and content. Oh, I don't deny that life was more peaceful under serfdom. The landlords found no advantage in having poor muzhiks; well-fed and empty-headed—that's how they wanted them. I say what I know, for didn't I live almost forty years in bondage to the landlords? Plenty of wisdom's been lashed into my hide."

I recalled that the drayman Pyotr, the one who had cut his throat, had spoken in the same way about the gentry, and I did not relish the fact that the thoughts of Osip should coincide with those of that vicious old man.

Osip placed his hand on **my leg** as he continued:

"You must be able to see through to the meaning in books and other writings. Nobody does anything without some purpose, even if they try to hide it. And there's a purpose in writing books, which is to muddle your head. Brain goes into everything, down to chopping wood and cobbling shoes. . . ."

He went on talking for a long time, now lying back on his bed, now jumping up to softly scatter his neat sayings into the silence and darkness:

"It's said: there's a big difference between the landlord and the muzhik. That's not true. We're both the same, only he's on top. To be sure, the nobleman learns from his books, while I learn from my bruises, but except that his backside's whiter, he's not any brighter. Oh no, young fellow, it's time to be bringing a new order into this world; drop those books, throw them away. Let everyone ask himself: Who am I anyway? A man. And who's the landlord? Also a man. So what's the difference? Or maybe God asks five kopeks more of him? Oh no, when it comes to paying, we're all the same in the eyes of God. . . ."

Finally, in the early morning, when the dawn had extinguished the stars, Osip said to me:

"Can't I talk though? I said a lot of things tonight I never thought before in my life. Don't take me serious, fellows—I made that up mostly because I couldn't sleep, not because I meant it. When you lay here with your eyes open you invent things just for the fun of it: once upon a time there was a crow, it flew from the fields to the hills, from farm to farm, lived out its hour, sickened and died, rotted and dried. What's the sense to a tale like that? No sense at all. Well, let's go to sleep. Have to be getting up soon. . . ."

XVIII

Like stoker Yakov at an earlier time, Osip grew in my eyes until he cut off my vision of everyone else. He had much in common with the stoker, but at the same time he reminded me of my grandfather and the dogmatist Pyotr Vasilyev and the cook Smury, and while reminding me of all these people, so deeply impressed on my memory, he left his own pattern there, biting deep, like acid into brass. It was clear that he had two manners of thinking: during the working day, his simple, quick thinking was more practical and comprehensible than at night when he could not sleep, or in the evening, when he and I would walk to town to visit his mistress, a pancake vendor. He had special thoughts at night. They shone brightly and from all sides, like the light in a lantern, but I could not make out which was the right side, or which the one he preferred.

It seemed to me that he was vastly more clever than anyone I had ever met, and I hovered about him as restively as I had hovered about stoker Yakov, eager to know and understand the man, but he wriggled and slipped away, escaping me. Wherein lay the truth about him? What aspect of him was I to accept as the true one?

I remembered how he had said to me:

"Use your brains to find me out; go ahead and try."

My pride was injured, but so was something more than pride. It became of vital importance to me that I comprehend the old man.

For all his elusiveness, he was a stable person. It seemed that if he should live another hundred years, he would remain the same, preserving himself changeless among these amazingly changeful folk. The dogmatist had roused in me the same impression of stability, but in him I had found this unpleasant. The stability of Osip was of a different sort, more desirable.

Human instability was constantly making itself felt, and the unexpected leaps people made from one position to another upset me. I was already weary of wondering at these inexplicable leaps, and they gradually dampened the lively interest I took in people, confounding my love for them.

One day at the beginning of July a rickety cab came dashing up to the spot where we were working. On the driver's seat sat a drunken izvozchik, hatless, with a bleeding lip, hiccoughing glumly into his beard. In the seat behind lolled the drunken Grigori Shishlin held by the arms of a fat, red-cheeked girl in a straw hat trimmed with scarlet ribbons and glass cherries and with galoshes on her bare feet. She was lurching with the movement of the cab and waving a parasol in her free hand, as she laughed and shouted:

"Hey, you devils! The fair's closed, there is no fair, but here they are dragging me to the fair!"

Crumpled and battered, Grigori crawled out of the cab, sat down on the ground, and announced to us with tears in his eyes:

"Here I am, down on my knees—I've sinned enormous! Thought it all out, and sinned—so there! Yefimushka says: Grigori, Grigori, says he. . . . And it's right what he says, but— forgive me! I'd like to treat the whole lot of you. It's true what he says: we only live once . . . can't live more than once. . . ."

The girl went off into peals of laughter and hopped about, losing her galoshes, while the izvozchik shouted:

"Come on, let's go! Come along—I can't hold the horse!"

The horse, an old, decrepit nag, foaming at the mouth, seemed to have become rooted to the spot, and the whole picture was indescribably funny. Grigori's workmen roared with laughter as they viewed their master, his resplendent lady, and the dazed driver.

The only one who did not laugh was Foma, who stood next to me in the doorway of the shop muttering:

"So he broke loose, the pig! Back home he's got a wife—and such a pretty one!"

The izvozchik kept urging them to get going, so the girl climbed down and pulled Grigori back into the cab, where he lay at her feet. Then she flourished her parasol and cried:

"We're off!"

At a shout from Foma, who seemed hurt at seeing Grigori make such a fool of himself, the men resumed their work; they exchanged a few good-natured remarks at their master's expense, but apparently they envied him.

"Calls himself the master," mumbled Foma. "There's less than a month left before we finish our work and go back to the village, and he couldn't wait. . . ."

I too was annoyed with Grigori—that girl with the cherries had looked so incongruous beside him!

Often I wondered why Grigori Shishlin was the master, and Foma Tuchkov a mere workman.

Foma was sturdy, blond, and curly-haired, with an aquiline nose, intelligent grey eyes, and a round face. He did not resemble a muzhik, and had he been well dressed, he might easily have passed for a merchant's son from a good family. He was morose, taciturn, matter-of-fact. Since he knew how to read and write, he kept the contractor's accounts and drew up the estimates; he could make his comrades work, though he himself showed little love for it.

"You can't do everything in one lifetime," he would say calmly. He was contemptuous of books: "Everything gets printed; here, I'll make up a story for you if you like—nothing very difficult about that."

But he listened attentively to whatever was said, and if something interested him, he would insist on finding out all the details, drawing his own conclusions and measuring things by his own measure.

Once I said to Foma that he ought to become a contractor, to which he answered lazily

"If I had thousands of rubles pouring in right from the start, that wouldn't be so bad, but to have the bother of handling a lot of workmen for a mere pittance—what's the sense? No, I'll bide my time, and then take myself off to the monastery in Oranka. I'm big and handsome; maybe some rich merchant's widow will fall in love with me. Such things happen. A fellow from Sergachi made a good match in two years, and with a maid from the townsfolk at that. She caught sight of him while he was carrying the icon from house to house. . . ."

That was his plan. He had heard many stories about how men had won soft livings for themselves by first becoming novices in a monastery. I had an aversion for such stories, and for Foma's way of thinking, but I was sure he would enter a monastery.

Yet when the fair opened, Foma, to everyone's surprise, became a waiter in a tavern. I can hardly say that this surprised his companions, but they began to mock him. When they

ere about to set out for tea on Sundays or
olidays, they would say to each other with
laugh:

"Let's go give Foma some business."

And once in the tavern, they would call
ut imperiously:

"Hey, waiter—you with the curly hair—
ome over here!"

He would come over, chin in the air, and
sk:

"What will you have?"

"Don't you recognize old friends?"

"I'm too busy."

He realized that his comrades were con-
emptuous of him and wanted to tease him,
nd he eyed them with bland endurance, his
ace freezing in an expression that seemed
o say:

"Well, hurry up and get it over with."

"I suppose you want a tip," they would
ay, elaborately fumbling with their purses
nd then leaving without giving him a kopek.

I asked Foma why he had become a waiter
when he had planned to become a monk.

"I never planned to become a monk,"

he answered, "and I don't intend being a waiter for long."

But four years later I met him in Tsaritsyn, still a waiter in a tavern, and finally I read in the paper that Foma Tuchkov had been arrested for attempted housebreaking.

I was particularly impressed by the story of stonemason Ardalion, the oldest and best worker in Pyotr's artel. This jolly, black-bearded, forty-year-old muzhik also made me wonder why Pyotr was the master instead of him. He rarely drank and almost never became drunk; he was skilled at his job and worked with zest, making the bricks fly like red pigeons. Alongside of him, the dour and ailing Pyotr seemed of no account. Pyotr was fond of saying:

"I build brick houses for others in order to build a wooden coffin for myself."

Ardalion would shout as he laid his bricks with joyful enthusiasm:

"Come on, fellows, lend a hand, to the glory of God!"

And he would tell them how he intended going to Tomsk the following spring, where his brother-in-law had signed a contract to build a church and had offered him a job as foreman.

"Everything's settled. Building churches— that's a job I love!" he said; then, turning to me: "Come along with me. Life's easy in Siberia for anyone who can read and write. There's a high price on learning out there."

I agreed to go along, and Ardalion cried triumphantly:

"Good! But in all seriousness, no joking."

His attitude toward Pyotr and Grigori was one of good-natured condescension, like an adult with children, and he said to Osip:

"The braggarts! They show each other everything that's in their heads, like a hand of cards. One says: look here, what a hand I've got, and the other: but just take a peek at these trumps of mine!"

"Why not?" replied Osip enigmatically. "Bragging is only human; all the girls wear their breasts in front."

"With them it's God this, and God that, but they're saving up money all the same," said Ardalion, unappeased.

"You can't tell me Grigori's saving up anything."

"I'm talking about the other. Why don't he go off into the woods, into the wilderness, alone with God? Lord, but I'm sick of everything here; in the spring I'm leaving for Siberia."

The other workmen, envying Ardalion, said:

"If we had someone to hook on to, like that brother-in-law of yours, Siberia wouldn't scare us either."

And then suddenly Ardalion disappeared. One Sunday he left the workshop, and for three days no one knew what had happened to him.

They made awed conjectures:

"Maybe somebody's done him in."

"Maybe he went swimming and drowned."

Finally Yefimushka came and announced, somewhat abashed:

"Ardalion's on a spree."

"That's a lie," cried Pyotr incredulously.

"On a spree, on a drunk. Just went up in smoke, like the hayloft, right from the centre. As if his wife had died. . . ."

"He's been a widower a long time. Where is he?"

Pyotr set out angrily to rescue Ardalion, but received a beating from him.

Then Osip tightened his lips, thrust his hands deep into his pockets, and announced:

"I'll go and have a look myself—see what's the cause. He's a good sort."

I went too.

"Just look at that, now," said Osip on the way. "A man goes living along, very respectable, and then all of a sudden—up goes his tail and he's off to the garbage pile. Keep your eyes open, Maximich, and take a lesson!"

We came to one of the cheapest brothels in "the gay town of Kunavino," where we were met by a thievish-looking old woman. Osip whispered something into her ear and she led us into a small, empty room, dark and dirty as a stable. A fat woman was tossing in her sleep on a cot. The old woman gave her a punch in the side and said:

"Get out, hear? Get out, you toad!"

The woman jumped up in fright, rubbing her face and crying:

"My God, what is it, who is it?"

"The detectives have come," said Osip gravely. With a gasp, the woman vanished, and he spat in her wake.

"They're more scared of detectives than of the devil himself," he explained.

The old woman took a little mirror off the wall and lifted a flap of wallpaper.

"Take a look. Is that the one?"

Osip peered through the opening.

"That's him. Get rid of the girl."

I also had a look. A lamp was burning on the sill of a tightly shuttered window in a room as wretched as the one we were in. Near the lamp stood a cross-eyed, naked Tatar girl sewing up her undershirt. Behind her could be seen the bloated face of Ardalion propped up on two pillows, his black, stiff beard splintering out in all directions. The Tatar girl gave a start, pulled her shirt on, walked past the bed, and suddenly appeared in our room.

Osip glanced at her and spat again:

"Phooh, you shameless hussy!"

"You an old fool!" she retorted with a laugh.

Osip laughed too and shook his finger at her.

We went into the Tatar girl's den, and the old man sat down at the feet of Ardalion. For a long time he tried to wake him up, but Ardalion only kept muttering:

"Oh, all right . . . wait a minute, we'll go. . . ."

At last he sat up, stared wildly at Osip and me, and then, closing his inflamed eyes, muttered:

"Well? . . ."

"What's happened?" asked Osip calmly and cheerlessly, but without reproach.

"Lost my head," explained Ardalion with a hoarse cough.

"How?"

"Simple enough."

"Looks pretty bad."

"I know. . . ."

Ardalion took an uncorked bottle of vodka from the table and began to pour it down his throat, then offered the bottle to Osip.

"Want some? Should be something to eat here too."

The old man took a swig, made a face, and began to chew a piece of bread very intently, while Ardalion drawled:

"See—I picked up with that Tatar girl. All Yefimushka's doings. He says she's young —an orphan from Kasimov—planned to go to the fair."

Through the wall came impudent words in a broken tongue:

"The Tatar's best! Like a young chicken. Chase old man away. He no your father."

"She's the one," muttered Ardalion, staring dully at the wall.

"I saw her," said Osip.

Ardalion turned to me:

"Just look what I've done, brother. . . ."

I expected that Osip would begin to scold Ardalion, or lecture him, and that the sinner would be shamed into repentance. But nothing of the sort occurred. They sat there shoulder to shoulder, calmly exchanging brief remarks. It was very sad to see them there in that dark, dirty hovel; the Tatar girl kept talking broken Russian through the hole in the wall, but they ignored her. Osip took a dried fish off the table, banged it against his boot, and began to skin it.

"Is all your money gone?" he asked.

"Pyotr owes me something."

"You should be leaving for Tomsk soon. Will you manage now?"

"I'm not so sure about Tomsk."

"Why, have you changed your mind?"

"If it wasn't my relatives inviting me. . . ."

"What?"

"My sister and her husband. . . ."

"Well?"

"It's not much fun working for your relatives."

"Employers are all the same, relatives or not."

"Even so. . . ."

They sat there speaking in such a grave, friendly way that the Tatar girl stopped teasing them. She slipped back into the room, silently took her dress off a nail, and disappeared.

"She's young," said Osip.

Ardalion looked at him and said good-naturedly:

"It's all Yefimushka's doings. All he thinks about is women. . . . The Tatar girl's jolly enough, always talking nonsense."

"Watch out, or you'll get stuck for good," warned Osip. With a last chew at the fish, he took his leave.

On the way back, I said to him:

"Why did you come?"

"Just to see what was happening. He's a friend of mine. I've known lots of such cases: a man goes living along, and then, all of a sudden it's like he was escaping from prison," he said, repeating himself: "Keep away from vodka!"

A minute later he added:

"But it's dull without it."

"Without vodka?"

"Yes. Once you take a swig, it's as if you was in another world."

Ardalion did get stuck for good. A few days later he returned to work, but soon disappeared again, and in the spring I met him with some other tramps chopping ice from around a river barge. We were glad to see each other and went into a tavern for tea.

"Remember what a workman I was?" he boasted over the tea. "There's no denying it, I was a wizard at my job. I could have made hundreds of rubles."

"But you didn't."

"Of course I didn't," he cried proudly. "A fig for a job!"

He had assumed a blustering air which attracted the attention of the people in the tavern.

"Remember what Pyotr, that quiet thief, used to say about work? 'Brick houses for others, a wooden coffin for yourself.' There you are; there's your job for you!"

"Pyotr's a sick man," I said. "He's afraid of dying."

"I'm a sick man too," shouted Ardalion. "My soul's sick!"

On Sundays I often left the centre of town and descended to "Millionaire" Street, where all the tramps lived. I saw how quickly Ardalion was becoming one of these outcasts. Only a year before he had been a cheerful, sober-minded workman; now he had adopted loud manners, a swaggering walk, and a defiant glance, as though challenging everyone to quarrel and fight.

"Just see how people listen to me. I'm a leader here," he would boast.

Unsparing of the money he earned, he would treat the tramps, and was always entering fights in defence of the loser. Often he could be heard crying:

"That's unjust, fellows! You must act just!"

And so they nicknamed him "The Just," which pleased him greatly.

I tried to understand the people crammed into the stone sack of that old and dirty street. All of them were people who had broken away from the main stream of life, but they seemed to have created a life of their own, which was gay and independent of others. Bold and carefree, they reminded me of grandfather's tales about the Volga boatmen, who so readily turned into highwaymen or hermits. When they were out of work, they did not hesitate to make petty thefts from the barges and steamers, but this did not shock me in the least. I saw that life was darned with thieving like an old coat with grey thread, but I also saw that sometimes, as during a fire, or the breaking up of the ice on the river, or an urgent loading, these people worked with tremendous enthusiasm and self-sacrifice, unsparing of their strength. And on the whole they were more gay than other people.

But when Osip noticed my friendship with Ardalion, he said to me paternally:

"Listen here, my boy, aren't you getting a bit too friendly with those 'Millionaires' down there? See they don't bring you to harm."

I explained as best I could that I liked these people, living so carefree, without working.

"Free as the birds!" he interrupted with a laugh. "That's just because they're lazy good-for-nothings. For them, work is a punishment."

"Does anybody enjoy it? 'Nobody ever built himself a mansion by honest labour,' as the saying goes."

I quoted it glibly, so often had I heard it and so true did it seem. But Osip flared up and shouted:

"Who says things like that? Fools and sluggards, and it's not for you to listen to such things, you puppy! It's only the envious ones or the failures who talk such nonsense; you better grow some feathers before you try flying! As for this friendship of yours, I'll tell your master about it, and you'll have only yourself to blame."

And he did tell him. My master said to me in the presence of Osip:

"Drop the 'Millionaires,' Peshkov. They're all thieves and prostitutes on that street, and it leads straight to prison or the hospital. Drop them!"

I began to hide the fact that I visited "Millionaire" Street, but soon I was forced to stop it.

One day Ardalion, The Kid and I were sitting on the roof of a shed in the yard of a lodginghouse. The Kid was giving us an amusing account of how he had made his way on foot from Rostov-on-the-Don to Moscow. He was an ex-soldier who had served in the engineers, had been decorated with the Cross of St. George, and received a wound in the knee during the Turkish war which had lamed him for life. Short and stocky, he had tremendous strength in his hands, a strength which found no outlet, since his lameness prevented him from working. Some disease had caused his hair and beard to fall out, so that his head was as bald as a baby's.

With a glitter in his amber eyes, he was saying:

"So I arrived at Serpukhov; there I saw a priest sitting in his back yard, so I went up to him and said: 'Could you spare a mite for a hero of the Turkish war? . . . '"

Ardalion shook his head and said:

"Oh, what a liar, what a liar!"

"Why a liar?" asked The Kid without taking offence, but Ardalion went on in a lazy tone of reproach:

"You ought to live upright. You ought to get a job as a night watchman, like all the lame ones, but instead you go prowling around and telling lies."

"I just do it for the fun of it—to make people laugh."

"Why don't you laugh yourself?"

Into the yard, dark and dirty in spite of the sunny weather, came a woman who began to wave something above her head and cry:

"Hey, girls, who wants to buy a skirt?"

Women came crawling out of the cracks in the houses and crowded around the seller. I immediately recognized her as Natalya, the washwoman. By the time I had jumped down off the roof she was already leaving the yard, having sold the skirt to the first bidder.

"Hello!" I cried joyfully on overtaking her outside the gate.

"Is that all you can say?" she asked, with a glance out of the corner of her eye. Suddenly she stopped and cried angrily:

"My God! What are you doing here?"

I was touched and embarrassed by her startled outcry. Fear and surprise were clearly written on her intelligent face, and I realized that it was for me she was afraid. I hastily explained that I did not live on that street, but only came occasionally to have a look.

"Have a look?" she repeated with mocking asperity. "Look where? Into the pockets of the passers-by, and down the blouses of the women, is that it?"

Her face looked worn, her lips were lax, and there were dark circles under her eyes.

At the door of a tavern she stopped and said:

"Come in for a glass of tea. You're dressed neat enough, not like these folks, but somehow I don't believe you."

But once we were inside she seemed to regain confidence in me. After pouring the tea, she began to talk dully about how she had waked up only an hour before and had not yet had anything to eat or drink.

"Last night I went to bed drunk as a cabby, but I don't remember where I drank or who I drank with."

I felt sorry for her and uncomfortable in her presence, and I wanted badly to ask about her daughter. When she had had some tea and vodka she began to speak in her usual brisk manner, with the coarseness common to all the women on this street. But when I asked her about her daughter she immediately became sober and said:

"Why do you ask? Oh no, my lad, you'll not be reaching my daughter, never in your life."

She took another drink and continued:

"My daughter has nothing to do with me. Who am I? A washwoman. What kind of a mother am I for the likes of her? She's learned and educated. That's something, brother! So she left me and went off to join a friend of hers, a rich girl, to become a governess, it seems. . . ."

After a short pause, she said softly:

"Nobody has any use for a washwoman. Maybe they have for a streetwalker, eh?"

That she was a streetwalker I had immediately guessed—all the women here were streetwalkers. But it was so shocking to hear her apply the name to herself that tears of shame and pity sprang to my eyes. The admission sounded particularly startling coming from Natalya, who only so recently had been a bold and clever and independent woman.

"You little fool," she said, glancing at me with a sigh. "Get away from here! And I advise you, *I* beg you, never to come back. It'll be your undoing."

Then she leaned over the table, tracing something on the tray with her finger, and began to speak softly and disconnectedly, as though to herself:

"But what do you care for my advice? If my own daughter wouldn't listen to me. . . . I used to say to her: you can't abandon your own mother! You can't! But she would answer: 'Then I'll kill myself.' So she went off to Kazan —wanted to learn nursing. All well and good. But what about me?. . . As for me, well, here I am. Who can I turn to? To the men out there in the street?. . ."

She sat there lost in thought, her lips moving soundlessly, apparently unaware of my presence. The corners of her lips drooped, turning her mouth into a crescent, and it was painful to see the twitching of her lips and the quivering of her wrinkles, speaking some silent message. Her face was hurt and childlike. A lock of hair had slipped from under the shawl on her head and lay on her cheek, curling back about her small ear. A tear fell into the glass of cold tea. Seeing this, she moved the glass away and closed her eyes tightly, squeezing out two more tears, and wiped her face with the ends of her shawl.

I could not bear sitting with her any longer and quietly got up.

"Goodbye."

"Eh? Be off, be off to the devil!" she said, waving me away without looking up, probably having forgotten who I was.

I returned to the yard in search of Ardalion, with whom I had planned to go fishing. I wanted to tell him about the woman, but he and The Kid were no longer up on the roof. While searching for them in the cluttered yard, I heard the clamour of one of the usual street rows.

I went out of the gate and almost ran into Natalya. She was stumbling blindly along the pavement, sniffling and wiping her bruised face on her shawl with one hand, pushing back her matted hair with the other. Behind her strode Ardalion and The Kid.

"Let her have it again, come on!" cried The Kid.

Ardalion ran up and shook his fist at her. She whirled around, her face distorted, her eyes blazing with hate: "Go on, strike me," she shouted.

I grabbed Ardalion's hand, and he looked at me in surprise:

"What's wrong with you?"

"Don't touch her," I gasped faintly.

He burst out laughing.

"Who is she, your mistress? Oh, Natalya, you skunk, even snared a monk!"

The Kid also guffawed, slapping himself on the thighs; then the two of them began taunting me abusively. But this gave Natalya time to escape. When I felt I could stand it no longer, I knocked down The Kid by butting him in the chest and ran away.

For a long time thereafter I kept away from "Millionaire" Street, but I met Ardalion once again—this time on a ferryboat.

"Hello," he said joyfully, "whatever happened to you?"

When I told him I had been offended by the way he had struck Natalya and insulted me, he laughed good-naturedly:

"Did you think we meant it? We teased you just for the fun of it. As for her—why shouldn't we hit her? She's only a streetwalker. If a man can beat his wife, why spare a slut like her? But we were just fooling. Fists don't teach you anything, I know that well enough."

"What do you think you could teach her? You're no better than she is."

He threw his arm over my shoulder and gave me a shake.

"That's the evil of it," he said with a snort. "Nobody's any better than anybody else. I can see it all, brother—the whole thing, inside and out. I'm not one of your village yokels."

He was tipsy and gay, and he gazed at me with the affectionate forbearance of a kind teacher coaching a dull pupil.

Occasionally I met Pavel Odintsov. Livelier than ever, he now dressed like a dandy and was condescending toward me. Once he said reprovingly:

"Why did you ever take a job like that? You'll never get anywhere, working with those muzhiks."

Then he sadly recounted the news from the workshop:

"Zhikharev still keeps company with that horse. Looks like Sitanov's pining over something or other—drinks more than's good for him. The wolves ate up Gogolev— he got drunk while he was home during Yuletide and the wolves just chewed him to pieces."

Pavel went off into a peal of laughter as he indulged his imagination:

"Chewed him up and got drunk themselves! Went walking about the forest on their hind legs like circus dogs, howling their heads off, and the next day they all dropped dead!"

I too laughed as I listened to him, but deep down in my heart I realized that the workshop and all it had meant to me was a thing of the past. This was rather sad.

XIX

During the winter there was almost no work at the fairgrounds. At home I did the same old tasks. They occupied the entire day, but my evenings were free, and to the assembled household I once more read novels from the *Niva* and *The Moscow Leaflet,* which I heartily disliked. At night I read good books and attempted to write verse.

One day when my mistresses were at vespers and my master, who was not feeling well, was at home with me, he said:

"Victor keeps joking about your writing poetry; is that true, Peshkov? Let's hear something you've written."

Finding it awkward to refuse, I read him a few of my poems. Apparently he did not like them, but he said:

"Keep it up, keep it up. Maybe you'll be another Pushkin. Ever read Pushkin?

> Do witches ever marry,
> And do goblins ever die?

In his day they still believed in goblins. But I don't think *he* did—just wrote that as a joke."

"Yes, brother, you should have been given an education," he mused. "But it's too late now. The devil only knows how you'll get on in the world. Hide that notebook of yours from the women, else they'll start teasing you. The women, brother, love hitting a person right on the sore spot!"

Of late my master had become quiet and meditative, often casting furtive glances about him and starting up at every ring of the doorbell. Sometimes he would become morbidly irritated by the slightest things, shouting at everyone and running out of the house to return home drunk at a late hour. It was clear that he was oppressed by something known to himself alone, something which had broken his spirit, so that he had lost confidence and interest in life and went on living just by force of habit.

After dinner on Sundays I would go out to walk until nine o'clock in the evening and then visit the tavern on Yamskaya Street. The keeper was an obese, sweaty creature with a passion for songs. Knowing this, choristers from all the surrounding churches would gather here in order to receive the vodka, beer, and tea to which he treated them in exchange for their songs. Choristers are a dull, drunken lot. They sing reluctantly, only for the sake of the treat, and rarely anything but church music. Since the pious topers protested that a tavern was no place for such music, the keeper would invite his guests into his private room, and I could catch the sounds only by listening at the door.

But often artisans and muzhiks from the village would perform in the tavern; the keeper combed the vicinity for singers, seeking them out among the peasants who came to town on market day, and inviting them to visit him.

A singer was always given a seat on a stool at the bar in front of the vodka barrel, the bottom forming a round frame for his head.

The best performer was Kleshchov, a skinny little saddler with a store of particularly fine songs. He had a mussed, crumpled appearance, and was tufted all over with red hair; his nose was as shiny as a corpse's and his dreamy little ferret-eyes seemed set immovable in their sockets.

Sometimes he would close them, rest his head against the bottom of the barrel, inflate his chest, and sing in a soft, but irresistible tenor:

Ah, the mist unrolled across the plain
And hid from sight the open road. . . .

Then he would get up and lean against the bar, his face lifted to the ceiling as he continued soulfully:

> *Ah, whither, whither shall I go,*
> *How shall I the pathway know?*

His voice was small, but inexhaustible. With a silver thread he stitched through the dull, dark mutter of the tavern, and there was not a soul who was proof against the mournful words of the music, and its sobbing accents. Even the drunkest of them would become wonderingly serious, staring hard at the table in front of them, while my own heart was nigh to bursting, brimming over with the powerful emotion always roused when fine music touches the depths of the soul.

Silent as a church grew the tavern, with the singer a benevolent priest. He preached no sermon, but earnestly prayed for the whole human race, and gave utterance to all the griefs of this poor human life. And on every hand these bearded folk gazed at him, their childlike eyes blinking meditatively in their beastlike faces. Occasionally one of them would give a deep sigh, convincing testimony to the force of the song. At such moments it seemed to me that all people lived a false, artificial life, whereas the true life—ah, here it was!

Off in one corner sat the pudgy-faced Lysukha, an unbridled creature, shamelessly wanton. She had withdrawn her head into her beefy shoulders and was weeping, the tears quietly laving her brazen eyes. Sprawling over a table not far away was the sombre chorister Mitropolsky, a hirsute giant with a fathomless bass voice and enormous eyes in a sodden face—a man resembling an unfrocked priest. He would gaze at the glass of vodka on the table in front of him, pick it up, lift it to his lips, then replace it untouched, cautiously, noiselessly, somehow unable to drink it.

And all the people in the tavern sat motionless, as though listening to something long forgotten, something very near and dear to their hearts.

When, having finished his song, Kleshchov humbly sank down on the stool, the tavern keeper would hand him a glass of vodka and say with a smile of satisfaction:

"Well done, to be sure! Though it's more a tale than a song you sing, you're a master at it, and that's the truth. There's none can deny it!"

Unhurriedly Kleshchov would drink his vodka, clear his throat, and say:

"As for singing, anyone can do that who has a voice, but I'm the only one can reveal the soul of a song."

"None of your bragging now!"

"Let him who has nothing to brag of hold his tongue," observed the singer unruffled, but with a note of stubbornness.

"You have a high opinion of yourself, Kleshchov!" exclaimed the tavern keeper in annoyance.

"High as my soul; I can go no higher."

From his corner Mitropolsky roared:

"How could you be expected to appreciate the singing of this ugly angel, you worms, you crawling things!"

He was always at loggerheads with everyone, quarrelling and finding fault, for which he was beaten almost every Sunday by the singers or anyone else who could or cared to attack him.

The tavern keeper loved Kleshchov's songs, but despised the man. He complained about him to everyone, obviously seeking some means of insulting him, or making fun of him. All the frequenters of the tavern, as well as Kleshchov himself, were aware of this.

"He's a good singer, but conceited; needs to be taken down a peg," was the tavern keeper's opinion, and some of his patrons agreed with him.

"There's truth in that; he's an uppity fellow!"

"And whatever he has to be uppity about! God gave him his voice—he didn't make it himself. And not much of a voice at that," insisted the tavern keeper.

"True enough, it's not so much his voice as how he uses it," joined in the others.

One day when the singer, drained of song, had left the tavern, the keeper began pressing Lysukha:

"You might try your hand at Kleshchov, Maria Yevdokimovna—maul him a bit, eh? You could do it easy."

"If I was younger," said the woman with a short laugh.

"What are the young ones good for!" urged the man. "You're the one to do it! It would do my heart good to see him slobbering over you! Give him the heartache! Wouldn't he sing then though? Do try, Yevdokimovna; you'll have my thanks for it."

But she refused. She just kept sitting there, enormously fat, with lowered lids, playing with the fringe of her shawl, and saying in a listless monotone:

"It's a young one you need here. If I was younger now, I wouldn't mind."

The tavern keeper kept trying to get Kleshchov drunk, but the latter, after singing two or three songs, each one punctuated by a glass of wine, would painstakingly wind a knitted scarf about his throat, pull a cap over his tousled head, and leave.

Often the tavern keeper would find competitors for Kleshchov; on such occasions, when the saddler had finished singing and been duly praised, the keeper would remark with suppressed excitement:

"By the by, there's another singer here tonight. Come right over, friend . . . be so kind!"

Sometimes the newcomer would have a good voice, but I never heard any of Kleshchov's rivals sing with his simplicity and fervour.

"Hm, that's very good, of course; you've got a voice, but as for the soul . . ." the tavern keeper would have to admit, not without regret.

Everyone would laugh.

"Looks like there's no beating the saddler!"

Kleshchov, gazing at everyone from under bristling red brows, would say to the tavern keeper with polite imperturbability:

"Try as you will, you'll not find a singer the likes of me, for my talent is the gift of God."

"We've all come from God."

"You'll never find one, not for all the wine in your shop."

A dark flush crept over the tavern keeper's face, and he muttered:

"We'll see about that—we'll see."

But Kleshchov kept insisting:

"Singing's none of your cockfights, you know."

"Who are you teaching?"

"I'm not teaching; I'm just showing you: a song's meant for the soul."

"Enough of this; let's have the song instead."

"I'm always ready to sing, even in my sleep," agreed Kleshchov, and with a slight cough he began.

All the pettiness, all the dross of words and intentions, all that was vulgar and of the tavern, miraculously vanished like smoke; everyone was conscious of the fresh breath of another sort of life, a life that was pure and pensive, full of love and sorrow.

I envied the man; with all my heart I envied his talent and the power he wielded over people. And how wonderfully he employed this power! I yearned to make the acquaintance of the saddler and to speak with him at length, but I lacked the courage to approach him, so strangely did he gaze about with his pale eyes which seemed to see no one. And there was something unpleasant about him which repulsed me, though I wanted to admire him not only when he sang. He had a disagreeable way of pulling down his cap like an old man, and ostentatiously winding a red knitted scarf about his neck and saying:

"It's my sweety made this for me,—a certain young lady. . . ."

When he was not singing he would puff himself up importantly, rub his frostbitten nose, and give reluctant, monosyllabic answers when questioned. Once when I sat down next to him and asked him something, he answered, without so much as looking at me:

"Get away, boy!"

I liked Mitropolsky much better. On entering the tavern he would make for a corner with the lumbering gait of a person carrying a heavy burden. Kicking out a chair, he would slump into it, his elbows resting on the table, his great shaggy head on his hands. Without a word he would gulp down two or three glasses of vodka, smacking his lips so loud that everyone started and turned to look at him; he would stare back defiantly, his chin in his hands, his matted mane falling in wild profusion over his flushed, puffy face.

"What are you looking at? What d'ye see?" he would suddenly burst forth.

"It's a goblin we see!" they would sometimes answer.

There were evenings when he drank in silence, and as silently went away, dragging his heavy feet after him. But several times I heard him denouncing people in the manner of the prophet:

"I am the incorruptible servant of the Lord, and as such do I condemn you, like Isaiah, of old. Woe to the city of Ariel, where thieves and malefactors do dwell in the loathsomeness of their lust! Woe to the ship of the earth sailing the waterways of the universe laden with pollution, which pollution is you, ye drunkards and gluttons, ye dregs of the earth! Your number is legion, oh ye accursed, yet the earth shall spurn your remains!"

The resonance of his voice shook the windowpanes, a thing which delighted his audience, and set them to singing his praises.

"Can't he lay it on, though, the shaggy old devil!"

It was easy to make his acquaintance—one had only to treat him. He would be sure to order a decanter of vodka and a serving of liver with red pepper, things which he loved for the searing they gave his throat and stomach. When I asked him what books I should read, he snapped back viciously:

"Why should you read?"

But he softened on seeing how his question shocked me, and murmured:

"Ever read Ecclesiastes?"

"Yes."

"Read Ecclesiastes. That's all. All the wisdom of the world's written there, only your squareheads don't understand it; nobody understands it. Who are you, a singer?"

"No."

"Why not? You ought to sing. That's the most stupid of all professions."

Someone at the next table said:

"What about you—aren't you a singer?"

"Me? I'm a loafer. Well?"

"Nothing."

"Naturally. Everybody knows there's nothing in that dome of yours. And there'll never be anything there. Amen!"

He used this tone with everybody, including me of course, although after I had treated him two or three times he softened toward me, even saying one day, in some surprise:

"Whenever I look at you I try to understand who you are, what you are, and why. But you can go to the devil for all I care!"

I could not find out his true opinion of Kleshchov. He listened to him with manifest pleasure, sometimes even smiling fondly, but he never sought to make his acquaintance and would speak of him gruffly and contemptuously:

"He's a clown! He knows how to breathe and understands what he's singing, but still he's an ass!"

"Why?"

"Because he was born one."

I would have enjoyed speaking to him when he was sober, but at such moments he only grunted and looked about with clouded, miserable eyes. From someone I learned that this man, drunk for the rest of his days, had once studied at the Kazan Academy and might have become a priest. At first I had discredited the story, but one day while talking to him, I happened to mention the name of Bishop Chrisanf.

"Chrisanf?" said Mitropolsky, with a toss of his head. "I knew him. He was my teacher and benefactor. That was in Kazan, at the Academy—I remember. Chrisanf means 'golden flower' as has been truly stated by Pamva Berynda. He was indeed golden, Chrisanf!"

"And who was Pamva Berynda?" I asked, but Mitropolsky replied curtly:

"That's none of your business."

When I reached home I wrote in my notebook: "Be sure to read 'Pamva Berynda.'" For some reason I got the notion that Berynda would answer all the questions troubling my soul.

The chorister loved to use bizarre names and unusual combinations of words. This annoyed me.

"Life is no Anisia!" he once said.

"Who is Anisia?" I asked.

"An anodyne," he replied, amused by my perplexity.

The use of such words and the fact that he had studied at the Academy led me to think that he had a great store of knowledge, and it was vexing that he should speak so reluctantly and so mystifyingly. Perhaps I did not know how to approach him.

Yet he left his mark on my soul. I liked the drunken boldness of his denunciations, made in the manner of the prophet Isaiah:

"Oh filth and stench of this earth!" he would roar. "Now art the wicked exalted, and the righteous cast down. But soon will dawn the judgment day, and then it will be too late, too late!"

On hearing this dispairing cry I would recall "That's Fine," and the washwoman Natalya, so grievously doomed, and Queen Margot, wreathed in clouds of unclean gossip. Already I had things to remember! . . .

My brief acquaintance with this man came to a curious end.

One spring day I met him in the fields near a soldiers' camp. He was walking alone, terribly bloated, nodding his head like a camel.

"Taking the air?" he asked hoarsely. "Let's do it together. I'm also out for a stroll. I'm a sick man, friend, indeed I am."

We walked along in silence for a while, and suddenly we caught sight of a man at the bottom of a pit. He was sitting slumped over against the wall, his coat jerked up over one ear as though he had tried to pull it off.

"Drunk!" decided the chorister, stopping to look.

But on the young grass not far away lay a large revolver and the man's cap and an unfinished bottle of vodka, up to the neck in grass. The man's face was buried in the collar of his coat, as though in shame.

For a minute we stood without a word, and then Mitropolsky planted his feet wide apart and said:

"Shot himself."

I had immediately seen that the man was dead rather than drunk, but it was so unexpected that I resisted the idea. I remember feeling neither fear nor pity as I gazed at the large, smooth skull and the blue ear poking above the coat collar. It was hard to believe that a person could kill himself on such a balmy spring day.

Mitropolsky briskly rubbed his unshaven cheeks, as though he were cold, and rasped:

"Oldish. Wife must have left him, or else he got into difficulties with money."

He sent me to town to fetch the police while he himself sat down on the edge of the pit, his legs hanging over, his seedy coat pulled tightly about his shoulders. As soon as I had informed the police of the suicide I ran back, but by that time the chorister had drunk up the remains of the suicide's vodka. On seeing me he brandished the empty bottle in the air.

"Here's what was his undoing!" he shouted, and hurled the bottle to the ground, smashing it to bits.

A policeman came running at my heels, glanced into the pit, took off his cap, and when he had crossed himself hesitantly, turned to the chorister:

"Who are you?"

"None of your business."

After brief consideration, the policeman said more politely:

"How's that now—a dead man lying here, and you drunk. . . ."

"I've been drunk for twenty years!" said the chorister proudly, thumping himself on the chest.

I was certain they would arrest him for drinking up the vodka. Some other people came running from the town, while a stern-visaged police officer rode up in a drozhky. He climbed down into the pit and lifted the man's coat to get a look at his face.

"Who was the first to find him?"

"I was," said Mitropolsky.

The police officer shot him a glance, and suddenly drawled, with menace in his voice:

"Ah, glad to see you, my fine man!"

Onlookers gathered, a couple of dozen of them; panting and excited, they gazed into the pit and circled about the edge. Someone shouted:

"He's a clerk from our street, I know him!"

The chorister stood swaying in front of the police officer, arguing inarticulately, shouting hoarsely. The officer gave him a push in the chest which caused him to lurch and sit down. Unhurriedly the first police-man took out a rope and tied the chorister's hands, held submissively behind his back, while the officer fumed at the crowd:

"Get away from here, you ragamuffins!"

Still another policeman with moist red eyes and a mouth flapping for breath came running up, seized the ends of the rope binding the chorister's hands, and quietly led him away into town.

Utterly crushed, I too left the field. My memory re-echoed with the words, like a raven's harsh cawing:

"Woe to the city of Ariel!"

Nor could I rid my mind of the sad picture of the policeman unhurriedly pulling the rope out of his pocket while the grim prophet meekly thrust his hairy red hands behind his back as though repeating the gesture for the thousandth time. . . .

Later I learned that the prophet was exiled. And not long afterward Kleshchov also dis-appeared. Having made a gainful marriage, he went to live in the country, where he opened a saddler's shop. . . .

But before his departure my master, to whom I had often praised the saddler's singing, had said to me:

"I must go to the tavern to hear him."

One day he did so, and sat at a table opposite me, wide-eyed, his brows raised in astonishment.

All the way to the tavern he had teased me, and even after we entered he kept poking fun at me and the other patrons and the stifling odours. When the saddler began to sing he gave a supercilious smile and started pouring himself a glass of beer. But he stopped halfway and said:

"Humph! . . . What the devil!"

Gently, and with a trembling hand, he replaced the bottle and began to listen.

"You're right, brother," he said with a sigh when Kleshchov had finished. "He knows how to sing, damn it all. He's even made me sweat."

Once more the saddler sang, throwing back his head, his eyes fixed on the ceiling.

Through the fields a lonely maiden made her way,
From the rich-men's houses she had come away.

"Yes, he can sing," muttered my master, with a short laugh and a shake of his head.

Kleshchov went on trilling like a flute:

Then the maiden told the stranger wearily:
No one needs a homeless orphan-girl like me.

"He's a wonder!" whispered my master, blinking his reddened eyes. "God damn it! He's a wonder!"

I watched him, my heart filled with gladness, while the sad words of the song rose victorious above the noise of the tavern, growing ever stronger, more beautiful, more soulful:

Not a friend in all our hamlet do I own,
When the young folks all make gay, I sit alone,
Not a swain in all the hamlet finds me fair,
For I lack the pretty clothes to make me fair.
An old widower would take me for his wife,
But I never will agree to such a life....

My master wept without shame. He sat with bowed head, snuffling loudly, letting the tears drip down onto his knees.

After the third song he said, deeply moved:

"I can't sit here any longer—no air—these damn smells—come along home!"

But once out in the street his mood changed.

"The devil with it all, Peshkov! Let's go to the hotel and have something to eat! I don't feel like going home!"

Without bickering over the price, he climbed into a sleigh and sat silent until we reached the hotel, where he took a table in a corner and immediately began to speak softly, frequently glancing about, roused by some deep hurt:

"That old goat took the wind out of me—put me in the blackest mood ever. Listen, you read a lot and think about things—how the devil can you explain this? Here I've been living along, year after year, forty of them behind me, with a wife and children, and not a soul in the world to talk to. Come moments when I think I just have to pour out my soul to somebody, to say all there is to say, and—no one to say it to! If you tell it to her—the wife, that is—it don't reach her. What's it to her? She's got her children, the house, her cares. She's outside my soul. Your wife's your friend till the first baby comes . . . that's how it is. And in general, my wife—well, you can see for yourself—no fun with her—just a lump of flesh, damn it all! Ah, brother, what a heart-ache!"

Convulsively he drank down the cold, bitter beer and sat on in silence, ruffling his long hair, until he began to speak again:

"On the whole, brother, people are bastards. I see you like to talk to those muzhiks—about this and that—I understand very well how wrong things are, how rotten they are—that's true, brother. All those men are thieves. But do you think your words touch them? Not the slightest bit. Take Pyotr and Osip—they're rotters. They come tell me everything you say—even if it's about me. Well, how do you like that?"

I was too taken aback to answer.

"There you are!" said my master with a short laugh. "That was a good idea of yours, to go to Persia. At least you wouldn't under-stand what people were saying there—a for-eign tongue. But in your own tongue—nothing but muck."

"Does Osip tell you what I say?" I asked.

"Of course. Are you surprised? He tells me more than anybody else, windbag that he is. He's a sly fox, brother. No, Peshkov, words don't touch people. The truth? Who the hell wants to hear it? It's like snow in the autumn—falls in the mud and melts. Nothing left but more mud. You'd do better to hold your tongue."

He drank down his beer, glass after glass, and spoke faster and more resentfully, without growing drunk:

"The saying goes: Silence is golden, words are dross. Ekh, brother—it's a sad and lonely life! It was true what he sang: *Not a friend in all our hamlet do I own.* . . . ."

With a glance about him, he lowered his voice:

"I almost found a kindred spirit not long ago—met a woman here, a widow— that is, her husband was sentenced to Siberia for counterfeiting—he's still here in prison. Well, I made her acquaintance—she hadn't a kopek to her name—so she decided— you know. . . . A matchmaker introduced us. I took one look at her—what a sweet little thing she was! A real beauty—so young, so pretty! So I started seeing her—once, twice—and then I said to her: How's that, I said, your husband in prison and you not keeping to the straight and narrow? Why should you go off to Siberia with him? You see she was planning to follow him into exile. And she says to me: Whatever he is, she says he's good enough for me because I love him. Maybe it's for my sake he did wrong, and it's for his sake I'm doing this with you. He needs money, she says. He's a gentleman and is used to living decent. If I was alone, she says, I'd live honest. You're a good man too, and I've grown fond of you, she says, but you mustn't talk about this to me any more. . . . Damn it all!. . . I gave her everything I had with me—something over eighty rubles, and I said to her: Forgive me, I said, but I can't see you any more, I just can't do it. And I went away, just like that. . . ."

After a pause, during which he grew drunk and seemed to collapse all at once, he muttered:

"I was with her six times. . . . You can't

imagine what that was like! I went up to her apartment another six times I guess, but hadn't the courage to go in—couldn't make myself. Now she's gone away. . . ."

He placed his hands on the table and started drumming with his fingers.

"I hope to God I never meet her again," he whispered. "God forbid! That would be the end of everything! Come along home—come on!"

We went out, he stumbling and muttering:

"Now, you see, brother. . . ."

I was not surprised by what he had told me. For some time I had sensed that something unusual was happening to him.

But I was greatly depressed by his views on life, and especially by what he had said about Osip.

XX

For three summers I served as an overseer in the dead city, among empty buildings, watching the workmen dismantle the clumsy stone stalls every autumn and put them up every spring.

My master made sure that I earned the five rubles he paid me. If a new floor was to be laid in one of the shops, I had to remove the earth of the whole surface to the depth of about two feet. Unskilled labourers were paid a ruble for such a job; I was paid nothing. But while busy at this, I could not keep my eye on the carpenters, who took advantage of the situation to unscrew the locks and knobs off the doors and make other petty thefts.

Both workmen and contractors tried in every way to deceive me, stealing almost openly, as though submitting to some pressing necessity. They never became angry when I caught them, but would say in astonishment:

"You strain yourself for those five rubles of yours as if they was twenty! Makes a person laugh to watch you!"

I pointed out to my master that in economizing a ruble on me, he lost much more, but he only replied with a wink:

"Don't try to fool me!"

I realized that he suspected me of cooperating with the thieves, and this, without offending me, made me contemptuous of him.

Such was the order of things. Everyone stole, and my master himself had no scruples about annexing another's property.

When the fair was over he would go through the shops to see what repairs were needed; often he would come upon forgotten samovars, dishes, rugs, scissors, and sometimes even boxes and crates with goods in them. He would say with a short laugh:

"Make a list of these things and put them in the storehouse."

From the storehouse he would have certain articles delivered to his own home, asking me to make new copies of the list with these articles omitted.

I had no love for property and did not wish to own anything; even books were a burden. My only possessions were a little volume of Béranger and the songs of Heine. I wanted to buy Pushkin, but the cantankerous old man who was the only second-hand book dealer in town asked too much for it. I disliked the furniture, rugs, mirrors, and other things which crowded my master's flat. They irritated me with their clumsy bulk and the odour of stain and varnish they exuded. In general I disliked my employers' rooms, which reminded me of trunks stuffed with all sorts of rubbish. All the more revolting was it, then, to see my master cart home other people's things, adding to the superfluity about him. Queen Margot's flat had also been crowded with furniture, but at least it had been beautiful.

Life itself seemed to me disjointed, incongruous, with too much that was obviously senseless. Here we were repairing stalls which would only be submerged by the spring floods, causing floors to bulge and doors to sag. When the water fell, the beams would rot. Year after year, over a period of dozens of years, the fairgrounds were flooded, damaging buildings and pavements. These annual inundations caused enormous losses, and everyone knew they would never cease of themselves.

Every spring the breaking up of the ice tore away barges and dozens of small boats. People would sigh and groan and build new boats which the breaking up of the ice would only tear away again. How could people go on revolving in such a vicious circle!

When I asked Osip about this he seemed surprised, and laughed at me:

"Look at the crow, how he's crowing! What does it matter? What do you care?"

Then he replied more seriously, without, however, extinguishing the little sparkle of derision in his blue eyes, which were unusually clear for his age:

"You're smart to notice things like that! Maybe it's none of your business, but again, maybe you'll make good use of it some day. Here's something else for you to notice. . . ."

And he went on pouring out dry little words interspersed with folk sayings, unexpected comparisons, and witticisms:

"Here's people complaining: too little land, and the Volga tearing the banks away every spring, carrying the earth out into midstream to make shallows: and here's others complaining: The Volga's gone shallow! Spring freshets and summer rains dig gullies, and down goes the land into the Volga again!"

He spoke without regret or complaint, as though revelling in his knowledge of the charges brought against life, and while his words corroborated my own thoughts, they were hard to hear.

"And there's another thing—fires."

I knew that not a summer passed but the forests beyond the Volga burned; every July the sky was veiled in safron smoke, while a lowering, rayless sun stared down at the earth like a sore eye.

"Forests—they're nothing," said Osip. "The forests belong to the gentles or the tsar; muzhiks own no forests. When cities burn down, that's no great evil either—the rich live in cities, and there's no pitying the rich. But take the towns and villages—how many villages burn down during a summer! At least a hundred, and that's a real loss!"

He gave a quiet laugh.

"We've got pains, but no brains. You and I can see that the benefit of a man's labour doesn't go to himself or the land, but to fire and water!"

"Why are you laughing?"

"Why not? You can't drown a fire with tears, and they only swell a flood."

I was convinced that this comely old man was the wisest person I had ever met, but I could not discover his likes and dislikes.

As I pondered over this, he continued to feed my fire with chips of words:

"Just look how wasteful of strength people are—of their own and others! Take how your master wears you out. Or the harm vodka does. There's no calculating it—too great for even a learned mind to grasp. If a hut burns down, you can build another, but if a good man goes to his ruin, there's no righting it. Ardalion, for example, or Grigori. Just look how that muzhik went up in smoke. He's not of the brightest, Grigori, but he's a soulful muzhik! Might've been a haystack, the way he flared up. The women attacked him like worms after a corpse."

"Why do you tell my master everything I say?" I asked him, merely out of curiosity, without any hard feelings.

And he replied simply, even gently:

"So's he'll know what harmful thoughts you have; it's up to him to teach you; who'll do it if your master don't? It's not out of malice

I tell him, but out of pity for you. You're not a stupid lad, but there's a demon stirring things up in that head of yours. If you steal something, I'll keep mum about it; if you go with the girls—still I'm mum; and I'll not say a word if you get drunk. But I'll always tell your master about those brazen ideas of yours, so you may as well know it."

"I'll not talk to you any more."

He was silent a while, picking at some tar on the palm of his hand, and then he looked at me fondly and said:

"Yes you will; you're lying. Who else will you talk to? There's nobody else."

In spite of his neatness and cleanness, Osip at this moment seemed to resemble the stoker Yakov, so indifferent was he to everyone and everything.

Sometimes he reminded me of the dogmatist Pyotr Vasilyev, sometimes of the drayman Pyotr, at other times he seemed to have something in common with my grandfather—in one way or another he resembled all the old men I had ever known. All of them were amazingly interesting old men, but I felt that it would be hard and disgusting to live with them. They seemed to eat into your soul and corrode your heart with their wise precepts. Was Osip a good man? No. A bad man? No. He was clever—that I clearly saw. But while marvelling at the versatility of his mind, I realized that his way of thinking had a deadening effect on me and was in every way antagonistic to my own.

Dark thoughts began to seethe within me:

"All people are alien to each other, in spite of fond words and smiles; all are alien. And no one, it seems, is bound to life with strong bonds of love. Granny alone truly loves life and people. Granny, and wonderful Queen Margot."

Sometimes these and similar thoughts piled up into dark clouds, making life cheerless and stifling. But what other sort of life was there? How could I escape? There was not even anyone but Osip with whom I could speak, and I turned to him ever more often.

He listened with evident interest to my ardent outpourings, asking me questions, finding things out, and then saying calmly:

"The woodpecker's a stubborn bird, but

not fearful; nobody's afraid of it. With all my heart I advise you to enter a monastery. There you can live until you come of age, comforting the faithful with fine words. Peace of mind for you; profit for the monks. With all my heart I advise you to do this. I'm afraid you're not able to cope with this world."

I had no wish to enter a monastery, but I felt that I was lost in a labyrinth of the incomprehensible. I longed for relief. Life was like an autumn woods with the mushrooms gone, leaving me with nothing to do in an emptiness where every nook and cranny was only too familiar.

I did not drink vodka or court the girls —these two means of intoxicating the soul were substituted for me by books. But the more I read, the harder it became to go on living in the empty, senseless manner in which most people appeared to live.

I had just turned fifteen, but there were times when I felt old. My heart seemed to have grown swollen and heavy with all I had lived through, all I had read and pondered so distractedly. The reservoir of my impressions was like a dark lumber-room stuffed with a multiplicity of things I had neither the strength nor the ability to sort.

And the weight of these impressions, despite their number, did not make me firm, but rocked and unsettled me like water in a shaky vessel.

I despised complaints, misery and unwholesomeness, while the sight of brutality—blood, blows, even oral abuse—roused in me an instinctive repulsion; this easily became transformed into a cold fury, and I would fight like a wild beast, only to suffer cruel pangs of remorse afterwards.

There were times when, seized by such an impassioned desire to flay someone's tormentor, I would fling myself blindly into a broil. To this very day I am overwhelmed by grief and shame on recalling these fits of despair born of impotence.

Two beings dwelt within me: one of them, having seen too much of filth and loathsomeness, had become chastened. Life's dreadful humdrum had made him sceptical and suspicious, and he looked with helpless compassion upon all people, including himself. This individual longed to lead a quiet, retired life far away from cities and people. He dreamed of going to Persia, of entering a monastery, of living in a forester's hut or the lodge of a railway-guard or becoming a night-watchman somewhere on the outskirts of town. The fewer the people and the more remote, the better.

The other individual, baptized by the holy spirit of wise and truthful books, realized that life's dreadful humdrum exerted a ruthless power which might easily lop off his head or crush him under a grimy heel. And so he summoned all his strength in self-defence, baring his teeth, clenching his fists, ever ready for a fight or an argument. His love and his pity found expression in action, and, as became the gallant hero of a French novel, he would unsheathe his sword and strike a fighting pose at the slightest provocation. . . .

At that time I had a vicious enemy—the porter of one of the brothels on Malaya Pokrovskaya Street. I had first made his acquaintance one morning on my way to the fairgrounds, when I had seen him removing a girl in a drunken stupor from a cab. Grabbing her by the legs, from which the stockings had rolled down, he jerked at her obscenely, baring her body to the waist, grunting and laughing and spitting on her, while the girl, dishevelled, unseeing, with hanging lips, slid down jerk by jerk; her limp arms, seemingly unsocketed, trailed above her head, which struck the seat of the carriage, then the step, finally the pavement.

The izvozchik whipped up his horse and drove away, while the porter, picking up the girl's legs like wagon shafts, dragged her along the pavement. I rushed at him in a mad frenzy, but fortunately for me I either threw down or accidentally dropped the seven-foot level I had been carrying, thus saving both the porter and myself serious consequences. Dashing into him at full speed, I knocked him down, leaped up on to the porch and gave the bell a desperate tug, in response to which some wild-looking people came running. Incapable of explaining anything, I recovered my instrument and rushed away.

Down on the river road I caught up with the izvozchik. He glanced down at me from the height of his box and said approvingly:

"You fixed him fine."

Angrily I asked him why he had allowed the porter to treat the girl so shamelessly.

"The hell with her," he replied with unruffled contempt. "The gentlemen paid me when they put her in the cab. That's all I care about."

"But what if he had killed her?"

"It's not so easy to kill her kind," he remarked with the assurance of one who made a specialty of killing off drunken strumpets.

After that I met the porter almost every morning. Whenever I came down the street he would be sweeping the sidewalk or sitting on the steps as though waiting for me. As I approached he would get up, roll up his sleeves, and say threateningly:

"Now I'll smash your mug for you all right!"

He was something over forty, small and bowlegged, with a belly like that of a pregnant woman. There he would stand laughing at me, and to my dismay his eyes had a kindly, good-natured twinkle. Unskilled at fighting, and with arms shorter than mine, he would surrender after two or three attacks, backing up against the fence and gasping in wonderment:

"Wait a second, you wildcat!"

I grew sick of these fights and said to him one day:

"Listen, you fool, leave me alone, will you?"

"Why did you start fighting?" he asked reproachfully.

I asked him why he had abused the girl.

"What do you care? Do you pity her?"

"Of course I do."

After a short pause, he wiped his lips and said:

"Do you pity cats too?"

"Yes I do."

Then he said:

"You're a fool and a liar! Just wait, I'll show you!"

I had to take this street, it being the shortest route to work. But I began to get up earlier in the morning so as to avoid meeting the porter. Despite my efforts, a few days later

I saw him sitting on the steps stroking a grey cat lying in his lap. When I was within three steps of him he jumped up, grabbed the cat by the hind legs and banged its head with such force against a stone post that I was splashed with the warm blood. Then he tossed it at my feet, took his stand in the gateway, and said:

"Well?"

What was I to do? We rolled about the yard like two dogs; later, stunned with misery, I flung myself down among the weeds along the road, biting my lips to keep from screaming or sobbing. I recall this with a shudder of repugnance, amazed that I did not go mad or commit murder.

Why should I recount anything so loathsome? So that you may know, gentle reader, that this is not a thing of the past! You enjoy invented terrors, you take pleasure in reading tales of horror, you are not averse to having your senses pleasantly tickled by harrowing fantasies. But I have known true horrors, the horrors of everyday life, and I hold it my right to tickle your senses unpleasantly by recounting them to you, that you may know exactly where you live and how you live.

It is a base and filthy life that all of us lead, and none can deny it.

Loving mankind as I do, and shrinking from causing pain, I see that we must not be sentimental, nor conceal the grim truth in bright verbiage and pretty lies. We must stand closer to life, closer! And we must pour into it all the goodness and humanity contained in our hearts and minds.

I was particularly outraged by the accepted attitude toward women. My reading had taught me that life held nothing finer or more meaningful than a woman. This view had been confirmed by my grandmother and her tales about the Virgin and Vasilissa the Wise; by the unfortunate washwoman Natalya; and by those hundreds and thousands of smiles and glances with which I had seen women, the mothers of life, beautify an existence only too wanting in joy and love.

The books of Turgenev sang the glory of women, and my Queen remained for me the incarnation of all the good things I had learned about them—a treasure of knowledge to which Heine and Turgenev had lavishly contributed.

On returning home from the fairgrounds I would often stop on a hill beside the Kremlin wall to watch the sun sink below the Volga, leaving flaming rivers streaming down the sky, while my beloved terrestrial river grew darkly purple. At such moments I sometimes felt that the earth was an enormous convict barge, or a pig being pulled along on some invisible rope.

But more often my thoughts turned to the vastness of the earth, to those other cities about which I had read in books, and to those strange lands where people lived differently. Books by foreign authors pictured a life more clean and desirable and less onerous than that which slowly and monotonously revolved about me. This calmed my fears and roused insistent hopes that a better way of life was possible.

And I kept thinking that some day I would meet a wise and simple person who would lead me out on to a broad, bright highway.

One day as I sat on a bench beside the Kremlin wall, I was joined by Uncle Yakov. I did not notice him approach, nor did I immediately recognize him. Although we had been living in the same town for many years, we rarely met, and then only briefly and by chance.

"You've been sprouting up," he said jokingly, giving me a little push, and we began to talk together like people who are not relatives, but have long known each other.

Granny had told me that Uncle Yakov had squandered all his means. For a while he had been the warder's assistant at a prison colony, but this had come to a sad end. When the warder was ill, Uncle Yakov had held gay parties for the convicts at his own flat. When this was discovered, he was dismissed and prosecuted on the charge of having set the convicts free at night. None of them had run away, but one had been caught in an attempt to strangle a deacon. The investigation dragged along for considerable time but never reached court— the convicts and prison guards managed to spare my kindhearted uncle such a disgrace. Now he was not working, but was supported by his son, who sang in the Rukavishnikov church choir, a famous one at that time. He spoke strangely about his son:

"He's become very serious of late, and very important. A soloist. He gets huffy if I'm late with the samovar or brushing his clothes. A very neat lad. And clean in his habits."

My uncle himself, who now looked old, was dirty and shabby and somehow pithy. His gay curls had thinned, his ears stuck out, and a network of red veins covered the whites of his eyes and the silky skin of his beardless cheeks. He spoke jestingly, but he seemed to have something in his mouth that impeded his speech, though his teeth were sound.

I was glad of the opportunity to speak with a person who knew how to be gay, who had seen much and must know many things. I well remembered his bold, comical songs and what grandfather had said of him:

"A David at singing, an Absolom at work!"

The more respectable townsfolk went promenading past us along the boulevard: officers and officials and fluffy young ladies. My uncle was wearing a shabby coat, a battered cap, and rusty-looking boots, and he shrank back on the bench, obviously ashamed of his appearance. We went to one of the taverns above the Pochainsky Gully where we took a table at a window overlooking the market place.

"Remember how you sang:

A beggar hung up his pants to dry,
Another beggar stole them. . . ."

As I repeated the words of the song, I sensed their irony for the first time, and it seemed to me that my seemingly gay uncle was really barbed and bitter.

But he only replied pensively, as he poured himself a glass of vodka:

"Ah yes, I've lived my life and had my fun, but not enough of it. That wasn't my song. It was written by one of the teachers at the seminary—what was his name now? I've forgotten. We were great friends, him and me. But he drank himself to death—froze out in the cold. The number of people I've seen drink themselves to death! Past counting! Do you drink? Don't. Wait a while. Do you often see your grandfather? A mournful old man. Seems he's grown feeble-minded."

After a drink or two he perked up, squared his shoulders, seemed to grow younger, and began to speak with more animation.

I asked him about the affair with the convicts.

"So you've heard about it?" he inquired. Lowering his voice and glancing about, he said:

"What if they were convicts? I'm not their judge. I could see they were people like the rest of us, so I said to them: come on, brothers, let's live together friendly, let's have some fun, as the song goes:

> *Let's be gay in spite of Fate,*
> *Till our journey here is done,*
> *A fool is he who bows to grief;*
> *We shall live for joy and fun!*"

With a laugh he glanced out the window at the darkening gully, with the row of trade stalls along the bottom.

"Of course they were glad—it was dull in that prison," he went on, stroking his moustaches. "So when roll call was over, they'd come visit me; food, vodka; sometimes mine, sometimes theirs, and Mother Russia off on a lark! I love a song and a dance, and there were some fine singers and dancers among them. Very fine indeed. You wouldn't believe it! Half of them in chains. Well, you can't dance in chains, so I permitted them to take them off, that's the truth. They could do it themselves, without the blacksmith. Clever people, very clever indeed. But it's all nonsense about my setting them free to go stealing in the town. Nobody could prove such a thing."

He fell silent and sat gazing down into the gully where the second-hand dealers were closing up their shops with a rattle of bolts, a screeching of locks, and a thumping of falling boards. Then he went on quietly, with a merry wink:

"If the truth's to be told, one of them really did go out nights, but he wasn't in chains—just a local thief from Nizhni-Novgorod. He had a mistress living nearby, on the Pechorka River. And the fuss with the deacon was just an accident. He took the deacon for a merchant. It happened on a stormy winter night—everybody in greatcoats; who could tell a deacon from a merchant?"

This struck me funny, and he too laughed as he added:

"Of course he couldn't tell."

Suddenly, and with strange facility, my uncle's mood switched to anger. He pushed away his plate, made a wry face, and muttered, lighting a cigarette:

"They rob each other, then catch each other, and send each other off to prison, or to hard labour in Siberia. But why drag me in? Spit on it all! I have my own soul to look after."

Before me rose the vision of the shaggy stoker. He too was fond of saying "spit on it!" and he too was named Yakov.

"What are you thinking about?" asked my uncle gently.

"Did you feel sorry for those convicts?"

"It's easy to feel sorry for them. Such fine fellows. Very fine indeed! Sometimes I'd look at them and think: I'm not fit to black your boots, and here I am, your keeper. Smart devils, and foxy."

The wine and the reminiscences had again stimulated him pleasantly; placing his elbows on the window sill and waving a yellow hand with a cigarette between the fingers, he continued in a lively tone:

"If you'd ever heard how one of them talked! A one-eyed fellow he was, an engraver and watchmaker, arrested for counterfeiting and tried to escape. Always flaring up like a torch. He sang like a bird. Explain this to me, he would say: why can the mint coin money, and I can't, eh? Go ahead and explain. Nobody could explain. Nobody, not even me. And me their keeper! Then there was another, a famous Moscow thief—quiet, and clean, and something of a dandy; he always spoke very polite. People, says he, work till they drop, and I have no desire to do such a thing. I tried it once, says he—worked my finger tips off, and what for? A mere pittance. Drink a thimbleful, lose a trifle at cards, slip a mite to a woman for her fondling, and there you are again, broke and hungry. No, says he, I'm not playing that game!"

Uncle Yakov leaned low over the table as he went on, red to the roots of his hair, and so excited that his tiny ears twitched:

"They're no fools, brother. They take the right view of things. To hell with all this bother! Take me, for instance: what's my life been like? It's shameful even to recall it. Everything good taken in spurts and underhand. Earned grief, stolen pleasure. My father shouting don't do this, and my wife shouting don't do that, and I myself scared to break my neck over a ruble. So life slipped past, and here I am in my old age, flunkey to my son. Why try to hide it? I serve him humble, brother, and he goes yelling at me like a true gentleman. He calls me 'father,' but it sounds to me like 'flunkey.' Is that what I got born for, what I went through it all for, to end up as flunkey to my own son? But even if it wasn't like this —what did I live for? How much pleasure did I ever get out of life?"

I was not listening very attentively. Falteringly, and with no thought of an answer, I said:

"I don't know how to go on living either. . . ."

He snorted.

"Humph! Who does? I've never met

anybody who knew! People just go on living, by habit. . . ."

Once more a note of anger and injury crept into his voice:

"There was another fellow from Orel—sent up for rape—he came from the gentles and was a marvellous dancer. He used to make folks laugh with his song about Vanka:

> Round the graveyard Vanka walks,
> With a very sober face.
> Vanka, Vanka, why walk here?
> Can't you find a better place?

"But it's my opinion there's nothing funny about that song. It's the living truth! Wriggle and squirm, but there's no escaping the graveyard. And when I reach it, I won't give a damn whether I was a convict or a warder."

Tired of speaking, he drank up his vodka and cocked one eye at the empty glass like a bird, smoking in silence, the smoke curling through his moustaches.

The stonemason Pyotr, who in no way resembled Uncle Yakov, had been fond of saying: "Try as a man will and hope as he may, he'll only come to a grave and a coffin." And how many folk sayings expressed the same idea!

I had no desire to ask my uncle anything else. I pitied him and felt depressed in his company. I could not help remembering his gay songs and the ring of his guitar, weaving joy through the gloom. Nor had I forgotten the merry Tsiganok. No, I had not forgotten him, and as I gazed at the crumpled figure of Uncle Yakov I couldn't help wondering if he remembered how he had crushed Tsiganok with the cross.

But I did not ask him.

I glanced down into the gully, now brimming with August mist. From its depths rose the fragrance of apples and melons. Lanterns flashed along the narrow road leading up to the town, and everything about me was poignantly familiar: this whistle came from the steamer bound for Rybinsk; that, from the steamer to Perm. . . .

"Ah, well—I must be going," said my uncle.

At the door of the tavern he shook my hand and said jestingly:

"Don't go moping now; you seem to be moping. Cheer up; you're young yet. Remember: 'Let's be gay in spite of fate.' Well, goodbye. My way lies past the Uspensky Cathedral."

And my gay uncle went away, leaving me more muddled than ever by what he had said.

I climbed the hill to the city and set off through the fields. The moon was full, and lowering clouds trailed across the sky, erasing my shadow with their own. Circling the town through the fields, I came to the Volga at the Otkos, where I lay down on the dusty grass and gazed for long at the river, at the meadowlands, at the motionless earth. Cloud shadows slowly streamed across the Volga, growing brighter on reaching the meadows, as though washed in passage over the waters. Everything about me was drowsy and subdued; everything moved reluctantly, under force of necessity, instead of being impelled by an ardent passion for life and movement.

And I longed to give that land and myself a good kick, so that everything—myself included—would spin about in a joyful whirl, in the rapturous dance of people who are in love with each other and with life, this life, conceived for the sake of another life, to be more honest, courageous, and beautiful. . . .

And I thought to myself: "If I don't do something, I shall be lost."

Often had I wandered through the woods on dull autumn days, when I could not see, nor even feel the sun, and was quite forgetful of its very existence. If I lost my way, I would search anxiously for bypaths leading me back, until, weary of searching, I would set my teeth and plunge boldly into the very heart of the woods, making my way through matted underbrush and across perilous bogs. And always, inevitably, I would come out on to the road!

And this was my decision.

In the autumn of that year I left for Kazan, secretly hoping that I would find some means of studying there.

52